Survival

GLOBAL POLITICS AND STRATEGY

Volume 51 Number 6 | December 2009–January 2010

The International Institute for Strategic Studies
1850 K Street, NW | Suite 300 | Washington, DC 20006 | USA
Tel +1 202 659 1490 Fax +1 202 296 1134 E-mail survival@iiss.org Web www.iiss.org

Arundel House | 13–15 Arundel Street | Temple Place | London | WC2R 3DX | UK
Tel +44 (0)20 7379 7676 Fax +44 (0)20 7836 3108 E-mail iiss@iiss.org

9 Raffles Place | #53-02 Republic Plaza | Singapore 048619
Tel +65 6499 0055 Fax +65 6499 0059 E-mail iiss-asia@iiss.org

Survival Online www.informaworld.com/survival

Aims and Scope *Survival* is one of the world's leading forums for analysis and debate of international and strategic affairs. Shaped by its editors to be both timely and forward thinking, the journal encourages writers to challenge conventional wisdom and bring fresh, often controversial, perspectives to bear on the strategic issues of the moment. With a diverse range of authors, *Survival* aims to be scholarly in depth while vivid, well written and policy relevant in approach. Through commentary, analytical articles, case studies, forums, review essays, reviews and letters to the editor, the journal promotes lively, critical debate on issues of international politics and strategy.

First published 2009 by Routledge Journals

Published 2019 by Routledge
2 Park Square, Milton Park, Abingdon, Oxon OX14 4RN
52 Vanderbilt Avenue, New York, NY 10017

Routledge is an imprint of the Taylor & Francis Group, an informa business

ISBN 13: 978-1-138-45878-9 (hbk)
ISBN 13: 978-0-415-49843-2 (pbk)

GLOBAL POLITICS AND STRATEGY
Volume 51 Number 6 | December 2009–January 2010

Contents

Cover: US Navy/Getty Images

On the cover
A Standard Missile-3 is launched from the *Aegis* cruiser USS *Lake Erie* as part of the Missile Defense Agency's latest Ballistic Missile Defense System test, 11 December 2003.

New on the web
Visit http://www.iiss.org/publicatons/survival for interviews and podcasts by authors in this issue.

IISS Voices
A blog from the editors of *Survival* and other IISS staff. Http://www.iiss.org/whats-new/iiss-voices.

Review Essays

Closing Argument

About the IISS The IISS, a registered charity with offices in Washington, London and Singapore, is the world's leading authority on political-military conflict. It is the primary independent source of accurate, objective information on international strategic issues. Publications include *The Military Balance*, an annual reference work on each nation's defence capabilities; *Strategic Survey*, an annual review of world affairs; *Survival*, a bi-monthly journal on international affairs; *Strategic Comments*, a monthly analysis of topical issues in international affairs; and the *Adelphi* series of books on issues of international security.

SUBMISSIONS

To submit an article, authors are advised to follow these guidelines:

- *Survival* articles are around 4,000–10,000 words long including endnotes. A word count should be included with a draft. Length is a consideration in the review process and shorter articles have an advantage.
- All text, including endnotes, should be double-spaced with wide margins.
- Any tables or artwork should be supplied in separate files, ideally not embedded in the document or linked to text around it.
- All *Survival* articles are expected to include endnote references. These should be complete and include first and last names of authors, titles of articles (even from newspapers), place of publication, publisher, exact publication dates, volume and issue number (if from a journal) and page numbers. Web sources should include complete URLs and DOIs if available.
- A summary of up to 150 words should be included with the article. The summary should state the main argument clearly and concisely, not simply say what the article is about.
- A short author's biography of one or two lines should also be included. This information will appear at the foot of the first page of the article.

Submissions should be made by email, in Microsoft Word format, to the Managing Editor, Jeffrey Mazo, survival@iiss.org. Alternatively, hard copies may be sent to *Survival*, IISS–US, 1850 K Street NW, Suite 300, Washington, DC 20006, USA. Please direct any queries to Jeffrey Mazo.

The editorial review process can take up to three months. *Survival*'s acceptance rate for unsolicited manuscripts is less than 20%. *Survival* does not normally provide referees' comments in the event of rejection. Authors are permitted to submit simultaneously elsewhere so long as this is consistent with the policy of the other publication and the Editors of *Survival* are informed of the dual submission.

Readers are encouraged to comment on articles from the previous issue. Letters should be concise, no longer than 750 words and relate directly to the argument or points made in the original article. A response from the author of the article will normally be solicited.

Back issues: Taylor & Francis retains a three-year back issue stock of journals. Older volumes are held by our official stockists: Periodicals Service Company, 11 Main Street, Germantown, NY 12526, USA to whom all orders and enquiries should be addressed. *Tel* +1 518 537 4700 *Fax* +1 518 537 5899 *e-mail* psc@periodicals.com *web* http://www.periodicals.com/tandf.html

The issue date is December 2009–January 2010.

A Prudent Decision on Missile Defence

Mark Fitzpatrick

President Barack Obama's decision to substitute a mobile, adaptable missile shield for President George W. Bush's plan to deploy silo-housed missile interceptors in Poland and an advanced tracking radar in the Czech Republic was wise on multiple grounds. Whether judged on its technical, military, strategic or diplomatic merits, the new missile-shield deployment plan is far superior to the dubious system it will replace.

Technological assessments played a major role in the decision. The Obama plan replaces systems that have experienced serious operational and developmental problems with radars and interceptors that are much more capable at present and that are likely to be even better in the future. The administration rightly insists that it is not scrapping missile defence in Europe, but strengthening it.

President Bush's decision in 2007 to deploy missile-defence systems in Central Europe was primarily intended to defend the continental United States against an intercontinental ballistic-missile (ICBM) threat from Iran that some believed would become imminent as early as 2015. The ten silo-based interceptors to be sited in Poland and the omnidirectional X-band tracking-radar base in the Czech Republic were collectively called the 'Third Site' system, because they were to complement the two US-based missile-defence sites in Alaska and California. This terminology was indicative of an American-centric defence against ICBMs. Defending western – but not southeastern – Europe against

Mark Fitzpatrick is Director of the IISS Non-Proliferation and Disarmament Programme.

Survival | vol. 51 no. 6 | December 2009–January 2010 | pp. 5–12 DOI 10.1080/00396330903461633

intermediate-range Iranian missiles was only a secondary purpose of the system.

The US intelligence community earlier this year concluded in a classified report that Iran's missile-development programme is focused on short- and medium-range rockets, not ICBM capabilities as previously predicted. An IISS threat assessment by a team of American, Russian and European experts to be published in early 2010 reaches a similar conclusion. Obama's plan to field sea- and land-based versions of the Navy's Standard Missile (SM)-3 is designed primarily to protect US allies and forces in Europe and the Middle East against the real Iranian threat. Meanwhile, it retains flexibility should signs emerge of an Iranian ICBM threat, which would be accompanied by ample warning time in the form of readily observable flight tests. Reflexive attacks from critics such as Republican Senator Lindsey Graham that the decision will cause joy in Tehran could not be more wrong.[1] Whatever strategic advantage Iran thought it would obtain by deploying nuclear-capable missiles capable of hitting American forces and US allies and friends in the Middle East and southeastern Europe will now be diminished by systems that can both detect and defeat any Iranian missile currently under development.

The only valid criticism of the new system is that the announcement was poorly timed (it coincided with the 70th anniversary of Russia's invasion of Poland) and badly coordinated. Far better than a midnight phone call to Polish and Czech leaders would have been a senior-level visit to discuss the plan in person and in advance, and then to have presented the decision as one made after consultations with allies. To be fair to the administration, however, any such careful roll-out plan probably would have been stymied in any case by the kind of leaks that forced the hurried announcement and belated, rushed trip by State Department and White House officials to Warsaw and Prague.

Welcome news

The deterrence and reassurance value of the new missile shield should be readily apparent to any unbiased observer. The range of Iran's missiles primarily encompasses the greater Middle East. Countries such as Egypt and Saudi Arabia that feel threatened by Iran's strategic capabilities will be less inclined to want to keep open nuclear options of their own if they feel protected by a US missile shield. This reassurance will be particularly important for Turkey, which is within easy reach of Iran's missiles but which fell outside the coverage of the Third Site. Although the Bush plan also called for optional deployment of theatre missile-defence systems to plug that gap, his emphasis on the Czech and Polish sites and the optional nature of the other systems left Turkish security planners feeling vulnerable. Turkey is also worried about falling behind Iran in terms of the regional power balance. Given Turkey's growing sense of estrangement from the Europe Union and Ankara's foreign-policy emphasis on 'zero problems with neighbours', a missile-defence system that both incorporates the country into a Europe-wide shield and reduces a major source of NATO–Russia tension is a godsend. For Israel, Obama's plan will complement the *Arrow* missile-defence system and thus provide more reassurance about the range of methods for deterring Iran. If diplomacy fails to stem Iran's nuclear capabilities, a pre-emptive military strike against its nuclear and missile facilities will not be Israel's only defence option.

In most of Europe, the response has been decidedly positive. The security communities in Western European capitals were never fully comfortable with a Bush missile-defence plan they felt was imposed upon them, and they instinctively appreciate policy decisions that are de-politicised. Western Europeans also clearly see the benefits of removing an unnecessary irritant in the relationship with Russia. In his first major foreign-policy address on 17 September 2009, NATO Secretary-General Anders Fogh Rasmussen spoke for many others when he praised the Obama decision as a 'positive step … in full accordance with the principle of solidarity within the alliance and the indivisibility of security in Europe'.[2] He undoubtedly hopes that the demise of the Third Site will bring the Central European states more closely into a truly European-centred security structure to replace their dependence on America. Indeed, the United States intends the new missile-defence effort to be multinational and integrated with NATO members' missile-defence capabilities.

To be sure, there were some in certain Central European capitals who greeted Obama's decision with scepticism, even trepidation. Inflammatory headlines in Poland and Prague claiming that 'Russia won' were eye-catching, but at least half the populations in these countries support Obama's decision.[3] Only a minority of right-wingers, recently voted out in both countries, joined with similarly ousted conservatives in Washington in criticising the decision as a betrayal to loyal allies and a capitulation to a menacing Russia. For Polish and Czech supporters, the Bush missile-defence plan had nothing to do with defending against Iran. It was all about strengthening military relations with the United States vis-à-vis Moscow. What these supporters wanted most of all was American boots on the ground. This will still happen, but now without the downside of a provoked Russian neighbour. America will probably still deploy a *Patriot*-missile battery to Poland, and has offered it a land-based SM-3 interceptor site. Command-and-control facilities are likely to go to the Czech Republic. The difference is that under the Bush plan the US troop presence would have been relatively permanent, stationed at fixed structures (silos and radar installations). Under Obama's scenario, the interceptors and sensors are 'transportable' and thus temporary, at least in theory.

The US–Russia dynamic became a caricature of circular causality

Bush's Eastern European supporters also saw his missile-defence plan as a way to ensure American solidarity in standing up to Russian intimidation. For the Bush administration, a similar political-strategic rationale grew in importance even as the technical merits of the Third Site waned. The US–Russia dynamic became a caricature of circular causality: the Bush team insisted that the plan had to go ahead, all the more so because of Moscow's fierce opposition. But by allowing the Polish and Czech deployments to become a symbol of strength against Russia, the Bush administration undercut its rebuttal of Russia's otherwise unfounded complaint that the shield would be used to counter its strategic forces. The shield would not have posed a military threat to Russia, unless vastly expanded, but Moscow had reason to wonder what its real purpose was. And by insisting on his Third Site deployment plan regardless of the technical merits, Bush sought to bind his successor to a fait accompli.

Although Obama's decision to realign the defence shield toward countering the real Iranian missile threat removes some of its more political problems, the effects of Bush's faulty plan remain toxic. Eastern Europeans do have reason to be concerned about Russian aggression and Moscow's view that they fall into its natural sphere of influence. Although Obama's decision to realign the defence shield was not made as a concession to Russia, many Russians believe otherwise, not least because Obama's opponents in the United States have said so. The danger is that Russia will believe this rhetoric and take to heart the lesson that belligerence pays.

Reaching out to Russia

The initial Russian responses to Obama's plan were mixed. Foreign Minister Sergei Lavrov said the new missile-shield plans presented no risks for Russia, and offered favourable conditions for bilateral dialogue.[4] But Russia's notoriously hostile envoy to NATO, Dmitry Rogozin, was less willing to let down his guard; he asked for more guarantees that the replacement missile-defence system would not be aimed against Russia's nuclear arsenal.[5] General Nikolai Makarov, the chief of the general staff of the Russian military, said Russia had 'a negative attitude to everything that concerns missile defence'. The only form of missile defence acceptable to Russia, he said, was joint missile defence with Russian involvement.[6]

Although couched in negative terms, Makarov's comments present an opportunity for the United States and NATO to forge a new security relationship with Russia by putting in place elements of a cooperative missile-defence system. Such cooperation has been a topic of desultory discussion for years. In 2000, then President Vladimir Putin proposed the creation of a pan-European missile-defence system. At the June 2007 G8 summit he called for joint use of Russia's radar-tracking facilities at Armavir in southern Russia and Gabala, Azerbaijan. But such Russian proposals were always cast as an alternative to America's National Missile Defense concept and the Czech-based radars, not as an addition to the Third Site, as promoted by the Bush administration. This was an intractable sticking point in the unsuccessful working-level discussions between the two countries on the subject. Obama's plan offers the first realistic prospect for complementary inclusion of Russian radars in a European missile-defence programme. For missile defence against Iran, there is a real need for forward-based radar, and Gabala's proximity to Iran makes it an attractive location. As Rasmussen reasoned, both NATO and Russia have a wealth of experience in missile defence that should be combined to mutual benefit.

Finding ways for NATO and Russia to cooperate on missile defence will not be easy. Interoperability problems posed by different technical standards, command-and-control procedures and operational doctrines will need to be overcome. Difficult policy decisions will need to be made on the sharing in real time of raw data from missile-detection radars, and on who has control of the data. If restrictive technology-transfer policies on the part of Western countries are changed in order to allow cooperation with Russia, safeguards will need to be put in place to preclude onward transfer of the technology to countries such as China. Underlying all these problems is a basic lack of trust between Russia and the United States, along with its NATO allies.

New challenges and issues concerning missile defence will undoubtedly arise to complicate prospects for US–Russia cooperation in this field. Putin has already reacted strongly to a suggestion by US Assistant Secretary of Defense for International Security Affairs Alexander Vershbow that Ukraine was being considered as a possible site for a radar station as part of the new missile defence.[7] Most of the other sites for ground-based sensors will similarly be fielded in the previous Soviet sphere in central and eastern Europe. The SM-3 interceptors on which the new shield is based, although currently designed primarily to protect against short- and medium-range missiles, will likely acquire a capability by 2020 to defend against intercontinental-range ballistic missiles. Once the capabilities of the new architecture become better known, the potential reach of the SM-3 could become an issue for Russia. In addition, US officials have said they will continue to develop the silo-based interceptors from the Bush plan in case they might be needed later. It will be useful for the United States and Russia to begin addressing these issues before political problems begin to overwhelm and confuse the policy debate, to the detriment of sound judgements about technology and actual threats.

Cooperation on missile defence is not a sop from either superpower to the other. Rather, it can be a key part of the solution to shared concerns about major national security challenges in both the short and long terms. One of the gravest security challenges facing the world today is the danger of nuclear-weapons proliferation. By sharing resources and strategies, the United States and Russia can collectively counter the most threatening means of delivering nuclear weapons. In the long term, the availability of missile defences to defend against rogue nuclear-armed states may become an important element in the strategy for realising the dream of a secure, nuclear-weapons-free world, which Obama and Russian President Dmitry Medvedev, among many other leaders, have set as national goals. However, unless missile defences are embarked upon in a spirit of cooperation rather than confrontation, they are more likely to block than foster the willingness of nuclear-armed states to dismantle their arsenals.

Notes

1 Ben Feller, 'Obama Says Missile Defense Decision is Not About Russia', Associated Press, 21 September 2009.

2 'Press Point with NATO Secretary General Anders Fogh Rasmussen and the Prime Minister of Belgium Herman Van Rompuy', North Atlantic Treaty Organisation, 17 September 2009, http://www.nato.int/cps/en/SID-0D774214-F07D90AA/natolive/opinions_57665.htm.

3 See, for example, Robert Marquand, 'Why Europe Welcomes US Missile Defense Shield Decision', *Christian Science Monitor*, 21 September 2009.

4 'New U.S. Missile Defense Plans Pose No Threat to Russia – Lavrov', RIA Novosti, 7 October 2009.

5 Conor Sweeney, 'Russia Still Cool On New U.S. Anti-Missile Scheme', Reuters, 29 September 2009.

6 'General Says Russia Favours Only Joint Missile Defence', Channel News Asia by AFP, 21 September 2009.

7 John T. Bennett, 'Behind the New European Missile Plan', *Defense News*, 12 October 2009.

Three Iraq Intelligence Failures Reconsidered

David Hannay

So pervasive is the criticism of the invasion of Iraq in 2003, and even more so of the policy decisions taken in its immediate aftermath, that little attempt is made to situate these developments in some kind of historical context that takes account of the events which preceded the Bush administration's decision to go to war. Of no aspect of these events is this more true than of the failure to find any serious trace of Iraq's programmes for the development of nuclear, biological and chemical weapons, which it had been confidently predicted ahead of the invasion still existed in considerable quantities and with the capacity to be re-constituted fairly rapidly. That particular story is read backwards, with the benefit of 20/20 hindsight, and not forwards as those who shape historical events are compelled to experience it. The potential threat from these programmes is simply assumed to have been a convenient, and possibly fabricated, pretext for invading Iraq, despite the fact that many of those who opposed the invasion were just as convinced of their continued existence as were those who supported it, and that even Hans Blix, head of the UN team set up to search them out (UNMOVIC), did not believe he had yet got to the bottom of the story. It is surely time to take a more careful look at this complex issue and try to understand rather better what lay behind it, and at the possible consequences of the actions taken at that time.

Saddam Hussein's drive to equip himself with the full panoply of weapons of mass destruction – nuclear, chemical and biological – goes back

David Hannay was British Ambassador to the United Nations from 1990–95. He is now an independent member of the upper house of the British parliament.

 DOI 10.1080/00396330903461641

a long way, and was pursued without the slightest regard for Iraq's status as a signatory of international treaties forswearing the possession of such weapons. The possibility that he might divert highly enriched uranium from the Osirak reactor into a nuclear-weapons programme had led the Israelis to bomb the reactor in 1981; the Iraqis had used chemical weapons liberally in their war with Iran in the 1980s and against their own Kurdish population. What was not by any means fully understood in the period before Iraq's invasion of Kuwait in August 1990 was the full extent of the programmes that were under way, including the development of missiles for the delivery of these weapons. When the UN's inspectors, mandated under the post-Gulf War Security Council Resolution 687, got to work they uncovered a massive nuclear programme designed to pursue several different routes to the production of fissile material and likely to reach fruition by the mid 1990s in a deliverable nuclear weapon; huge stockpiles of chemical weapons, including the nerve agent VX; and, eventually, a nascent biological programme which had not yet proceeded far along the road to weaponisation. All this is fully documented in the reports of the International Atomic Energy Agency and of UNSCOM, the first of the UN agencies set up to get rid of all Iraq's weapons of mass destruction and of the means of their delivery. So that part of the tale is not in doubt.

What conclusions can be drawn from this first intelligence failure? Firstly and most obviously, it was only Saddam Hussein's impetuosity in invading Kuwait in 1990, before his nuclear- and biological-weapons programmes had reached the stage of creating deployable weapons, that saved the world from a far worse crisis. A second conclusion is that the Security Council's decision, in the aftermath of the hostilities, to send in UN inspectors with an unprecedentedly intrusive mandate and powers was fully justified and, indeed, a far-sighted anticipation of what might be required to rise to the challenge to international peace and security from the proliferation of nuclear, biological and chemical weapons in a post-Cold War world. A third conclusion was less positive: that neither the intelligence agencies of the Western World nor the UN inspectors would again allow themselves to be hoodwinked into underestimating Iraq's determination and capacity to develop these weapons. That first intelligence failure to spot how wide and how far advanced Iraq's weapons programmes were before the invasion of Kuwait thus cast a heavy shadow over assessments of Iraq's intentions and potential during the decade-long struggle to implement the provisions of Security Council Resolution 687. The seeds of the groupthink that prevailed in 2002–03 were planted then.

From the very outset of UNSCOM's work in the summer of 1991, Saddam Hussein played a cat-and-mouse game with the inspectors. Their work was impeded and sometimes prevented at every step. An early example was when the inspectors were held in the courtyard of the Ministry of Agriculture for 24 hours while lorry-loads of documents were ferried away from the back of the building. There were plenty of other, less spectacular instances of obfuscation and evasion. The Iraqis also became practised at tabling successive 'full, final and complete' statements on their programmes which revealed precisely as much and no more than the inspectors already knew. As the inspectors came to know more, successive statements were adjusted to take account of that. This practice was continued right up to Iraq's final submission in December 2002, when UNMOVIC took over the task which had been left by UNSCOM when it was withdrawn from Iraq in 1998. It was an approach hardly likely to inspire confidence in the value or completeness of the information being submitted. On their biological programme, Iraq remained in total denial for four years until the gaff was blown by the flight to Jordan of two of Saddam's sons-in-law who had been closely involved in its inception. Another Iraqi tactic was to exclude the inspectors from a range of installations named as 'presidential sites', whose number and extent threw new light on even Saddam Hussein's rather expansive approach to residential accommodation. This game of cat-and-mouse was interspersed with occasions of open confrontation, in 1992 and 1998 in particular, when the United States and Britain launched air attacks against targets connected with the weapons programmes. UNSCOM inspectors were finally withdrawn from Iraq in 1998 ahead of the launching of air attacks and there ensued a hiatus of more than four years when there was no presence or activity of international inspectors in Iraq until the arrival of UNMOVIC

> Saddam played cat-and-mouse with the inspectors

following the Security Council's unanimous decision to give Saddam 'one last chance' to come clean on the totality of his nuclear-, biological- and chemical-weapons programmes.

The cumulative effect of this sorry saga, taken in conjunction with the first intelligence failure prior to the Iraqi invasion of Kuwait, was to instil in all those concerned a deep suspicion that Iraq was still managing to conceal the remnants of its earlier activities and that it was determined to reconstitute those programmes as soon as it could possibly do so. To say this is not to condone some of the manipulative objectives to which intelligence pointing in that direction was put in the run-up to the 2003 invasion of Iraq, but simply to try to understand why such intelligence fell on fertile ground and contributed to a second intelligence failure: the mistaken belief that Iraq actually had some nuclear-, biological- or chemical-weapons assets at its disposal in 2003. It is perhaps also worth asking whether this cat-and-mouse game could have been avoided or brought to an earlier, non-violent conclusion. One reason why it was not was that the United States and Britain gradually drained of all credibility the bargain explicitly set out in UNSCR 687 that, if Iraq rid itself of all its nuclear-, biological- and chemical-weapons programmes, received a clean bill of health from the international inspectors and accepted continuing international monitoring and surveillance of all its dual-use facilities, then the economic sanctions against Iraq would be lifted. We shall never know whether an explicit willingness by Washington and London to honour that bargain might have persuaded Saddam to fulfil his side of it rather than continue to prevaricate and to seek relief from sanctions by successfully subverting the UN's oil-for-food programme. What should not be in doubt is that Iraq could have come clean if it had wanted to and could have got a clean bill of health from the UN inspectors, and that that would have made the maintenance of economic sanctions even more problematic. That, after all, was what South Africa did when it abandoned its nuclear-weapons programme following the end of the apartheid regime, and what Libya did after the invasion of Iraq. The main reason for being cautious over reaching any so potentially benign a conclusion is the considerable evidence that

Iraq could have come clean if it wanted

Saddam Hussein attached overriding importance to being able to continue to convince his neighbours and his own people, as a key part of his aggressive and repressive policies, that he still possessed the potential for nuclear, biological or chemical weapons, and was ready to use it.

This brings us to the third intelligence failure, not often recognised: Saddam's failure, both in 1991 and in 2003, to understand the main drivers behind American policy and the way and the lengths to which it would be pursued. When Saddam invaded Kuwait in August 1990, he clearly thought that he would get away with a slap on the wrist. He completely failed to spot the tectonic shifts that were taking place in international diplomacy as a result of the end of the Cold War; and, even when the Soviet Union's willingness to give UN authority to the forceful reversal of his occupation of Kuwait was signalled ever more clearly during autumn 1990, he paid no attention. Faced with the UN ultimatum expiring in mid January 1991, he chose to believe that the United States, traumatised by its experience in Vietnam, would never dare actually to use force to expel Iraq from Kuwait. Added to that, he grossly overestimated the capacity of his own armed forces, weakened by the long war with Iran which he had himself precipitated on the basis of an earlier intelligence failure, to hold Kuwait. In the run-up to the invasion of Iraq in 2003 he similarly miscalculated, apparently believing that French and Russian opposition in the Security Council would prevent any action by the United States. In the last few weeks before the invasion he passed up every opportunity to make a major shift in policy on nuclear, biological and chemical weapons, which would at the least have greatly complicated the Bush administration's plans and would probably have frustrated their hopes of mustering an international coalition in support of the invasion. To a considerable extent, therefore, in both 1991 and 2003 he brought the roof down on his own head as well as those of his luckless compatriots.

In a dictatorship like Saddam's Iraq, where every major domestic- and foreign-policy decision was taken by a single person, it is well-nigh impossible to establish what role was played in these decisions by the intelligence assessments he received, especially when the person in question is now dead. Certainly there was no lack of resources directed to intelligence work in Saddam's Iraq, although much of it was concentrated on the internal repression of opposition to his rule. But a ruler in power as long as Saddam, and with as brutal an approach as he took to opinions which did not chime with his own, was unlikely to receive objective analyses of the possible consequences of his actions and of the reactions of others to them. This amounts to saying that dictatorships are particularly prone to intelligence failures, as was also demonstrated, for example, in the case of the Argentine junta's seizure of the Falkland Islands in 1982.

What conclusions should one draw and what consequences are likely to flow from this trio of intelligence failures? The most obvious point, and the one most frequently overlooked in the continuing ferocious debate over the rights and wrongs of the invasion of Iraq in 2003, is that, due partly to the fact that these failures had a tendency to cancel each other out, Iraq's nuclear, biological and chemical weapons and programmes have all been removed or destroyed and the risk of their being re-constituted in the future has largely, if not totally, disappeared with the dictator himself. Thus the failure to spot just how far advanced Iraq's programmes were before the invasion of Kuwait was cancelled out by Saddam's impetuosity and failure to identify the likely reaction of the international community when he decided to act before most of his potential nuclear, biological or chemical assets were usable. And the failure to realise these assets had all been destroyed was cancelled out by Saddam's determination to prevent that being clearly and verifiably established. A second point is that this outcome was achieved by concerted international action under the aegis of the UN, which authorised the reversal of Iraq's aggression and carried out the destruction of Iraq's remaining nuclear-, biological- and chemical-weapons programmes. The same could not be said of the invasion of Iraq and the overthrow of Saddam in 2003, but it is hard to deny that those later actions did plug the biggest weakness in the UN's coercive disarmament strategy, namely how to prevent Saddam re-constituting his programmes once sanctions were lifted or had been eroded to the point of futility. Whether or not that justifies those actions is quite another matter, for a wider debate.

Iraq's success during the 1980s in hoodwinking the International Atomic Energy Agency and the rest of the international community about the extent of its nuclear-weapons programme, and its cavalier disregard for its obligations under the Biological and Toxic Weapons Convention (supplemented as it has been since then in the nuclear field by similar successful evasions of safeguards by North Korea and Iran) has surely underlined that more effective preventive international mechanisms need to be put in place to deter others from going down this road. Absolute certainty of prevention may not be obtainable, but the bar to successful evasion can be raised much higher than it is at present. This points to making the International Atomic Energy Agency's Additional Protocol universal, either by agreement, by mandatory action or by making its adoption a condition of supply of civil nuclear technology; to ensuring that the withdrawal option in the Nuclear Non-Proliferation Treaty cannot be used as an easy and cost-free exit from its obligations; and to encouraging multinational, internationally guaranteed provision of uranium-enrichment and reprocessing services to bona fide civil nuclear users. And it also points to the need, at the next review conference on the Biological and Toxic Weapons Convention in 2011, to finally grasp the nettle of verification and the need for challenge inspections if the provisions of that treaty are not in future to be flouted with impunity.

One very evident consequence of the failure to realise that Iraq no longer had any usable nuclear, biological or chemical assets or delivery vehicles by the time the invasion took place in 2003 is the damage that has been done to the credibility of intelligence about such programmes in countries known to be, or suspected of, breaking their international obligations; and that damage has been compounded by the unjustified and excessive public-relations use to which that intelligence was put in the case of Iraq. Here we face a paradox. Any country which has embarked on a course of evading its international obligations not to develop nuclear-, biological- or chemical-weapons programmes is bound to surround its activities with the tightest secrecy it can achieve. Obtaining intelligence that penetrates that blanket security is likely only to be partially successful. The picture provided by intelligence will therefore inevitably be patchy and often hard to interpret. But it may well be the only picture available to the international community before the country in question completes a successful breakout from its international obligations with obviously damaging consequences for international peace and security. It would thus seem to be a high priority to re-establish and strengthen the credibility of such intelligence material. To do that may require those countries possessing the intelligence and wishing to convince others of its validity to accept its being reviewed by some international peer group or panel. That will not be easily accepted or achieved. But, if the alternative is ingrained scepticism and opposition to the taking of collective action, it is a course that may need to be tried.

This assessment is designed to throw some light on a complex series of issues which have recently become so heavily politicised as to resist objective analysis. No doubt it will anger both protagonists of the invasion of Iraq in 2003 and those who believe that that course of action had no legitimacy and was in fact contrary to international law. It does not position itself in either of those camps. But, as we move into a period when proliferation of weapons of mass destruction looks likely to occupy an ever more prominent place in international diplomacy, it could be important to be able to deal with the different shades of grey that will prevail in this field rather than with a black and white picture which is unlikely to be obtainable.

Climate Change and Copenhagen: Many Paths Forward

Paula J. Dobriansky and Vaughan C. Turekian

As talks get under way in December 2009 in Copenhagen, Denmark to negotiate a successor to the 1997 Kyoto Protocol, few believe that the nearly 190 countries taking part will have an easy time finalising a global climate treaty under the UN Framework Convention on Climate Change (UNFCCC). Fortunately, the 12 years since the conclusion of Kyoto have provided an abundance of ideas and experiences that can contribute to effective global action to address climate change.

The ultimate issue for Copenhagen is whether a critical mass of major greenhouse-gas-emitting nations, particularly rapidly developing countries and the United States, is willing to sign on to a legally binding international treaty on climate change that identifies targets and timetables for greenhouse-gas reductions. Without this critical mass, Copenhagen is unlikely to produce results of historic significance.

While the stakes of this process are high, the intense focus on Copenhagen among diplomats, the environmental community, industry and the media should not obscure the fact that these talks are only one facet of the intricate and diverse set of discussions and activities that have emerged globally to develop both technical and policy solutions to climate change. Individually, developed and developing countries are establishing and implementing

Paula J. Dobriansky is a former Under Secretary of State for Global Affairs and is currently a Senior Fellow at Harvard University's Belfer Center for Science and International Affairs. **Vaughan C. Turekian** is the Chief International Officer and Director for the Center for Science Diplomacy at the American Association for the Advancement of Science. He served previously as an adviser on science and climate-change issues at the US Department of State.

Survival | vol. 51 no. 6 | December 2009–January 2010 | pp. 21–28 DOI 10.1080/00396330903461658

national policies and investing in new technologies. Internationally, governments, companies and non-governmental organisations (NGOs) are working together in numerous venues to share ideas, coordinate policies in such areas as regulation, research and investment, and distil lessons that can be incorporated into new policies. Linking these many efforts, which range from large international exchanges to targeted multilateral groups to action-oriented partnerships, will be crucial to any successful outcome in Copenhagen and beyond. Together, these broad and diverse efforts can become powerful and mutually reinforcing tools. And they are central to success in combating climate change.

International efforts

The UN Framework Convention on Climate Change is the premier international forum for climate-change negotiations, and the results of its December 2009 Copenhagen conference will strongly shape global attitudes toward international efforts to reduce emissions. Created during the 1992 UN Conference on Environment and Development, the UNFCCC defines its core objective as the 'stabilisation of greenhouse gas concentrations in the atmosphere at a level that would prevent dangerous anthropogenic interference with the climate system' – in other words, limiting the impact of human activity on the global climate. In working towards this goal, the convention codifies national commitments for developing policies to reduce greenhouse-gas emissions, promotes technology transfer from developed to developing countries, and shares information about national policies and their effectiveness.

Negotiations between and during the UNFCCC's annual Conference of Parties (COP) meetings usually focus on setting a single emissions target for developed countries while eschewing targets for rapidly developing countries. While this is in keeping with the UNFCCC's principle of 'common but differentiated responsibility' for developed and developing countries in reducing emissions, it has predictably led to gridlock and frustration as each group presses the other to make a more significant commitment. Our own experiences, informed by collectively attending over half the COP meetings to date, suggest that the greatest strengths of the COP process lie in its role as a forum for coordinating national and multilateral efforts. COP meetings enjoy a unique status as inclusive venues in which each country, regardless of size, has a voice and an ability to highlight its efforts, and as forums for countries to pledge actions and review lessons from concrete experiences. Focusing on these positive elements rather than target-based regulations could enhance the UNFCCC's potentially powerful but often unrealised contribution to the overall climate-change challenge.

Multilateral groups

Another important lesson of the last 12 years has been that more manageable conversations among smaller groups of countries are often more effective in identifying practical solutions, especially when they focus on major emitters or specific regions.

The G8 was the initial vehicle for many important climate discussions. Over time, however, it became increasingly clear that its potential impact was limited by the exclusion of large developing economies. As a result, the G8 launched the G8+5, including Brazil, China, India, Mexico and South Africa, at its 2005 Summit in Gleneagles, Scotland. Building on the concept of the G8+5, the George W. Bush administration announced the creation of the Major Economies Meeting (MEM) on Energy Security and Climate Change in 2007. The MEM brought together the 17 largest economies, which together represented over 80% of annual greenhouse-gas emissions. The overarching goal of the MEM was to seek agreement among top developed and developing economies on a long-term goal for emissions reductions, and to discuss national policies and international actions to achieve these objectives. Earlier this year, US President Barack Obama replaced the MEM process with the Major Economies Forum on Energy and Climate (MEFEC), which brought together the same 17 economies to try to build consensus on climate-change policy in advance of Copenhagen. Both the MEM and MEFEC processes have been instrumental in building consensus for developing action plans to increase financing for mitigation and adaptation activities, particularly in developing countries. In addition, the meetings have led to general agreement among the major greenhouse emitters on the need for regularised reporting of national emissions inventories.

Regionally based organisations, including the European Union and the Arctic Council, have also done a great deal to develop broad agreement on climate-change policies and a deeper understanding of region-specific climate impacts. The EU process has been instrumental in developing and implementing a regional approach to addressing climate change, including the creation of the novel European-wide Emissions Trading System. As the world's largest multinational emissions-trading scheme, it provides an important model and experience as countries beyond Europe work to identify potential mechanisms for efficiently reducing greenhouse-gas emissions. The EU process is also working to develop a regional target for energy production from renewable sources.

The Arctic Council has been a particularly valuable forum to bring together the various stakeholders of the Arctic region (NGOs, ethnic communities, national governments) at the political and technical levels to evaluate the economic and ecological implications of climate change. The Arctic Council's landmark 2004 Arctic Climate Impact Assessment provided decision-makers and scientists with critical information about observed and predicted changes in the Arctic climate system that, in turn, facilitated important policy discussions.

Action-oriented partnerships

While action-oriented partnerships, like the groups described above, are also multilateral in structure, they differ from other groupings in that they have been established specifically to develop and implement projects to reduce greenhouse-gas emissions while forging close relationships, sharing resources and coordinating activities. As a rule, these partnerships work with a targeted group of countries that have both the necessary technical expertise and the capacity to affect the overall rate of growth in greenhouse-gas emissions; focus on practical projects that advance the development or utilisation of technology; and leverage private-sector investment to accelerate action.

The Asia-Pacific Partnership on Clean Development and Climate (APP) is an excellent example of such a partnership. The APP brings together Australia, China, India, Japan, South Korea, the United States and Canada

– which collectively account for over 50% of the world's greenhouse-gas emissions, economic activity and population – to mobilise resources, promote trade policies, and develop specific projects to address energy security, national air-pollution reduction and climate change. It includes public–private partnerships with companies and trade associations and has begun more than 100 projects to expand investment and trade in cleaner energy technologies as well as goods and services in key market sectors.

The Renewable Energy and Energy Efficiency Partnership, launched by the United Kingdom during the 2002 World Summit on Sustainable Development and based in Vienna, uses innovative financing techniques to implement small- to medium-scale technology-deployment projects and helps to develop and promote policies to create and expand markets for renewable energy in major developing economies. This helps to meet two critical goals for developing nations: increasing access to energy essential for economic growth, and limiting or reducing the greenhouse-gas emissions that result from the increasing prosperity their citizens want, need and deserve.

The focus on methane reduction has particular benefit

Other partnerships focus on specific problems or particular technologies, such as the Methane to Markets Partnership, intended to bring cost-effective methane-capture technology to developing countries. The focus on methane reduction has particular benefit given that this gas, a powerful contributor to the greenhouse effect, has a shorter atmospheric lifetime and is easier to remove from the atmosphere than carbon dioxide. Methane is also a key low-carbon energy source in itself (natural gas). Thus, policies and technologies that decrease its leakage into the atmosphere or assist in capturing it can meet the dual objectives of increasing energy supplies while decreasing greenhouse-gas emissions. Other examples include the International Partnership for a Hydrogen Economy, which works to pioneer the development and deployment of hydrogen technologies as a clean energy carrier, the Carbon Sequestration Leadership Forum, which is developing and demonstrating cost-effective methods to capture and store carbon emissions from fossil fuels, and the Global Nuclear Energy Partnership, which is leading nuclear-technology research and development. Finally, China, the European Commission, India, Japan, Russia, South Korea and the United States are cooperating in a cutting-edge partnership – International Thermonuclear Experimental Reactor – that aims to develop fusion energy. While clearly a long-term effort, success in this research could fundamentally change the global energy-production and -delivery system, providing cheap, reliable and abundant energy that will massively reduce greenhouse-gas emissions on a global scale.

Other action

Bilateral partnerships can also significantly advance specific projects that build on areas of commonality. For example, America's Strategic and Economic Dialogue with China has been useful in harmonising climate policies and identifying financial tools to promote clean energy technologies. The United States has also had important dialogues with Japan, on technology and efficiency, and with India, through the US–India Global Issues Forum. The EU and China are working through climate-change partnerships on carbon-reducing strategies, including an agreement to co-finance a carbon-capture and -storage coal plant in China. This demonstration project will serve as a test bed for determining the feasibility of large-scale deployment, especially in rapidly developing and coal-intensive countries.

Additionally, development-bank and NGO activities have shown great promise in providing concrete steps and models for addressing greenhouse-gas emissions. For example, the World Bank's Prototype Carbon Fund creates a public–private partnership to finance specific projects in borrowing countries that lead to greenhouse-gas reductions. It also helps build capacity in these countries by focusing on training and 'learning by doing' approaches to projects. The Congo Basin Forest Partnership demonstrates the potential role of track-two partnerships to develop programmes, policies and projects designed to address forest management. Given the important role that deforestation plays in producing the greenhouse effect, governmental and NGO-led programmes that reduce forest loss are important to a comprehensive global climate-change strategy.

National climate-change efforts are diverse and provide valuable experiences and insights that can also be effectively applied to a global framework. For example, Spain's activities in increasing renewable-energy production, especially wind and solar energy, offer a valuable road map for other countries to learn from. And Brazil's recent experience in developing a biofuel-based energy system, while balancing other sustainability objectives including forest management, will allow for more informed decisions about whether these low-carbon fuels are a practical alternative energy source.

In the United States, there is an ongoing debate about how best to move forward on climate change. Legislation currently under consideration would enact a 'cap and trade' approach. Significantly, although there may be differences over what approach is optimal, there is broad consensus that some form of legislation mandating reduced greenhouse-gas emissions for the US economy will be enacted. In addition, the Environmental Protection Agency has embarked on the path of promulgating, under the existing statutory authority (the Clean Air Act), a bevy of new rules, which would reduce greenhouse-gas emissions from mobile and stationary sources. While such rules are likely to be challenged by industry, there is still widespread belief that, at least eventually, they will come into force. Moreover, there is also a rising tide of litigation by private individuals as well as states against major industrial greenhouse-gas emitters.

In addition to these legislative and regulatory efforts, the United States has invested over the past decade billions of dollars in clean energy technologies. These investments, combined with efficiency standards for automobiles and appliances, provide important drivers for the development and deployment of clean and efficient energy systems. In addition, US states and regions have been important laboratories for different climate and energy policies, such as renewable-energy standards in Texas and cooperative regional greenhouse programmes in the New England states.

* * *

The current global economic crisis highlights the fact that environmental objectives exist in a balance with economic growth, a balance that political leaders struggle to find in their own countries and at the global level. The UNFCCC contributes importantly to achieving a healthy balance by providing an overall framework for action to address climate change and as a regular gathering point for diplomats, policymakers and technical experts from the widest range of countries. As such, it is a unique forum for building partnerships to help countries meet their own national objectives and to forge the consensus needed for success in global efforts to address climate change. It could also help to coordinate international efforts, creating synergies and avoiding duplication.

Despite these many advantages, however, it would be a mistake either to rely solely on UNFCCC processes or to give insufficient resources and attention to the many other venues and partnerships that advance global climate objectives. No agreement in Copenhagen or at any future UNFCCC conferences can succeed without rich and diverse contributions from governments, companies, NGOs and other groups acting individually and collectively.

Great-Power Relations in Asia: A Japanese Perspective

Yukio Okamoto

Japan, the United States and China will need to cooperate to secure the peace, stability and prosperity of Asia-Pacific and indeed the wider world. The three countries must work together to address such problems as climate change, threats to energy security, pandemic diseases, poverty and other urgent problems. With the inclusion of other countries from Europe and Asia in this framework, positive results can be expected.

The alignment of each country's national interests is complicated, however, by differing views about human rights and other basic values, differences that, particularly in the case of China, can be fundamental. One such difference can be found in the field of national security. Japan and the United States wish to maintain the political status quo in Asia; China aims to challenge that status quo. In such cases there is a risk that the defenders of the status quo and its challengers will become trapped in a dangerous and counterproductive competition.

Sea change

Of particular concern to Japan is China's expansionary strategy and its efforts to develop a powerful blue-water navy. Beijing has claimed the greater part of the South China Sea as its territorial waters. It has sought the means of controlling the waters east of what China calls 'First Island Chain' linking

Yukio Okamoto is President of Okamoto Associates, Inc., and Adjunct Professor, Faculty of International Relations, Ritsumeikan University. He served as Special Advisor to Prime Minister Ryutaro Hashimoto (1996–98) and Prime Minister Junichiro Koizumi (2003–04) and as Chairman of the Prime Minister's Task Force on Foreign Relations (2001–03).

Survival | vol. 51 no. 6 | December 2009–January 2010 | pp. 29–35 DOI 10.1080/00396330903465212

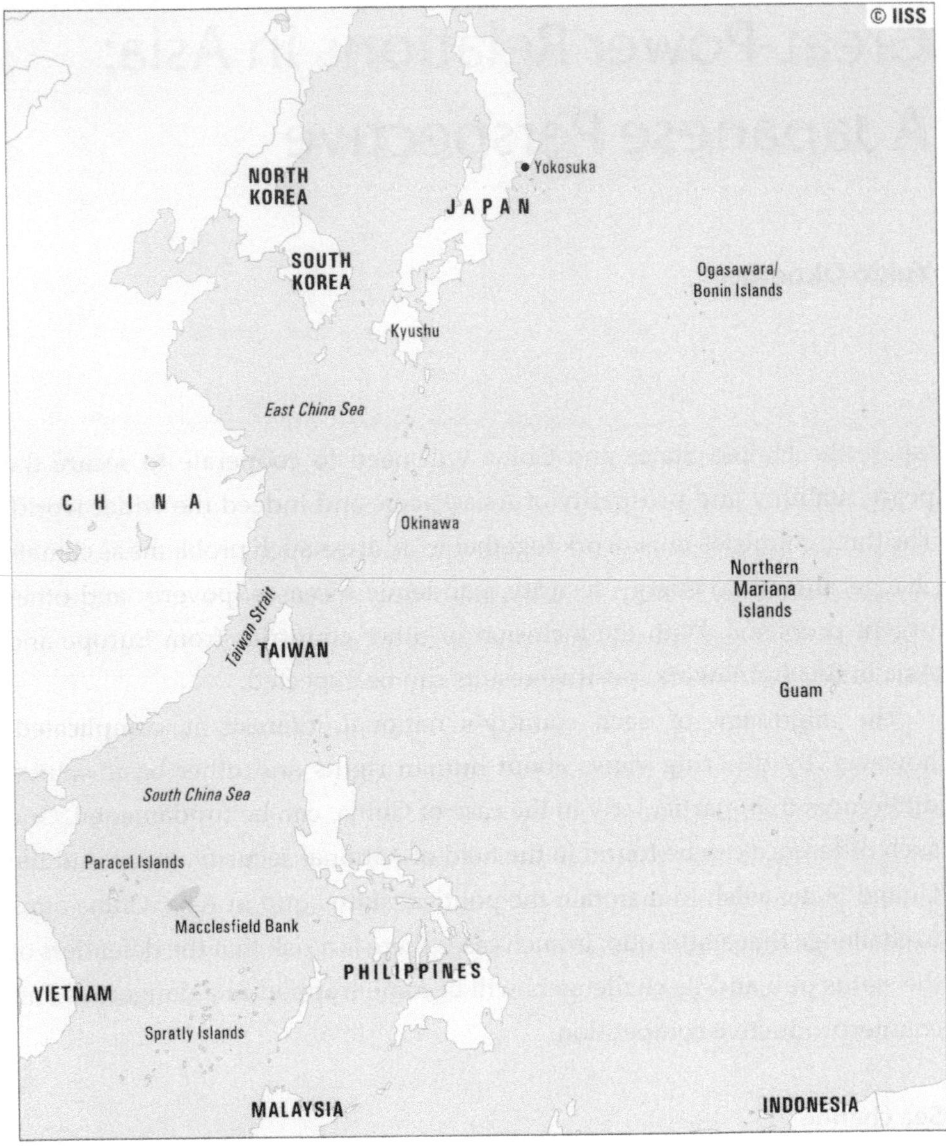

Kyushu, one of the main islands of Japan; the islands of Okinawa; Taiwan; and the Philippines. Recently, five Chinese ships harassed a US Navy surveillance vessel in international waters, while in late 2007 a new city was established to exercise administrative control over a district encompassing the Paracels, the Spratlys and the Macclesfield Bank. It is as though the East China Sea, the Taiwan Straits and the South China Sea have become China's internal waters.

China will soon possess aircraft carriers. It already possesses a formidable 62-vessel submarine fleet. Its strategic nuclear submarines are stacked with nuclear missiles. The country has demonstrated the ability to destroy satellites, and to sneak up on a US carrier strike group. All this suggests that China is equipping itself with the capabilities to go westward beyond the First Island Chain and project power into the western Pacific. China also has a determined policy of denying the US Navy access, during times of contingency, to the Pacific west of the Second Island Chain, stretching from Yokosuka to the Ogasawara/Bonin Islands to Guam and the Marianas. Indeed, many analysts agree that by the year 2030 China will possess such a capability.[1] China's strategy is to prevent US forces from coming to the aid of Taiwan within the waters between the First and Second Island Chains. This would mean that the US and Japanese fleets could no longer operate freely in the West Pacific.

The problem of history

Another destabilising problem is the fact that Japan has still not achieved reconciliation with China over historical grievances. Indeed, the gap between the feelings of the citizens of both countries has widened, not shrunk, in the 60 years since the end of the Second World War. Since 1945, there has been a strong sense of remorse in Japan for having started the Pacific War, which resulted in the total devastation of the Japanese homeland and parts of East Asia. But the Japanese people tend to forget that the original war – the Sino-Japanese War – started in 1931 in Manchuria, ten years before the attack on Pearl Harbor. Japan was the aggressor in the Pacific War, but the country's sense of guilt over this conflict is considerably offset by the terrible price Japan had to pay, with 3 million Japanese victims, including those lost in Hiroshima and Nagasaki. In the case of the Sino-Japanese War, however, there is no way of finding psychological equivalence. Japan was the unequivocal aggressor; China was the unequivocal victim. This is something many Japanese forget. Japan must make great efforts to teach its children about their country's undeniable history of invading China. On the other hand, China must stop using the actions of the Imperial Army of Japan as the foundation for a patriotic education that nurtures antipathy, if not outright hatred, toward Japan among Chinese young people.

Given the gap separating Chinese and Japanese feelings about the war, it will probably be a long time before Japan and China achieve final reconciliation. It may be necessary to establish a framework for reconciliation in East Asia similar to the one established in Europe to achieve reconciliation with Germany. This framework eventually expanded to become the European Union, in which nations that were once enemies – particularly France and Germany – are now able to work together cooperatively. Students in France and Germany today learn history from shared textbooks. I am unsure whether Japan and China could go quite so far on their own. For scholars to craft a joint textbook, there has to be complete freedom of expression and thought among those taking part in the exercise. When one side is not allowed to deviate from the official party line, such an undertaking is unlikely to succeed.

The problem of nuclear proliferation

The actions of North Korea have added a further complicating factor to relations among the Asia-Pacific powers. Pyongyang tested a ballistic missile on 5 April 2009 and a nuclear device on 25 May. It would seem these tests were not attempts to strengthen the North's bargaining position in negotiations or to draw the attention of the United States, but rather were part of a determined plan to eventually acquire nuclear inter-continental ballistic missiles (ICBMs) capable of reaching the western shores of the United States.

The North Koreans are probably not seeking nuclear ICBMs in order to actually launch them against someone. Instead, they seem primarily interested in demonstrating a power-projection capability. Once North Korea has such missiles in hand, it will no longer have to beg the United States for security guarantees. North Korean leaders must also believe that the possession of such weapons will give them an advantage in future negotiations over the unification of the Korean Peninsula. In the interim, the country will be able to sell its nuclear and missile technologies for much-needed hard currency.

There is a tendency, particularly among Americans, to understate the significance of North Korea's actions because its missile and nuclear capabilities are still at a primitive stage of development. But these tests are a sign that the global nuclear non-proliferation system is failing. It is clear that merely extending the Nuclear Non-proliferation Treaty (NPT) will not be enough to keep the world safe from nuclear weapons. India, Pakistan and Israel all obtained nuclear weapons outside the framework of the treaty. North Korea, once an NPT member, is now a primitive nuclear-weapons state. Iran will likely follow suit. President Barack Obama has presented an optimistic and uplifting vision of a world without nuclear weapons, but getting to that point over the long term will be no simple task. The difficult issues of process and procedures should not be underemphasised. Japan welcomes Obama's initiative; however, the country cannot allow itself to be carried away by euphoria based upon a manifesto.

The global nuclear non-proliferation system is failing

If the further nuclear armament of North Korea is to be restrained even a little, it will be due to pressure from China, rather than the United States. North Korea is dependent on China for food and energy. China, however, is not likely to pressure Pyongyang for fear of triggering the regime's collapse, which could result in the creation of a unified, pro-America Korea facing China across the Yalu River. The United States should recognise that it needs to negotiate with China more than with North Korea. Before China can agree to work with the United States, however, Beijing will need a guarantee that, in the event of Korea's reunification, China's worries will not come true.

Both China and the United States need to take on the task of reducing nuclear weapons in East Asia in a serious way. The international community, including Japan, have registered their protests at the illegality of North Korea's acquisition of nuclear weapons. For Japan, however, once North Korea's possession of nuclear weapons becomes a fait accompli, the threat will not lie in whether the acquisition process was legal but rather in the capabilities and policy intentions of the countries that possess nuclear weapons.

Of these, the intentions of China are of no less interest than those of North Korea. China has deployed over 170 missiles fitted with nuclear warheads.

In 1998 the Chinese government announced that China would de-target its missiles pointed at the United States. The question being asked in Tokyo is where those missiles are being aimed now, besides Taiwan.

* * *

Japan chose to enter an alliance with the United States as a means of maintaining its security after the Second World War. This was the country's only real option, as a constitutional ban on the possession of offensive weapons precluded the option of 'armed neutrality'. This alliance has served Japan well, enabling it to enjoy peace and stability for more than half a century. At the time the alliance was concluded, however, the current dynamism and growing importance of China was not foreseen. While Japan has to steadfastly maintain its alliance with the United States, the new geopolitical situation in East Asia and the need for a cooperative relationship with China must be included in the equation.

In China in 1990, only 1% of the population had incomes of over $6,000 a year. Today the proportion is 35%. By 2020, that proportion will double again.[2] As China grows in affluence and its relations with other countries mature, tripartite cooperation among Beijing, Washington and Tokyo offers the best way to secure the future stability and prosperity of the Asia-Pacific region. The advent of the government of Yukio Hatoyama has raised hopes of improvement in Japan–Asia relations. With Asia projected to produce half of the world's GDP in the year 2030,[3] Asian countries need to be responsible in managing their relations and must strive to develop a cohesive relationship. Improvement in the Japan–Asia relationship, however, should not come at the cost of the close Japan–US relationship. The two are perfectly compatible.

Notes

1 US Department of Defense, *Military Power of the People's Republic of China 2009* (Washington DC: Government Printing Office, 2009), p. 18.

2 Dominic Wilson and Raluca Dragusanu, 'The Expanding Middle: The Exploding World Middle Class and Falling Global Inequality',

Goldman Sachs Economics Papers No. 170, 7 July 2008, p. 10, http://www2.goldmansachs.com/ideas/global-economic-outlook/expanding-middle.pdf.

3 Angus Maddison, 'Shares of the Rich and the Rest of the World in the World Economy: Income Divergence Between Nations, 1820–2030', *Asian Economic Policy Review*, 2008, p. 8, http://www2.warwick.ac.uk/fac/soc/economics/news/forums/conferences/econchange/programme/maddison.pdf.

Noteworthy

Debating Afghanistan

'Had the Taliban given up the al-Qaeda leadership we might not have gone into Afghanistan ... In Pakistan, we are relatively content to deal with the al-Qaeda problem with *Predator* drone strikes ... So would an indicator of success for you in Afghanistan be if in 18 months or two years we could be treating the residual problem the way we are now treating the problem in Pakistan?'

John Chipman, Director-General of the IISS, poses a question to ISAF commander General Stanley McChrystal during his visit to the IISS on 1 October 2009

'The short, glib answer is no. You have to navigate from where you are, not from where you wish you were … A strategy that does not leave Afghanistan in a stable position is probably a short-sighted strategy.'

General McChrystal replies[1]

'Ideally, it's better for military advice to come up through the chain of command.'

US National Security Adviser James Jones reacts to McChrystal's IISS speech[2]

'It is imperative that all of us taking part in these deliberations – civilian and military alike – provide our best advice to the president candidly but privately.'

US Defense Secretary Robert Gates speaks in Washington on 5 October 2009[3]

'We are running the risk of replicating – obviously unintentionally – the fate of the Soviets.'

Former US National Security Adviser Zbigniew Brzezinski speaks on the challenges faced by US and allied forces in Afghanistan at the IISS 2009 Global Strategic Review in Geneva, 11 September 2009[4]

The price of recovery

'There will be some inflation coming through – that's not what we need to worry about now … When inflation comes it's a price you pay. If you get into this kind of hole as you have been, don't imagine one is going to come out of it without very bad side effects. The important thing is to avoid getting into the hole in the first place. Once you're there, the choices aren't brilliant, but I'm sure they've been made in the right direction.'

Keynes biographer Robert Skidelsky responds to a question during the IISS Global Strategic Review Conference about the potential risks of inflation caused by economic stimulus programmes in recession-affected countries[5]

Blame all around

'While the onus of having actually triggered off the war lies with the Georgian side, the Russian side, too, carries the blame for a substantial number of violations of international law.'

Heidi Tagliavini, head of Independent International Fact-Finding Mission on the Conflict in Georgia, delivers a report critical of both sides of the 2008 Georgia–Russia conflict[6]

Survival | vol. 51 no. 6 | December 2009–January 2010 | pp. 36–38 DOI 10.1080/00396330903465246

Iran's little secret

'Iran has been on the wrong side of the law.'

IAEA head Mohamed ElBaradei maintains that Iran should have notified the agency as soon as it began construction on the uranium-enrichment facility near Qom it declared in September 2009[7]

'We are working out a timetable for the inspection and we will soon be writing a letter to [the IAEA] about the location of the facility and others.'

Ali Akbar Salehi, head of Iran's Atomic Energy Organisation, suggests that Iran will allow inspectors to visit not just its newly declared Qom facility but perhaps other sites as well[8]

'Iran seems to have escaped the noose.'

Mark Fitzpatrick, IISS Senior Fellow for Non-proliferation, discusses the implications of Iran's agreement to allow inspectors at its Qom facility and to ship its enriched uranium to Russia and France for processing into nuclear fuel[9]

300

Approximate number of US Special Forces troops that supported the overthrow of Afghanistan's Taliban government in 2001

67,000

Approximate number of US troops in Afghanistan today[13]

Lecturing the UN

'It should not be called the Security Council, it should be called the terror council.'

Libyan leader Muammar Gadhafi delivers his maiden speech before the UN General Assembly on 23 September 2009[10]

'I just can't take it any more!'

Muammar Gadhafi's personal interpreter breaks down 75 minutes into the Libyan leader's speech at the United Nations on 23 September 2009[11]

'I am not going to speak any more than Gadhafi. Gadhafi has said all there is to say.'

President Hugo Chávez addresses the UN General Assembly[12]

7

Rank of the United States in list of most-admired countries globally, 2008

1

Rank in 2009[14]

Monster madness

'We [face] an ideological monster which was also created by us sitting here in the free world as an instrument of war. Now the instrument of war has tried to change the world.'

Pakistani President Asif Ali Zardari speaks at the IISS in London on 18 September 2009[15]

Sources: 1 General Stanley McChrystal, Address, London, 1 October 2009, http://www.iiss.org/recent-key-addresses/general-stanley-mcchrystal-address/; **2** 'State of the Union with John King', CNN.com, 4 October 2009, http://transcripts.cnn.com/TRANSCRIPTS/0910/04/sotu.04.html; **3** Robert M. Gates, speech for the Association of the United States Army, 5 October 2009, http://www.defenselink.mil/speeches/speech.aspx?speechid=1383; **4** Zbigniew Brzezinski, Keynote Address, The 7th IISS Global Strategic Review, Geneva, 11 September 2009, http://www.iiss.org/conferences/global-strategic-review/global-strategic-review-2009/plenary-sessions-and-speeches-2009/keynote-address-dr-zbigniew-brzezinski/; **5** Robert Skidelsky, 'The Economic Crisis and International Order', Fourth Plenary Session, The 7th IISS Global Strategic Review, Geneva, 13 September 2009, http://www.iiss.org/conferences/global-strategic-review/global-strategic-review-2009/plenary-sessions-and-speeches-2009/lord-robert-skidelsky/; **6** Stefan Wagstyl and Charles Clover, 'Georgia Fired First Shots in War – Report', FT.com, 30 September 2009, http://www.ft.com/cms/s/0/830d20ec-adc5-11de-bb8a-00144feabdc0.html?catid=6&SID=google; **7** 'IAEA: Iran Broke Law by Not Revealing Nuclear Facility', CNN.com, 30 September 2009, http://edition.cnn.com/2009/WORLD/meast/09/30/iran.iaea.nuclear/index.html; **8** 'Iran To Give Time Soon for Atom Plant Inspection: TV', Reuters, 29 September 2009, http://www.reuters.com/article/topNews/idUSTRE58S0W220090929; **9** Mark Fitzpatrick, 'Assessing Iranian Nuclear Developments', London, 7 October 2009, http://www.iiss.org/whats-new/iiss-podcasts/event-webcasts/assessing-iranian-nuclear-developments/; **10** Muammar Gadhafi, official statement, General Debate of the 64th Session of the United Nations General Assembly, 23 September 2009, http://www.un.org/ga/64/generaldebate/LY.shtml; **11** Chuck Bennett and Jeremy Olshan, 'Translator Collapsed During Khadafy's Rambling Diatribe', *New York Post*, 24 September 2009, http://www.nypost.com/p/news/international/translator_collapsed_during_khadafy_EAHR9j2jHOt8Y6TFRhrcQM; **12** Hugo Chávez, official statement, General Debate of the 64th Session of the United Nations General Assembly, 24 September 2009, http://www.un.org/ga/64/generaldebate/VE.shtml; **13** Alison Smale, 'A Somber Warning on Afghanistan', *New York Times*, 13 September 2009, http://www.nytimes.com/2009/09/14/world/europe/14nato.html; 'Bleak U.S. Job Market Boosts Military Recruitment', Reuters, 13 October 2009, http://www.reuters.com/article/topNews/idUSTRE59C5O320091013; **14** Patricia Reaney, 'U.S. Most Admired Country Globally: Survey', Yahoo News, 5 October 2009, http://news.yahoo.com/s/nm/20091005/lf_nm_life/us_usa_status; **15** President Asif Ali Zardari, Address, London, 18 September 2009, http://www.iiss.org/recent-key-addresses/he-president-asif-ali-zardari-address/.

The Unravelling of the Cold War Settlement

Daniel Deudney and G. John Ikenberry

Twenty years ago, as the Cold War was being ushered to a close, American and Russian leaders together articulated a vision of an emerging world order. They also crafted a settlement with principles and arrangements intended to constitute a great-power peace as well as to extend the liberal international order. Unlike any previous settlement, the Cold War settlement's arms-control centrepiece was based not on the strength of the victor and weakness of the defeated but rather the mutual vulnerability both parties faced from a new type of weapon. Coming after five decades of intense antagonism and rivalry, this diplomatic realignment of Russia and the West seemed to mark an epochal shift in world politics. Today, the promise these arrangements once held now seems distant. Over the last decade, the relationship between Russia and the West has become increasingly acrimonious and conflictual. For both sides, relations are now marked by a sense of grievance, disappointment and dashed expectations. Many expect a future based not on a cooperative partnership but rather renewed rivalry and geopolitical conflict, in effect a return to the nineteenth century.[1]

The new administration of President Barack Obama sees the repair of the relationship with Russia as a major foreign-policy objective, and is ambitiously attempting to reset it and place it on a more positive footing. These efforts began with conversations during Obama's July 2009 trip to Moscow

Daniel Deudney is Associate Professor of Political Science, Johns Hopkins University. His most recent book is *Bounding Power: Republican Security Theory from the Polis to the Global Village* (Princeton University Press, 2007). **G. John Ikenberry** is Albert G. Milbank Professor of Politics and International Affairs at Princeton University and a Global Eminence Scholar at Kyung Hee University, Korea.

Survival | vol. 51 no. 6 | December 2009–January 2010 | pp. 39–62 DOI 10.1080/00396330903461666

and have already produced a major foreign-policy shift with the decision to replace the deployment of silo-based ballistic-missile interceptors and radars in Eastern Europe with a more flexible sea- and land-based system. Already this new policy has provoked a chorus of condemnation that the United States is appeasing Russia and sacrificing both its national interests and the interests of democratic allies in Eastern Europe and the former Soviet region.[2] In reality, the Obama policy is a move toward recovering some of America's most successful foreign-policy approaches that reached a zenith at the end of the Cold War under the later Reagan administration and the George H.W. Bush administration.

The premise of the new Obama policy is that the stakes in the relationship with Russia are very large – even larger than is widely appreciated. Its proponents recognise that achieving the goals of an American interest-based foreign policy in many areas – nuclear weapons and non-proliferation, terrorism, energy supply and climate change, and peaceful change in the former Soviet sphere – requires a cooperative relationship with Russia.[3] A further deterioration of relations will not only undermine these goals, but also holds the unappealing prospect of a return to the type of full-blown great-power rivalry that the Cold War seemed to end. Russia is not powerful enough to dominate the international system or to even be a full peer competitor, but it is capable of playing the role of spoiler. The reigniting of a nuclear arms race and a full-spectrum competitive relationship with Russia would be a major setback for fundamental American security interests. US stakes in the relationship with Russia are not as great as during the Cold War, but remain important because of the two countries' joint vulnerability to nuclear devastation.

The past – both distant and recent – casts a long shadow over current efforts to reset the relationship. Russia's character and dealings with the world labour under a burden, centuries in the making, of anti-democratic and anti-liberal domestic politics and an often violently antagonistic relationship with the international system. Given Russia's past and much of its present, it is all too easy for Americans to conclude that Russia and the United States are doomed to have an inimical relationship. This understandable reaction fails, however, to acknowledge the key role of the Cold War settlement and Russian expectations stemming from it as an independent, and correctable, part of Russia's hostility to the West. The basic fact of the current relationship is that many Russians think, with good reason, that the United States has essentially reneged on key parts of its settlement with post-Soviet Russia. As a result, what most marks Russia's orientation to the world, and to the United States in particular, is a thick and toxic narrative of grievance. The key to a successful reset policy is for the United States to address these grievances, which are intelligible only in terms of the Cold War settlement.

The basic reason for Russian antagonism toward the United States is the widespread Russian perception that Washington has encroached upon legitimate and historical Russian national and security interests, which were accommodated in the settlement. Three issues dominate this narrative: two decades of NATO expansion into former Warsaw Pact and post-Soviet areas, and the prospect that Georgia and Ukraine could join as well; the termination of the Anti-Ballistic Missile (ABM) Treaty and George W. Bush administration plans for deployment of missile-defence systems in Eastern Europe; and American efforts to orchestrate oil-pipeline routes from the Caspian Basin that circumvent Russia. These American moves underscore and exacerbate the deeper Russian malaise stemming from lost status and diminished influence. Meanwhile, shortfalls on the Russian side, particularly Prime Minister Vladimir Putin's neo-authoritarian tendencies, have undermined America's forbearance toward Moscow and helped justify America's retreat from the principles of the Cold War settlement. It is not today's policy differences but the shadow of the past that most plagues the US–Russian relationship.

Many Russians think that the US has essentially reneged

Successfully resetting the relationship will require not just looking ahead and building upon current common national interests, as the Obama administration is now attempting to do, but also looking back and addressing the poisoned legacies that have resulted from the unravelling of the Cold War settlement. This settlement had many elements but a major, if not central, feature was a combination of great-power restraint and liberal order building. The principles of accommodation, restraint and integration that defined the settlement were, in turn, expressions of a larger and older agenda of great-power peacemaking and American and Western liberal order building. The key, therefore, to resetting relations is to return to and refurbish the architecture and principles of the Cold War settlement.

Settling the Cold War

In thinking about the shadow of the recent past on the American–Russian relationship, it is vital to put the settlement of the Cold War into proper historical and theoretical perspective. The Cold War did not just end, it was settled. As such, it invites comparison with other conflicts that produced important settlements in world political history. Across the history of the modern state system, settlements in the wake of great conflicts have become ordering moments, at which the rules and institutions of the international order were on the table for negotiation and change. The principle components of settlements are peace conferences, comprehensive treaties and post-war agreements on principles of order. At these rare junctures, the great powers are forced to grapple with and come to agreement on the general principles and arrangements of international order. These ordering moments not only ratify the outcome of the war, they also lay out common understandings, rules and expectations, and procedures for conflict resolution. Settlements have thus performed a 'quasi-constitutional' function. In effect, they have provided the baseline framework within which subsequent international relations have occurred.[4] Their logic and consequence are unlike those of 'ordinary' foreign policies and grand strategies, which tend to be dominated by short-term, incremental and routine considerations. But there is a tendency for the regular pursuit of the national interest to take for granted these frameworks, and statesmen often fail to take steps to protect and sustain them.

Although settlements vary in their success and features, over the last several centuries there has been a progression of relatively successful ones. These settlements have been a major feature of international order and of the American liberal order, and have emerged in two overlapping phases. In the first, which occurred under the European great-power state system, successful settlements came increasingly to be understood as reflecting principles of restraint associated with the 'society of states'. This way of thinking continues to be a major part of moderate realist practices for maintaining international peace and order. A second phase was American in inspiration, bursting onto the European scene in 1919 with Woodrow Wilson's bold liberal agenda articulated at the Versailles conference. Although not a central piece of the actual First World War peace agreement, this American agenda was picked up and much more extensively elaborated as the basis for the settlement among Western states after the Second World War.

Within the history of the modern state system, diplomatic historians commonly identify the settlements of Westphalia, Utrecht, Vienna, Versailles and Potsdam/Yalta as major international-constitutional moments. Particularly paradigmatic for the first phase of settlement practice and for the moderate realist model of success is the Vienna settlement of the French Revolutionary and Napoleonic Wars. Diplomatic historians characterise the Vienna settlement as particularly successful because it was based on great-power restraint. It integrated the defeated French, recognised legitimate French national and security interests, and put in place a diplomatic process for resolving emergent problems on the basis of shared principles and understandings. The resulting Concert of Europe is widely seen as a model of a stable and peaceful international order.[5]

In contrast, the Versailles settlement was a contradictory combination of punitive and progressive measures. It was punitive in that it embodied British and French demands for retribution; imposed heavy reparations, asymmetrical disarmament and the partial territorial occupation of Germany; and neglected legitimate German national-security interests. Diplomatic historians and moderate realists point to these punitive features as a major reason for its ultimate failure. At the same time, the Versailles settlement launched the League of Nations, which its progressive advocates hoped would usher in an entirely new system of inter-state relations based on advanced liberal principles.

The settlement of the Second World War was more complicated than that of previous conflicts. There was no negotiation with the defeated adversaries, Germany and Japan, and the negotiations that did occur at Potsdam and

Yalta were among the victors, who essentially partitioned Europe between them. Meanwhile, the United States undertook the comprehensive reconstruction of Germany and Japan as liberal-democratic, constitutional states, and championed their integration into the post-war, American-led, liberal international order. This American settlement differed from Vienna, which respected the internal integrity of the defeated regime, but resembled the progressive side of Versailles agreement because it sought to integrate the defeated states into a collective security system. These accomplishments have tended to be overshadowed by the subsequent Cold War antagonism between the major victors of the war, but they mark important advances in liberal order building.

The logic of the Cold War settlement can be more clearly understood in comparison with these previous settlements.[6] As with earlier conflicts, the Cold War was brought to an end with a far-reaching negotiated settlement that its architects optimistically hoped would be the framework for a new international order. This settlement did not come about after any one event but unfolded through a sequence of steps and agreements: the collapse of communism in Eastern Europe, the negotiated withdrawal of the Soviet military and the reunification of Germany, the mutual disarmament of nuclear and conventional forces, and the unexpected collapse of the Soviet Union.[7] All of this occurred rapidly, peacefully and unexpectedly. And these developments were marked by a continuous process of negotiation. Potentially explosive developments were skilfully managed by intensive diplomacy and negotiated agreements and understandings.[8]

To a greater degree than in any previous major conflict, the settlement that ended the Cold War was centred around several major arms-control treaties. Competitive development of nuclear weaponry was the central theatre of rivalry between the United States and the Soviet Union and came to completely overshadow other differences and issues. What made the Soviet–American rivalry radically unlike any previous great-power conflict was that the superpowers had the ability not only to instantly obliterate each other but perhaps all human civilisation as well. How to manage this vulnerability was the central grand-strategy question of the era, and over time, in a long process of fits and starts, came to be the basis for its peaceful conclusion. The central turning point came in the 1980s with the unexpected convergence of US President Ronald Reagan and Soviet leader Mikhail Gorbachev on a view of the nuclear problem that went far beyond the conventional deterrence and war-fighting wisdom of both the Soviet and American security establishments. The crucial point, often forgotten now, is that mutual vulnerability, not superior American strength, was the foundation for the end of the Cold War.

Given this mutual vulnerability, the diplomatic centrepiece of the settlement comprised several arms-control treaties. The Intermediate Nuclear Forces (INF) Treaty completely banned entire classes of weapons based in the European region, and the START I Treaty mandated deep cuts in the Soviet and American long-range strategic nuclear arsenals. These treaties built upon the legacies of the earlier détente period, particularly the ABM Treaty of 1970. That treaty's draconian restraints on defensive deployments were widely understood to be the prerequisites for subsequent offensive-arms reductions. The animating vision of the Cold War settlement was that nuclear arms control would continue, with further rounds of arms-control measures and expansions of security institutions.

The Soviet Union did not view itself as defeated

Of course, previous settlements had also contained arms-control provisions, but these were often highly asymmetrical in character. The common pattern was for arms-control provisions to essentially ratify the paramount position achieved by the victor by the end of the war. What was radically novel about the Cold War settlement was that the arms-control arrangements were explicitly and thoroughly symmetrical. This not only reflected the rough parity in the parties' deployed nuclear forces but also the fundamental equality of vulnerability that motivated the transformation in relations.

The Cold War was also unlike previous conflicts that ended in settlements in that it was, fortunately, a cold rather than a hot war. The Soviet Union did not view itself as defeated and was certainly not devastated or occupied, thus providing very different kinds of opportunities for reconstruction. The Cold War settlement was a hybrid, a mixture of Vienna-like great-power accommodation and Versailles-like liberal international institution building.

Russia's interests would be respected and accommodated, and on the basis of this great-power comity a new architecture of international institutions and cooperation could be built. Unlike Versailles, the punitive element was absent, and post-Soviet Russia (unlike Weimar Germany) would not bear the onus of retribution or diplomatic isolation. And unlike the League of Nations, which excluded Germany, the United Nations after the Cold War would continue to have a major role for the new Russia. Russian reformers hoped that the United Nations after the Cold War would be restored and extended now that it was free of the paralysis caused by the East–West conflict.[9]

Western liberal order and the Cold War settlement

Within the United States, the dominance of the 'Reagan victory' school of Cold War thought has obscured the importance of great-power self-restraint in bringing the war to an end. In this view, an exertion of American ideas and power, catalysed by Reagan's ideological assertiveness and military build-up, and coming after decades of containment and economic weakness under communism, pushed the Soviet Union to make concessions.[10] But this view is too simple, because it suggests that US assertiveness and not self-restraint was decisive. It overlooks the role of Western accommodation, engagement and restraint in making foreign-policy reorientation attractive to the Soviet Union. Moscow was not only checked by American power and purpose, but acted in the context of a wider Western system that made American power more restrained and less threatening. This system and the active diplomacy that embodied its principles made Soviet reorientation and retrenchment possible.

The Russian reformers realised that they lived in a very different international setting, one that was less threatening and potentially more accommodating. Over many centuries, the Russian empire and the Soviet Union had faced a threatening security environment from the West, culminating in the Third Reich's onslaught in the Second World War. Moscow's posture toward the world was understandably one of distrust, paranoia and over-armed vigilance. In earlier eras, Russia and then the Soviet Union faced an international system of aggressive, anti-liberal empires, a world of states and blocs with low interdependence and interaction. In contrast to the Russian historical experience, the relatively benign Western system prevailing in the second half of the twentieth century was starkly novel. The ascent of the United States and the post-war reconstruction of Western Europe as integrated liberal democracies marked a watershed transformation of the Soviet Union's security environment.

This new reality made Soviet reorientation possible.[11] In the sequence of events that marked the end of the Cold War, the pivotal juncture was the Soviet Union's decision to withdraw from its extended ramparts in Central and Eastern Europe. This decision was premised upon the judgement of Soviet leaders that the West would not exploit Soviet vulnerability by encroaching on its historic defensive parameter and sphere of influence to threaten core Soviet security interests. In other words, the United States and its Western allies were successful in signalling restraint to the Soviet leadership. Their retrenchment would not be exploited and their fundamental interests would not be jeopardised. In broader historical perspective, Moscow's voluntary retrenchment from Germany and Eastern Europe has few precedents. Germany had been the lethal adversary of the Soviet Union, and the East European client states were the hard-won fruit of the great sacrifices of the Second World War. In making this historically unprecedented retrenchment, the Soviet Union was signalling its confidence that the NATO allies would not exploit its newly exposed position.

Moscow's voluntary retrenchment has few precedents

This new security environment was not only less threatening, but also offered positive opportunities. The Soviet Union could do more than retrench from its global adversarial posture. It could become, as Gorbachev frequently articulated, a leader in cooperative global problem-solving and institution building. Reformers in Moscow believed that a reoriented Soviet Union could reform, grow and integrate only if the Cold War could be ended. The international system had not only become more benign, it had changed in other important ways as well. With the emergence of the American-led Western system since the Second World War, the international system had become increasingly densely populated with international organisations, transnational networks and market relationships. In all of its complexity, the modern Western-oriented system beckoned the Soviets to join and reap the benefits of interaction and integration. Not only had estrangement become costly and unnecessary, but reconciliation offered opportunities for membership and possibly even leadership.

Of course, the end of the Cold War and its settlement were not simply a matter of international relations, but were also heavily shaped by expectations and agendas for the domestic transformation of the Soviet Union and then Russia. Various domestic-reform agendas required cessation of international antagonism and were thus intimately related to the receptiveness of Soviet rivals to reduced antagonism. Moreover, the Western state system not only provided a suitable international context for major domestic change, it also provided a series of models for what the reformers hoped and expected to accomplish. Initially, Gorbachev and his circle of Soviet reformers held that the project of socialism had been seriously perverted during the decades from Stalin through Brezhnev. They viewed socialism as the realisation and not the violation of democracy and human rights. Their programme of perestroika and glasnost was not a rejection of socialism but rather aimed at its reformation and a return to lost first principles. They optimistically anticipated that their refurbished and revitalised socialist regime would incorporate democratic elements and come to resemble the advanced social democracies of northern Europe. This programme seemed plausible because it was associated with the expectation that modern industrial societies would eventually converge.

After the collapse of the Soviet Union and the ascent of Boris Yeltsin in Russia's first free election, the reformers' goal shifted to another essentially Western model. No longer was Western social democracy the aim, but rather a capitalist-democratic constitutional state. The second wave of reformers also held to a version of convergence, but now the preferred model was much closer to the Anglo-American neo-liberalist paradigm than the social-democratic welfare state.

Despite their profound differences, these two visions of domestic reform had two things in common. Firstly, they were essentially Western models. Secondly, Russian advocates of each model expected that their preferred reconfiguration of the Soviet system could be achieved rapidly. Western observers and leaders also had high expectations that these domestic-reform agendas could be realised, expectations that played a key role in Western thinking about the new international order and Russia's role in it. Thus, the end of the Cold War and its settlement would not only achieve the complete reconfiguration of international relations but also the complete reconfiguration of Russia itself so as to operate within this new world order.

The breakdown of the Cold War settlement

The 20 years since the ending of the Cold War have seen a slow but sure erosion of the principles and architecture of the settlement. Instead of a new world order of comity and integration, the relationship between Russia and the West is marked by grievance, disappointment and unfulfilled expectations. The sources of this deterioration are several. Certainly, the failure of the Soviet and Russian domestic-reform agenda to realise its heady vision of rapid reform and convergence is partly to blame. Instead of Sweden or Texas, Russia still looks a lot like the Soviet Union and the imperial state that came before it.

But much of this souring is the result of American policies. American foreign policy, so successful at the moment of settlement, has pursued goals contrary to the settlement's principles. This occurred through the administrations of both Bill Clinton and George W. Bush as the United States pursued short-term and secondary aims at the expense of more fundamental interests. One reason is that domestic interest groups have excessively shaped American grand strategy. The United States has also undermined the settlement by exploiting its advantages without considering Russian interests. An inflated sense of American unipolar prerogatives, combined with the ascent of an aggressive neo-conservative ideology, has generated an American foreign policy that has lost its sense of restraint and sensitivity to the interest of others. In the overall trajectory of deterioration, three specific issues loom particularly large: NATO expansion and rivalries over former Soviet republics; the termination of the ABM Treaty and the deployment of missile-defence systems; and controversies over oil-pipeline routes from the Caspian Basin.

NATO expansion and arms control

At the top of the list of American violations stoking Russian grievance is the expansion of NATO. The major foreign-policy development in Russian–American relations in the 1990s was the expansion of NATO to include not just former Soviet satellites in Eastern Europe but also parts of the former Soviet Union and empire. Had Gorbachev and the Soviet leadership understood that former Warsaw Pact allies and parts of the Soviet Union itself would become parts of the Western military alliance, it is hard to imagine they would have retrenched so extensively. Russians across the political spectrum view NATO expansion as a major violation of their understanding of the settlement, and this has generated fears of encirclement and encroachment. Advocates of expansion point out that there was no explicit agreement not to expand NATO,[12] but this is misleading because the idea of extensive NATO expansion was simply outside the realm of the thinkable at the time. Rather, the diplomatic conversation at the end of the Cold War concerned architectures that would *integrate* the Soviets (and Russians) into pan-European and pan-Atlantic institutions.[13] The conversation centred on reconfiguring NATO as a political rather than a military alliance, and on questions of whether the Conference for Security and Cooperation in Europe would be expanded to replace or complement NATO.

How did this extensive NATO expansion, so unanticipated in the settlement period, come about so quickly? NATO expansion was both opposed and supported by diverse groups and perspectives. The most prominent critics of NATO expansion were diplomatic historians, Russia specialists and moderate realists, such as George Kennan and John Lewis Gaddis, who argued that NATO expansion violated the principles of great-power restraint embodied in the settlement and was therefore likely to trigger Russian antagonism.[14] In contrast, many East Europeans and hardline, realpolitik analysts viewed NATO expansion as an appealing and prudent hedge against the inevitable reassertion of Russian power. American domestic politics also contributed to the race to expand NATO. The appeal of charismatic Eastern European leaders, most notably Lech Walesa and Václav Havel, combined with the mobilisation of ethnic Eastern European lobby groups in the United States, created powerful pressures for NATO expansion. Domestic American politics, not grand-strategic calculations, carried the day.[15] Liberal internationalists also championed NATO expansion as a tool of democratic consolidation. Locking transitioning Eastern European countries into Western institutions seemed like a useful means of avoiding instability and anti-democratic backsliding. Indeed, the integration of Eastern Europe and former Soviet areas into NATO was seen as an extension of the integrative principles of the overall Cold War settlement. The problem was not with the occurrence of integration but rather with the insufficiency of its reach: integration needed to incorporate Russia itself. But in contrast to the heady visions of the settlement period, the 1990s were marked by the steady atrophy of serious efforts to integrate Russia and to reconfigure Western institutions to accommodate it. And the fact that NATO expansion was occurring at the same time that the Alliance was fighting its first hot war, against Serbia (long the 'little Slavic brother' of Russia in the Balkans), reinforced the Russian perception that NATO was essentially anti-Russian in purpose.

Integration needed to incorporate Russia itself

Nuclear arms control is a second major source of Russian grievance that is rooted in the terms of the Cold War settlement. The deterioration of the nuclear arms-control regime began in the 1990s with a loss of momentum toward further reductions, and culminated in the arms-control rollbacks of the George W. Bush years. The Clinton administration, though committed to the goals of arms control, did not make it a central political objective, and failed to push through either the completion of the START II Treaty or the ratification of the Comprehensive Nuclear Test-Ban Treaty. With the arrival of the G.W. Bush administration, atrophy turned into active opposition. In a move that signalled a major reversal of 50 years of American nuclear policy, the administration announced America's withdrawal from the ABM Treaty and indeed from negotiations across the board.

The causes of this reversal were several. In part, the policies of the Bush administration were simply the product of the long-standing views of the conservative critics of détente and arms control generally. Where Reagan had dramatically broken from his allies on the right, George W. Bush was very much their captive. Like ghosts from the past, arms-control sceptics from previous administrations occupied key positions under Bush, and quickly set about implementing their agenda.[16] At the same time, the near evaporation of popular anti-nuclear sentiment – itself a product of the successful end of the Cold War – meant that the enemies of arms control were unchecked in the American political arena. Also at play was the unexpected divergence during the 1990s in American and Russian power, and in the countries' economic and organisational capabilities. The architecture of the settlement was bipolar, but over the course of the 1990s it became increasingly evident that the distribution of power between the two states was ever more unipolar. Thus, some of the deterioration in the post-Cold War understanding occurred because the American military establishment kept advancing while the Russians largely stopped, creating a growing gap in their capabilities and willingness to adhere to the terms of the settlement. As American capabilities surged and Russian capabilities waned, Washington policymakers increasingly acted as though Russia no longer mattered and the United States could do whatever it wanted. In the American vision of a unipolar world, particularly as understood by the neo-conservatives, the United States could increasingly secure itself and its allies without the hindrance of multilateral cooperation and institutions. Russia's and America's responsibilities and burdens in the broader global system also dramatically diverged as the United States' role, already large, expanded in Europe, the Middle East, South Asia and East Asia, diverting American attention from Russia and making it seem as though the United States could largely discount its concerns.

Western encroachments

A further unexpected source of stress on the relationship between Russia and the West emerged over the newly independent parts of the former Soviet Union. Tensions have arisen over oil and pipelines, the rights of Russian minorities, borders inherited from the Soviet Union, and democratisation in former Soviet states. Questions surrounding the exploitation of energy resources in the Caspian basin, for example, have proven problematic. The sudden independence of the poorer Soviet republics created something of a geopolitical power vacuum in the 1990s. Russian rule over the Central Asian peoples had dated back centuries, and both the Russian empire and the Soviet Union had been multinational empires overlaid with an extensive Russian diaspora community. The picture was further complicated by the fact that the regions surrounding the Caspian Basin contained substantial unexploited reserves of oil and natural gas. Into this volatile mix came American and Western energy companies seeking concessions for exploration and development. The Soviet Union had been organised as an integrated economy with few connections to the outside world. In the 1990s, the United States, at the urging of the energy companies, sought to orchestrate a network of oil pipelines from and through former parts of the Soviet Union in such a way as to bypass and exclude Russian participation and the use of Russian territory. Not surprisingly, this produced Russian fears that the United States was attempting to dominate areas with a historic Russian presence.

Questions concerning the borders and internal politics of the newly independent states are another source of tension within the Russian–American relationship. Some 25 million Russian nationals found themselves outside the borders of Russia after 1991, and their status in the tumultuous new states has been a continuing source of Russian interest, giving Russia both a stake and a set of allies in these fragile areas. An additional complication emerges from the fact that the borders of the newly independent states were taken without adjustment from the borders of the former Soviet republics, which had been essentially administrative units within the Soviet state. A particular flashpoint is the Crimean peninsula on the Black Sea. Historically part of Russia, largely populated by Russians and host to the Russian Black Sea fleet, Crimea became part of Ukraine due to the whim of Nikita Khrushchev, who transferred it from Russia to the Ukrainian Republic in 1954. Finally, Russian suspicions of Western encroachment have been produced by the active role of Americans, Europeans and transnational groups seeking democratic political change in the authoritarian regimes that sprang up in the wake of the Soviet Union's dissolution. Taken together, these complicated and often intractable inherited points of conflict and grievance have weighed heavily upon the Russian–American relationship and undermined Russian expectations about the settlement.

Russian domestic transitions

The unravelling of the Cold War settlement also stems in part from the incomplete democratic-capitalist transition in Russia itself. In the heady days of the early post-Cold War period, many Westerners and Russians anticipated that Russia could make a relatively rapid transition to liberal-democratic capitalism. But a key feature of the Russian transition was its extreme inequality. For the vast majority of Russians, the transition from socialism to capitalism was marked by a catastrophic decline in wages, living standards and social benefits, while key assets of the Soviet state found their way into the hands of a tiny stratum of the population. In retrospect, the legacies of 75 years of communist rule in Russia posed heavy obstacles to the development of a healthy capitalist system.

But the United States and its Western allies also played a key role in the decisions of the 1990s that shaped the direction of the transition. Firstly, the template employed by Westerners seeking to shape the transition was largely inattentive to equality and the fair distribution of assets. It amounted to the export of the prevailing neoliberal, radical market ideologies that were ascendant in the United States in the later decades of the twentieth century.[17] This strain of capitalism, whatever its other virtues and vices, places no emphasis on social equality and is widely associated with rising concentrations of wealth. The extremely oligarchic distribution of wealth in modern Russia is to some significant measure a result of this indifference to asset distribution.

Against this dismal record in Russia, it is worth recalling that another variant of capitalism associated with the New Deal had been the template for the reconstruction of Japan and Germany by American occupation forces after the Second World War. The liberal reconstruction of Germany and Japan had the advantage of operating against completely defeated and discredited adversaries, a circumstance unlike that of the dissolution of the Soviet Union. But the reconstruction of Germany and Japan was also guided by a New Deal variant of Western liberalism that placed heavy emphasis on social and economic equity and the economic empowerment of previously marginal groups such as labour unions, small businesses and farmers.[18] Had the transition in Russia been to a New Deal type of democratic capitalism, the prospects for Russian political liberalisation and stability would have been much greater. The liberalism exported to Russia was not the liberalism of the successful middle years of the twentieth century but rather a radical and lopsided version whose primary beneficiaries were an elite, wealthy minority.

Lessons for liberal grand strategy

Developments since the end of the Cold War hold important lessons for the conduct of American grand strategy and its agenda of liberal order building. How liberal goals are meshed with the pursuit of great-power politics is an enduring problem in American foreign policy. Acknowledging these dilemmas does not resolve them but rather points to deep tensions and trade-offs that must be successfully negotiated on a case-by-case basis. As a starting point, it is vital to reflect upon the deeper dilemmas of liberal order building in a world of great-power relations. Importantly, Washington's deviations from the principles of the Cold War settlement were in part the result of the incomplete and inappropriate pursuit of liberal ends. NATO expansion, while deeply problematic for the relationship with Russia, did play a role in stabilising Eastern Europe, and continues to embody the liberal principles of integration.[19] Similarly, American indifference to the historical legacies of Russian interests in its 'near-abroad' embodies the liberal principles of anti-imperialism, though it does provoke Russian hostility.

Liberal grand strategy necessarily occurs in a world of great-power politics. Although the ultimate liberal agenda is to replace such politics with expanding and deepening democratic accountability, capitalist prosperity and international institutional cooperation, great-power accommodation must precede liberal order building. Paradoxically, unrestrained liberal order building subverts the necessary precondition for its own realisation. This suggests the need for a 'higher liberalism' – a more strategic liberalism – in which the pursuit of liberal order building is tempered by appropriate regard for the historically rooted interests and aspirations of other great powers. The alternative risks triggering nationalist and statist backlashes. In the case of Russia, the liberal agenda embodied in NATO expansion and democracy promotion was blind to its potential effects on Russian historical great-power interests. Ultimately, the prospects for Russian domestic democratisation are retarded by American encroachment and the unravelling of the Cold War settlement. Just as Hitler came to power exploiting German grievances against the punitive Versailles settlement, so too Russia's authoritarian turn is reinforced by grievances against American policies.

A second source of liberal grand-strategic difficulty emerges from the prevailing American attitude toward historical legacies. The Obama administration wants to reset the relationship with Moscow, but the metaphor of 'resetting' is itself revealing of chronic and deep-seated American amnesia about history. A key feature of American exceptionalism is the belief that the world can, in the words Thomas Paine, be 'made new again'. This orientation toward the past is an important part of the positive appeal of the liberal and modernist agenda because it suggests the possibility of escaping from the 'dead hand of history'. The presumption of this worldview is well captured by the reset metaphor, which suggests that it is feasible and desirable to respond to difficulties by simply wiping the slate clean and starting over on the basis of present and future interests. This perspective under-appreciates the extent to which the legacies of the past – memories, grievances, identities – define the present. Successfully repairing the US–Russia relationship will require the United States to not just 'reset' but also 'rewind'. To do this it will be necessary to review and correct the legacies of the recent past that so heavily overshadow the relationship.

Repairing the relationship will require not just 'reset' but 'rewind'

A final lesson for the pursuit of liberal grand strategy concerns the relationship between international settlements and domestic politics. The unravelling of the Cold War settlement points to the way in which architectonic settlements can be undermined by routine foreign-policymaking under the influence of domestic popular interests. At moments of great crisis and opportunity, American leaders have successfully pursued grand-strategic initiatives that both reflected enduring realities of great-power politics and longstanding American liberal principles. This occurred at the end of the Cold War when the George H.W. Bush administration, although incremental by temperament, rose brilliantly to the challenge of shaping a constitutional settlement with the Soviets. Unfortunately, during the 1990s, with attention focused elsewhere, American foreign policy towards Russia and the former Soviet Union drifted from this framework. A combination of hardcore realists and neo-conservatives, together with domestic interest groups representing, in particular, corporations and ethnic communities with foreign attachments, shaped American policy toward Russia. This experience reflects an enduring basic tension in liberal societies: on the one hand, constitutional principles and structures reflect fundamental liberal ideas but, on the other, popular pressures and short-sighted interest groups can subvert them. This problem is particularly acute for international constitutional settlements, which are much less codified and institutionalised than most domestic constitutions. The principles of inter-state constitutional settlements are particularly fragile in the face of incremental pressures and interests because they are negotiated by national security elites and only partially embodied in formal treaties. In the case of the end of the Cold War, the status of the settlement within the American political system was weakened from the outset by the pervasive domestic discourse of 'victory through strength'. This interpretation completely contradicted the 'mutual restraint because of mutual vulnerability' principles of the settlement. The broader lesson is that the United States must find a way to more deeply institutionalise inter-state agreements so that they may be more firmly established. Only by doing this can the United States make these agreements commensurate with their importance in a world of intense and growing interdependence.

Rebuilding the Cold War settlement

The project of restoring the Cold War settlement and its logic to the centre of American foreign policy is vital to realising fundamental American interests. It also constitutes a return to some of America's most successful foreign-policy moments and traditions. The Obama administration's policy toward Russia is not so much a break from the past as an attempt to recover and refurbish a long and successful grand-strategic orientation. Given that it is less than a year old, however, it has not yet gone far enough towards overturning the trademark attributes of the recent George W. Bush administration and returning to the spectacularly successful approaches of the later Reagan and George H.W. Bush administrations. These earlier administrations were successful in part because of unprecedented openings and reversals on the Soviet and Russian side, which created both a necessity and an opportunity for settlement-grade diplomacy. But these earlier administrations were also successful because they made addressing the joint vulnerability created by nuclear weapons central to American grand strategy. In taking advantage of this opening and addressing this central problem, Reagan and Bush drew on a diplomatic toolkit that combined traditional great-power accommodation with the principles of liberal order building. This toolkit still contains the most effective instruments and best roadmap for success.

The Obama administration, in breaking with the tendencies seen under the George W. Bush administration toward unilateralism, hegemonic primacy and active hostility toward most treaties, multilateral approaches and institution building, is restoring the two pillars of successful American grand strategy over the last century. The first pillar, founded on the best practices of the great settlements of the European state system, emphasises the principles of restraint and accommodation. The second pillar is more distinctively American, more recent and more liberal. Over the last century, liberal internationalism has defined some of the most successful accomplishments of American grand strategy. Building on the principles of earlier great-power settlement diplomacy, the liberal programme seeks to institutionalise links across borders to restrain the actions of states and bind them together in a cooperative relationship. The liberal international programme is still a work in progress and its ability to solve today's problems will depend upon the ability of policymakers to demonstrate the same types of creativity and improvisation that have marked its progress to date.

It will not be easy to achieve the restoration of the Cold War settlement and the needed repair of the relationship with Russia. To realise this agenda, Americans will have to discipline themselves to abandon habits and mindsets, recently acquired, that are obsolete and counterproductive. Firstly, it will be necessary for Americans to give up visions of global unipolar dominance. They will have to stop thinking of any concession to Russia as 'appeasement'. And they will have to abandon their 'victory through strength' narrative of the end of the Cold War. This will also require American grand strategy to be set with fundamental, long-term national interests as their primary and overriding goal. Doing this will, in turn, require that the United States stop 'letting the tail wag the dog' through the intrusion of narrow but highly mobilised domestic ethnic, corporate and bureaucratic groups into the policymaking process. Most importantly, Americans will need to cultivate a mindset that puts their interdependence and vulnerability at the centre of their understanding of world affairs.

Notes

1 See Robert Kagan, *The Return of History and the End of Dreams* (New York: Knopf, 2008).

2 For criticism of Obama's Russia policy, see David J. Kramer, 'No 'Grand Bargain'', *Washington Post*, 6 March 2009.

3 Dimitri K. Simes, 'Losing Russia: The Costs of Renewed Confrontation', *Foreign Affairs*, vol. 86, no. 6, November–December 2007, pp. 36–52; Robert Legvold, 'The Russia File: How to Move toward a Strategic Partnership', *Foreign Affairs*, vol. 88, no. 4, July–August 2009, pp. 78–93; Michael Mandlebaum, 'Modest Expectations: Facing Up to Our Russia Options', *The American Interest*, Summer 2009, pp. 50–57; James M. Goldgeier, 'A Realist Reset for Russia: Practical Expectations for U.S.–Russian Relations', *Policy Review*, August–September 2009.

4 See G. John Ikenberry, *After Victory: Institutions, Strategic Restraint, and the Rebuilding of Order after Major War* (Princeton, NJ: Princeton University Press, 2001); Kalevi J. Holsti, *Peace and War: Armed Conflicts and International Orders, 1648–1989* (New York: Cambridge University Press, 1991); Andreas Osiander, *The States System of Europe, 1640–1990: Peacemaking and the Conditions of International Stability* (Oxford: Oxford University Press, 1994); and Jeff Legro, *Rethinking the World: Great Power Strategies and International Order* (Ithaca, NY: Cornell University Press, 2007).

5 See Hedley Bull, *The Anarchical Society*, 3rd ed. (New York: Columbia University Press, 2002).

6 For other discussions of the end of the Cold War as a post-war settlement, see K.J. Holsti, 'The Post-Cold War "Settlement" in Comparative Perspective', in Douglas T. Stuart and Stephen F. Szabo (eds), *Discord and Collaboration in a New Era: Essays in Honor of Arnold Wolfers* (Washington DC: Foreign Policy Institute, Johns Hopkins University, 1994), pp. 37–69; John G. Ruggie, 'Third Try at World Order? America and Multilateralism after the Cold War', *Political Science Quarterly*, vol. 109, no. 4, Autumn, 1994, pp. 553–70; and Ronald Steel, 'Prologue: 1919–1945–1989', in Manfred F. Boemeke, Gerald D. Feldman and Elisabeth Glaser (eds), *The Treaty of Versailles: A Reassessment after 75 Years* (New

York: Cambridge University Press, 1998), pp. 21–34.

7 For accounts of the end of the Cold War, see Raymond L. Garthoff, *The Great Transition: American–Soviet Relations and the End of the Cold War* (Washington DC: The Brookings Institution, 1994); and Don Oberdorfer, *The Turn: From the Cold War to a New Era* (New York: Poseidon Press, 1991).

8 For accounts of the negotiations that followed the fall of the Berlin Wall over the unification of Germany and the wider Cold War settlement, see Philip Zelikow and Condoleezza Rice, *Germany Unified and Europe Transformed: A Study in Statecraft* (Cambridge, MA: Harvard University Press, 1995); and Robert Hutchins, *American Diplomacy and the End of the Cold War: An Insider's Account of U.S. Policy in Europe, 1989–1992* (Baltimore, MD: Johns Hopkins University Press, 1997).

9 See Gorbachev's speeches at the United Nations, especially his address to the General Assembly, 7 December 1988, available at 'The Gorbachev Visit; Excerpts From Speech to U.N. on Major Soviet Military Cuts', *New York Times*, 8 December 1988, http://www.nytimes.com/1988/12/08/world/the-gorbachev-visit-excerpts-from-speech-to-un-on-major-soviet-military-cuts.html.

10 For a popular version of this account, see Peter Schweizer, *Victory: The Reagan Administration's Secret Strategy that Hastened the Collapse of the Soviet Union* (New York: Atlantic Monthly Press, 1994); and Paul Kengor, *The Crusader: Ronald Reagan and the Fall of Communism* (New York: Harper Perennial, 2007).

11 See Daniel Deudney and G. John Ikenberry, 'The International Sources of Soviet Change', *International Security*, vol. 16, no. 3, Winter 1991–92, pp. 74–118.

12 Mark Kramer, 'The Myth of a No-NATO-Enlargement Pledge to Russia', *Washington Quarterly*, April 2009, pp. 39–61.

13 Among the many accounts of these negotiations, see Stephan F. Szabo, *The Diplomacy of German Unification* (New York: St Martin's Press, 1992); Manfred Gortemaker, *Unifying Germany, 1989–90* (New York: St Martin's Press, 1994); and Mary Elise Sarotte, *1989: The Struggle to Create Post-Cold War Europe* (Princeton, NJ: Princeton University Press, 2009). See also James A. Baker, III, *The Politics of Diplomacy: Revolution, War, and Peace, 1989–1992* (New York: Putnam, 1995).

14 See George Kennan, 'A Fateful Error', *New York Times*, 5 February 1997; Michael Mandlebaum, 'Preserving the Peace: The Case Against NATO Expansion', *Foreign Affairs*, vol. 74, no. 3, May–June 1995, pp. 9–13; Paul Kennedy, 'The False Pretense of NATO Expansion', *New Perspectives Quarterly*, vol. 14, no. 3, Summer 1997, pp. 62–3; and John Lewis Gaddis, 'History, Grand Strategy, and NATO Enlargement', *Survival*, vol. 40, no. 1, Spring 1998, pp. 145–51.

15 James M. Goldgeier, *Not Whether But When: The U.S. Decision to Enlarge NATO* (Washington DC: The Brookings Institution, 1999).

16 See James Mann, *Rise of the Vulcans: The History of Bush's War Cabinet* (New York: Viking Press, 2004); and Ivo Daalder and James Lindsay, *America*

Unbound: The Bush Revolution in Foreign Policy (New York: Wiley, 2005).

17 See Marshall Goldman, *Lost Opportunity: What Has Made Reform in Russia So Difficult?* (New York: Norton, 1996).

18 See John Montgomery, *Forced to be Free: The Artificial Revolution in Germany and Japan* (Chicago, IL: University of Chicago Press, 1957).

19 For reflections on the liberal sources of NATO and NATO expansion, see Mary Hampton, *The Wilsonian Impulse: U.S. Foreign Policy, the Alliance, and German Unification* (Boulder, CO: Praeger, 1996).

NATO, Missile Defence and Extended Deterrence

Oliver Thränert

In September 2009 US President Barack Obama announced his decision to shelve the previous Bush administration's plans to install missile-defence components in Poland and the Czech Republic. Obama said that his administration would refocus missile-defence efforts on more proven technology using sea-based interceptors closer to the anticipated launch sites of Iranian missiles. The new administration also indicated that it would base future missile-defence architecture on enhanced collaboration with NATO allies more broadly, rather than bilateral arrangements with specific allies in Central Europe.

Along with the president's Prague speech of April 2009 endorsing the goal of global elimination of nuclear weapons, his decision on missile defence sets the stage for an important reconsideration of the role of nuclear weapons in NATO's defence plans. Although their numbers have been greatly reduced, nuclear weapons still play a significant role in those plans. This will not change any time soon, but the recent American initiatives do suggest that the Alliance should start thinking about a future in which those weapons are no longer deployed in Europe. In particular, technological advances should make it possible for NATO to consider a future in which the security of its members is based more on missile defences than on US nuclear weapons based on European NATO territories.

Oliver Thränert is a Senior Fellow in the International Security Research Division of the Stiftung Wissenschaft und Politik, Berlin.

Survival | vol. 51 no. 6 | December 2009–January 2010 | pp. 63–76 DOI 10.1080/00396330903461674

Since the 1960s, NATO has practiced 'nuclear sharing': the United States deploys nuclear weapons and delivery systems under its strict control in Europe, while some European allies maintain aircraft and (formerly) ballistic missiles for delivery of US nuclear weapons during wartime, and most other members participate in the NATO Nuclear Planning Group. This arrangement has had four functions: to deter the Soviet Union and latterly to hedge against Russian recidivism; to bind the United States to Europe by making the American commitment more credible and visible; to remove incentives for US allies to develop their own nuclear weapons; and to give allies a voice in nuclear force planning.

Today, many believe this arrangement is obsolete. In particular, some German politicians and non-governmental experts argue that US nuclear weapons should be removed from the country as a contribution to the goal of global elimination of nuclear weapons declared by US President Barack Obama in his Prague speech of April 2009.[1] Others in Europe and America maintain that terminating nuclear-sharing arrangements and removing all US nuclear forces from Europe would sharpen the difference within the Alliance between nuclear haves and have-nots. Nuclear weapons would again become symbols of national power and prestige, with negative effects on the political dynamic within NATO.[2] With political decisions looming over modernisation of ageing nuclear delivery systems in Europe, the controversy is set to heat up.

Modernising nuclear forces

The Alliance is already practicing a strategy of minimum nuclear deterrence. At the peak of the Cold War, more than 7,000 US non-strategic nuclear weapons on a wide variety of platforms were available in Europe. Today, only about 200 B61 gravity bombs remain.[3] This weapon, introduced in 1966 and subsequently modified several times, is nominally one of oldest in the US nuclear arsenal but can be regarded as reliable for several more years. More urgent is the reliability of delivery systems. In addition to US fighter wings based at Aviano in Italy and Incirlik in Turkey, the air forces of the Netherlands, Belgium, Italy, Greece, Turkey and Germany maintain in different states of readiness aircraft and crews to use these nuclear weapons during wartime. These aircraft are ageing and their military value is often called into question. The US Air Force has gradually lost interest in stationing nuclear forces in Europe, resulting in the quiet drawdown of such weapons from the UK, Greece, Germany and Turkey.

There is a huge difference between maintaining nuclear forces in Europe and modernising them. Without modernisation, extended nuclear deterrence will wither away over time as ageing weapons and platforms become obsolete. But modernisation would be very difficult both politically and in terms of hardware. The decision process would trigger a debate about strategic requirements, relationships with Russia and other countries to be deterred, the impact of such a decision on the nuclear non-proliferation regime, technical issues and costs. Most importantly, a decision to modernise nuclear forces in Europe would signal that the Alliance is inclined to use nuclear weapons for deterrence until 2050 or beyond – a proposition in stark contrast to Obama's vision of global zero.

Modernising US nuclear forces in Europe was, of course, controversial even during the Cold War. There was, most famously, a general European furore when NATO implemented its 'two-track' decision that included deployment of US *Pershing* II and ground-launched cruise missiles in Europe. With the East–West confrontation now history and the US government aiming at the complete elimination of nuclear weapons, it seems unlikely that the public could now be persuaded in favour of modernisation. It would be an uphill battle for politicians in all countries currently hosting US nuclear forces, with the possible exception of Turkey. In Germany a stable majority of the population has for many years favoured the complete removal of US nuclear forces from national territory.[4] The new conservative–liberal coalition elected in September 2009 aims at the complete elimination of US nuclear forces in Germany, albeit within a NATO context. Against this background, modernisation of German delivery systems for nuclear missions can probably be ruled out, and if Germany refuses, other NATO partners are unlikely to go it alone. Some Central and Eastern European NATO partners might be interested in filling the gap, but they are barred from hosting nuclear weapons by NATO's three 'no's' – no intention, no plan and no reason to deploy nuclear weapons on the territory of new members – first articulated in 1996 and reiterated in the NATO–Russia Founding Act of 1997.[5]

Currently, Belgium and the Netherlands operate F-16 aircraft for nuclear missions, while Germany and Italy use *Tornados*. Both weapons systems could remain in operation until at least about 2020. Two replacement options are under consideration: the F-35 Joint Strike Fighter and the Eurofighter *Typhoon*. The Hague's decision to participate in the F-35 Joint Strike Fighter programme is based on the assumption that this aircraft could be used in both conventional and nuclear roles, although no decision has yet been made whether it should be used for nuclear missions. Belgian policymakers are considering abandoning fighter aircraft altogether and working with France and the Netherlands to secure Belgian airspace, and is thus likely to end participation in nuclear sharing. Italy, like the Netherlands, is participating in the F-35 development and production programme, and may too eventually use the aircraft in a nuclear role. But it cannot be taken for granted that Rome will decide to adopt the F-35. Turkey and Greece, which continue to earmark F-16 aircraft for nuclear missions (albeit in limited states of readiness) have not yet decided whether to replace their F-16s with Joint Strike Fighters. The US Air Force, moreover, uses F-16s based in Italy and Turkey in nuclear roles. If its European partners are unwilling to introduce the F-35 for nuclear missions, the United States can hardly be expected to replace its own nuclear F-16s with F-35s.[6]

Germany has been introducing the *Typhoon* into its air force in a conventional role since 2004, despite many technical and financial problems. It could also be used in a nuclear role, replacing the *Tornado*, if the United States decides to license it for such missions. This is far from certain. For such a license to be issued the Eurofighter consortium would need to allow US authorities to inspect the fighter in ways that might be deemed too intrusive. If it is not possible to license the *Typhoon* for nuclear missions, considerations of cost make it unlikely that Germany would instead purchase the F-35 for use in a nuclear role in addition to the conventional *Typhoon*.

Any decision over modernising NATO's nuclear forces in Europe would be taken in light of NATO–Russia relations. This relationship has deteriorated for several reasons, including the Russia–Georgia war of summer

2008 and Russian complaints about NATO's enlargement policy. Although the Obama administration aims to improve relations, the NATO–Russian relationship will likely continue to experience ups and downs. If relations were to deteriorate to the point where direct military confrontation became more likely, NATO would confront an adversary with a powerful nuclear arsenal. But Moscow no longer has the huge numerical superiority in conventional weapons it enjoyed during the Cold War. NATO now has conventional superiority and does not need to contemplate using forward-based nuclear weapons in the early hours of a military conflict. Even in this worst-case scenario, the value of forward-based US nuclear forces in Europe seems questionable. From the Russian perspective, the presence of a small number of US nuclear weapons in Europe with limited capabilities to penetrate Russian airspace would make little difference to its military calculations. Furthermore a decision to modernise NATO's nuclear forces might be perceived in Moscow as an act of intimidation which would severely damage NATO–Russia relations.

The value of US nuclear forces in Europe seems questionable

Similarly, if Iran becomes nuclear-armed and at the same time more assertive vis-à-vis Israel and its other neighbours, NATO would be affected, not least because Turkey shares a border with Iran and the Alliance is cooperating with Israel and Arab countries through the Mediterranean Dialogue and the Istanbul Cooperation Initiative. Although unlikely, a confrontation between Iran and the United States and NATO in which nuclear weapons could play a role cannot be ruled out entirely. But, again, it would seem unnecessary to have nuclear forces available in Europe. The United States could deter Iran with strategic and sea-based non-strategic forces (sea-launched cruise missiles on attack submarines), and advanced conventional weapons could perform in many ways almost as well as nuclear weapons in many missions.

From a purely military point of view, then, land-based US nuclear weapons in Europe are already of negligible importance. Modernisation would not be necessary even if the political and military environment were to change dramatically. But while no future modernisation is one thing, withdrawal in the foreseeable future is quite a different matter.

Holding the Alliance together

Extended deterrence has always been a complicated endeavour, particularly because credible deterrence is not the same as credible reassurance for allies. During the Cold War, there were numerous discussions within NATO about the requirements for extended deterrence, with the United States often differing from European allies directly exposed to the Soviet threat. Today, things are becoming even more complicated within the Alliance.

Eastern Europeans particularly value America's presence in Europe to counterbalance Russia in light of their 40 years as unwilling parts of the Soviet empire, which distinguishes them from NATO members who experienced the Cold War from the other side of the Iron Curtain. Today, many new NATO members view Russia as increasingly authoritarian, and Moscow's foreign and security policy as assertive, if not aggressive. After the Caucasus crisis of 2008 Eastern Europeans feel the need more than ever to engage the United States militarily in Europe for their protection. These new NATO members are likely to oppose any development that might lead to the imminent withdrawal of US nuclear forces from Europe, fearing a weakening of the US commitment. But threat perceptions do not only differ between NATO members old and new. While Norway does not share the Eastern Europeans' Cold War experiences, it is increasingly concerned about Russian security policy, not least because Moscow has re-introduced its former practice of strategic bomber patrols over the North Sea. Turkey does not worry so much about Moscow, but is concerned about developments in Iran more than other NATO countries. Ankara has a reasonably sound working relationship with Tehran, but from the Turkish perspective its basis is a balance of power between the countries. If Iran were to develop nuclear weapons this balance would change.

A full-scale debate could undermine NATO

Given these threat perceptions, a full-scale debate about US nuclear withdrawal from Europe could trigger a controversy that would undermine NATO cohesion. Many members could lose confidence in the Alliance's defence commitments in general, and the US commitment to defend Europe in particular. Ending the US nuclear presence in Europe would also end

Allies' influence on NATO's nuclear policymaking. Only Washington and London would remain directly involved in NATO nuclear policy (even now that France has become a full NATO member, Paris still does not participate in Nuclear Planning Group meetings). True, the Nuclear Planning Group would continue to work, but it would quickly lose its salience, and NATO members would lose their nuclear competences.

NATO's nuclear sharing has, too, always been a non-proliferation endeavour. The concept was born in the 1960s, when the United States needed to convince the Federal Republic of Germany to forgo a nuclear-weapons option and to adhere to the Nuclear Non-Proliferation Treaty as a non-nuclear state. To reassure Germany and to give Bonn as well as other European allies a say regarding NATO's nuclear policy, the Nuclear Planning Group was created and nuclear sharing implemented. Today, Turkey is perhaps the member state most likely to want to develop its own nuclear weapons. It would not be easy for Ankara to conduct a clandestine programme, but if Iran develops nuclear weapons and at the same time the United States were to withdraw its nuclear installations from Incirlik, those voices in Turkey already talking about a Turkish bomb could become stronger and more influential. Turkish officials already apparently maintain in internal NATO discussions that if the United States were to remove its nuclear weapons from Europe, Ankara would no longer feel bound to the grand bargain of the 1960s to refrain from developing its own nuclear weapons in return for a US nuclear presence in Europe.[7]

Finally, if all US nuclear assets were removed from Europe, only British and French nuclear forces would remain. Paris might feel invited to offer its nuclear umbrella for European NATO allies, as it has done several times in the past. But many Allies, including Germany, could be expected to oppose such an undertaking. In many European capitals it would be argued that if nuclear extended deterrence was indeed felt necessary, it should be provided by the most powerful and most experienced nuclear country in the West. French and British nuclear forces would be seen as inadequate for the requirements of extended deterrence. And there would be status issues; Germany and other medium powers such as Italy could hardly accept a situation in which France compensated for an American removal and became

Europe's nuclear guarantor. Finally, there is the question of whether France, with its heritage of a strictly national nuclear-weapons programme, would ever be prepared to allow European partners to engage in consultations about its nuclear forces. In France's 2008 Defence White Paper it is argued that Paris cannot participate in the Nuclear Planning Group because its nuclear forces remain totally independent.[8] Moreover, in light of the global zero debate, France's rhetoric about nuclear disarmament does not match US and British visions, contributing to irritations between France and some of its European partners.[9]

The end of US nuclear bases in Europe would not automatically be the end of extended deterrence. Nuclear options could be replaced by advanced conventional capabilities. Moreover, US sea-based nuclear forces such as cruise missiles deployed on attack submarines could become more important for extended deterrence in Europe, as is already the case regarding Japan. But an important NATO symbol would be phased out irrevocably, unless a severe crisis involving Russia or the Middle East were to occur. In such a case, redeployment of nuclear forces to Europe would not only create tremendous logistical problems but would contribute to escalation of the crisis.

Arms control

Currently, Russia has about 3,800 tactical nuclear warheads, with a large additional number in reserve.[10] Moscow sees its numerical superiority compared to NATO's non-strategic nuclear forces in Europe as a counterbalance to NATO's conventional advantages and NATO enlargement. Russian military planners are apparently putting increasing emphasis on non-strategic forces to defend their country. Reportedly, they are even discussing using low-yield nuclear 'scalpels' to defeat NATO conventional forces,[11] a development that worries Western analysts. Moreover, the START follow-on agreement currently being negotiated, limiting both Russian and American strategic nuclear forces, is likely to increase the significance of the imbalance in non-strategic weapons. Both American and European analysts argue, therefore, that non-strategic nuclear forces should be included in future arms-control treaties. At the very least, confidence should be improved through transparency measures.

Moscow, however, seems uninterested. Still angered by NATO enlargement, many Russian experts and politicians take the view that Russia should not offer any more concessions. As a matter of principle, they say Russia should not agree to any arms-control activity regarding non-strategic forces as long as US nuclear forces remain in Europe. According to the dominant Russian view, there is no justification for this deployment. Russian analysts oppose transparency measures on the grounds they would be too intrusive, involving the nuclear warheads themselves rather than simply the delivery systems.[12]

But if NATO were to unilaterally remove all US nuclear forces from Europe as a contribution to nuclear disarmament, as many in Western Europe advocate, what incentive would Moscow then have to accept arms-control initiatives aimed at transparency and reductions? A more convincing political strategy would be to use the existing US nuclear assets in Europe as bargaining chips to involve Russia in new arms-control efforts covering non-strategic forces. A first step could be to arrange for transparency measures such as declarations and visits to non-strategic nuclear-force deployments sites. A two-track approach, announcing the modernisation of US nuclear forces in Europe if arms control does not result in significant reductions of Russian non-strategic nuclear weapons, would not be convincing; it would only encourage Moscow to launch yet another public-diplomacy offensive aimed at splitting NATO, one Russia might this time be expected to win because of the changes in attitude among European publics since the 1980s.

A decision to modernise US nuclear forces in Europe would also have a negative effect on the nuclear non-proliferation regime. Egypt, for example, has for many years complained that the continued deployment of nuclear weapons in territories of non-nuclear-weapon states through nuclear-sharing arrangements undermines the objectives of the non-proliferation treaty, particularly with a view to the presumed equality among non-nuclear-weapon states.[13] This view is shared by other non-nuclear states parties to the treaty. A NATO decision to modernise would be seen as yet another, typical Western double standard. Many countries could thus be expected to oppose Western efforts to improve verification and enforcement mechanisms under the treaty.

Moving to missile defence

While US nuclear forces still remain in Europe, NATO should develop missile defences as an ever more important element of its defence posture, adding a strong element of deterrence by denial. An effective missile-defence system could substitute for nuclear sharing as a means to keep the United States committed to European defence. Obama made it clear in September 2009 that he favours a multilateral approach on missile defence including all NATO allies rather than bilateral arrangements with certain Alliance members, as preferred by the previous administration. Effective missile defences – sea-based SM-3 missiles and *Aegis* systems to be deployed in the Mediterranean and North Sea by 2011 and SM-3s to be stationed on the territory of southern and central European NATO partners by 2015 – would provide protection for NATO as a whole.[14] Allies could have new opportunities to actively participate in NATO force planning through arrangements similar to the Nuclear Planning Group. In particular, member states such as Turkey would not feel a need to develop their own nuclear weapons. Finally, a NATO missile-defence endeavour would not differentiate between nuclear and non-nuclear European NATO countries, avoiding special status for France or Great Britain. The aim would be to have a NATO missile defence as a substitute for the US nuclear presence in Europe by the time the decision to modernise nuclear forces would need to be made.

NATO missile defence makes sense militarily

In contrast to a decision to modernise nuclear assets in Europe, such a NATO missile-defence project would make sense militarily. It would deal with one of the most likely military threats the Alliance will face in the medium term. More nuclear powers may emerge, particularly in NATO's immediate neighbourhood in the Middle East, some possessing advanced ballistic missiles. While such nuclear newcomers would not be so irrational as to attack NATO, still the most powerful military alliance in the world, they might conduct aggression against their non-nuclear neighbours. As an alliance that might be mandated by the UN Security Council for military operations to reconstitute order, NATO could face the need to decide whether it wanted to intervene with conventional forces in a contingency that might end up in intentional or unintentional nuclear escalation. Deliberately accepting one's own vulnerability, as during the Cold War, does not seem the appropriate strategic approach in such a context. But even limited missile defences would affect an aggressor's calculations. Despite technical limitations, missile defences could provide a damage-limitation option for situations where escalation to the nuclear level could not be ruled out.[15]

NATO already is developing its Active Layered Theatre Ballistic Missile Defense system to protect troops against short- and medium-range missiles. At the 2009 NATO summit in Strasbourg and Kehl, the allies reaffirmed that missile proliferation poses an increasing threat and that missile defence is part of a broad response. The Obama administration remains committed to defend both the US homeland as well as the territories of its allies against missile threats. As Obama pointed out, the new missile-defence architecture will provide stronger, smarter and swifter defences for American forces and allies by changing the emphasis from untested interceptors deployed in Poland to already proven sea-based systems such as *Aegis* or mobile land-based systems such as Terminal High Altitude Area Defense.

There is one important problem in making missile defence a substitute for nuclear sharing. Although US/NATO missile-defence activities are not directed against Russia, Moscow perceives them as an activity that can easily upset strategic parity. Now that the US plans to install missile-defence components in Poland and the Czech Republic have been abandoned, it should be easier to convince Russia that American or NATO missile defences are not aimed at undermining Moscow's nuclear deterrent. After all, as then Russian President Vladimir Putin explained in June 2007, Russia is not opposed to stationing missile-defence interceptors in Turkey or to sea-based systems in the Mediterranean.

The most persuasive way to convince Moscow that Western efforts are not directed against it is to establish missile-defence cooperation between the two sides. Indeed, at their summit meeting in Moscow in July 2009, Obama and Russian President Dmitry Medvedev reached agreement on the establishment of a joint data-exchange centre and on a joint threat assessment on ballistic missiles. It appears it may be possible to make missile defence less of a controversial issue. Russia and NATO face more or less the same threats from ballistic-missile proliferation. To be sure, NATO/US–Russian missile-defence cooperation is not an easy undertaking; most importantly, both sides would need to develop trust and confidence over time to allow for transparency in technical cooperation. Given the growing dangers resulting from nuclear and ballistic-missile proliferation, however, there is no real alternative to this approach. And, if successful, NATO–Russian missile-defence cooperation could become the nucleus for a wider missile defence that could provide some reassurance against nuclear breakout if a world free of nuclear weapons is ever achieved.

Acknowledgements

This article is based on a presentation given at the conference 'The Future of Extended Deterrence' organised by the Fondation pour la recherche stratégique, Paris, 16 November 2009. I wish to thank Mark Fitzpatrick of the IISS for his useful comments on an earlier version of this article.

Notes

1 See Oliver Meier, 'Steinmeier Calls for U.S. to Withdraw Nukes', *Arms Control Today*, May 2009, pp. 34–6; The White House, Office of the Press Secretary, 'Remarks by President Barack Obama, Hradcany Square Prague, Czech Republic, April 5, 2009', http://www.whitehouse.gov/the_press_office/Remarks-By-President-Barack-Obama-In-Prague-As-Delivered/.

2 See David S. Yost, 'Assurance and US Extended Deterrence in NATO', *International Affairs*, vol. 85, no. 4, July 2009, pp. 755–80; Michael Rühle, 'NATO and Extended Deterrence in a Multinuclear World', *Comparative Strategy*, vol. 28, no. 1, 2009, pp. 10–16.

3 See Robert S. Norris and Hans M. Kristensen, 'Nuclear Notebook: U.S. Nuclear Forces, 2009', *The Bulletin of the Atomic Scientists*, March–April 2009, pp. 59–69.

4 See *Der Spiegel*, May 2005.

5 Press conference by Secretary of State Warren Christopher, NATO Headquarters Brussels, Belgium, 10 December, 1996; Founding Act on Mutual Relations, Cooperation and Security between NATO and the Russian Federation signed in Paris, France, 27 May 1997, http://www.nato.int/cps/en/natolive/official_texts_25468.htm.

6 See Ian Anthony, 'The Future of Nuclear Weapons in NATO', paper presented at the 20th Cercle Stratégique Franco-Allemand, 11–12 June 2009.

7 See Catherine M. Kelleher and Scott L. Warren, 'Getting to Zero Starts Here: Tactical Nuclear Weapons', *Arms*

Control Today, October 2009, www.armscontrol.org/act/2009_10/Kelleher.

8 Yost, 'Assurance and US Extended Deterrence'.

9 See Bruno Tertrais, 'France and Nuclear Abolition: The Odd Country Out?', *Proliferation Analysis*, 3 September 2009, http://www.carnegieendowment.org/publications/index.cfm?fa=view&id=23789.

10 These numbers are taken from *America's Strategic Posture: The Final Report of the Congressional Commission on the Strategic Posture of the United States, William J. Perry (Chairman), James R. Schlesinger (Vice Chairman)* (Washington DC: United States Institute of Peace, 2009), p. 13.

11 *Ibid.*

12 See Nikolai N. Sokov (lead author), 'Tactical (Substrategic) Nuclear Weapons', in *Four Emerging Issues in Arms Control, Disarmament, and Nonproliferation: Opportunities for German Leadership*, The James Martin Centre for Nonproliferation Studies, prepared for the Policy Planning Staff of the Foreign Office of the Federal Republic of Germany, July 2009, pp. 69–100.

13 See statement by H.E. Ambassador Maged Abdel Fatah Abdel Aziz before the Third Session of the Preparatory Committee to the 2010 NPT Review Conference, New York, 4 May 2009.

14 See Robert M. Gates, 'A Better Missile Defense for a Safer Europe', *New York Times*, 20 September 2009.

15 See this argumentation in more detail in Oliver Thränert, 'Europe's Need for a Damage-Limitation Option', in Michael Emerson (ed.), *Readings in European Security*, Volume 5 (Brussels: European Security Forum, 2009), pp. 62–77.

South America: Framing Regional Security

John Chipman and James Lockhart Smith

Summits rarely make for exciting television viewing, but the meeting in August 2009 of the Union of South American Nations (Unasur) in Argentina, convening all heads of state of the organisation, came close. Unasur, uniting 12 South American states into a single institution, had been created in 2008 after several years of negotiation.[1] Originally envisaged as a continental organisation bringing together the region's trade blocs, as from March 2008 it has begun to be used as a forum for regional security management, especially in the Andes. The August 2009 meeting had been called to discuss the controversy surrounding an agreement by which Colombia was to allow the United States access to seven facilities and bases on its soil.[2] Presidents Alvaro Uribe of Colombia and Hugo Chávez of Venezuela, the main parties to the heated regional argument, claimed equal but differing threats to their national and personal security, and expressed opposite views of the US role. Uribe had the previous month leaked information implying that President Chávez continued to assist Colombian insurgents to buy shoulder-launched surface-to-air missiles to be used to bring down the presidential plane,[3] and now spoke harshly of Chávez's affection for them; Chávez referred, in turn, to a plot for his assassination hatched between members of his own opposition and Colombian paramilitaries,[4] and presented an obscure US Air Force White Paper as allegedly disquieting evidence of US imperialism.[5] President Luiz Inácio 'Lula' da Silva of Brazil, Unasur's principal promoter, elicited at

John Chipman is Director-General and Chief Executive of the IISS. **James Lockhart Smith** is Research Associate for Latin America at the IISS. This essay grew out of a speech originally delivered by John Chipman in Santiago, Chile, in August 2009.

Survival | vol. 51 no. 6 | December 2009–January 2010 | pp. 77–104 DOI 10.1080/00396330903461690

the summit a final collective declaration that made token references to drug trafficking and other non-state threats, and promised to build sovereignty-respecting trust in matters of defence and security, but principally warned against the destabilising effects of 'the presence of foreign military forces'.[6] The live coverage of the event, on which Uribe had insisted as a guarantee of transparency and insurance against excessive verbal aggression by his Venezuelan counterpart, in the event served to infect this new regional security institution with the familiar and unproductive rhetoric of megaphone diplomacy. Leaders took turns striking poses for their respective electorates rather than talking to each other and solving issues, in the process presenting distorted vignettes of strategic reality. The summit showed the difficulties in building an effective regional security institution from the top down and revealed the need for Unasur to develop a stronger institutional base. The Defence Council of Unasur, which convenes defence ministers for a more focused agenda, offers the promise of being just the right vehicle, if heads of government are willing to empower it with the means of carrying out a pragmatic agenda of consultations. A measured programme of regular meetings on agreed subjects could in time serve to cultivate a more common strategic culture among South American states and develop settled norms to govern conflict resolution. Summits of heads of government might still be characterised by aggressive rhetoric and grandstanding, but if the Defence Council were to build the underpinnings of professional security relations, the malign effects of theatrical summitry would be containable. The form of Defence Council consultations would have to be closely aligned to the reality of current South American security dilemmas and responsive to the historical suspicions and current political divisions that exist.

In Latin America as elsewhere, the development of effective regional security institutions has been wracked by regional disputes and conflicting attitudes towards the legitimate role of outside powers. For long periods Latin American states suffered from domestic revolutions, military coups and state repression and have struggled to find different forms of independence from the exercise of US power. With the end of the Cold War and the emergence in most cases of imperfect but promising democracies, new threats emerged and were identified. These were predominantly non-state and transnational in nature – for example the trafficking of illegal narcotics, people and weapons, and persistent violent crime, including human-rights violations by state security forces. Human security and democracy were given greater priority. The Organisation of American States (OAS), discredited to varying degrees among Latin American countries during the Cold War because of its perceived manipulation by the United States, found new life as the guarantor of democracy. Sub-regional institutions such as the Andean Community were presented as frameworks for cooperation against drug trafficking and related crime.

In this emerging context, the relevance of recent diplomacy conducted through Unasur is that it exposes clearly the divisions in South American security perspectives. A number of threats that are publicly spoken about are more perceived than real and turn on perceptions of strategic motives that are rooted more in the distant past than in present ambition. Other threats are indeed very real, even if they take on an apparently principally rhetorical form, as in the nationalist posturing of autocratic leaders who want to animate in other countries the populist fervour that they have led in their own. Certainly relations with external powers can appear suspicious unless clearly explained. But if their introduction is related to pre-existing regional tensions, these too have to be more honestly debated. The extent to which Latin American governments might generate or represent security problems for one another remains largely unaddressed in regional forums. Impelled by crisis – the Colombian attack on a Revolutionary Armed Forces of Colombia (FARC) camp in Ecuador in March 2008 and the protracted diplomatic conflict that ensued – South American nations are now seeking to address their security- and defence-related interests and disagreements collectively and in an institutional medium. However, this approach is still no more than embryonic. The enduring desire to hold successful summits rather than admit clear differences leads to communiqués that patch rhetorical disputes, but do not reflect strategic reality. Inspiring more transparency and discussion of defence and foreign policy would be a proper priority of a more effective regional security institution.

A number of threats are more perceived than real

The centre of attention after August's summit in Argentina has continued to be the interests of foreign powers, particularly the United States. As a specific outcome of that meeting, it was decided that confidence-building mechanisms should be designed to give transparency to the implementation of regional and extra-regional military agreements. To that end South American ministers of defence and foreign affairs met in Quito, Ecuador on 16 September. A package of proposals was supposed to be covered: information sharing, transparency and ultimately harmonisation of defence expenditure, and the need for consultation and cooperation regarding unforeseen military operations. In practice, participants again discussed the possible impact of the Bogotá–Washington agreement on relations among South American states, made competing claims about the destabilising effects of increasing military procurement and debated the use of extra-regional alliances to bolster defence capabilities. Unasur's preoccupation with external powers to the near exclusion of intramural issues is unbalanced and a trend in need of repair for the organisation to become useful.

For Latin America at the beginning of the twenty-first century, both regional security problems and regional security management start not with the penetration of foreign powers, but at home, with the quality of governance. The difficulties encountered towards the construction of a Latin American security community occur in four dimensions – domestic, transnational, regional and international – and domestic determinants of conflict are not only among the most important, their consideration is essential for understanding the other three. Good governance is the primary driver of sound strategic policy. Achieving that is a political task, but better habits could also be bred by requiring states to be more transparent in their reporting to regional security structures and therefore, perhaps, more transparent at home.

Domestic and transnational security issues

As has been exhaustively discussed in recent years, Latin American politics have taken a left turn. International observers' initial warnings of a 'red tide' of left-of-centre governments across the region have since been replaced by a more nuanced awareness of the many hues of red and pink involved. The majority of these changes have few security consequences, but in the case of Venezuela, where President Chávez came to power in 1999, the implementation of his national project of the 'Bolivarian Revolution' has an obvious and immediate geopolitical impact. It involves intervention in the politics of neighbouring states with the aim of reviving the original 'Gran Colombia', a single pan-Andean state, and beyond that seeks the emancipation of Latin America as a whole from what are perceived as its oppressive economic and political ties to the United States. Furthermore, Venezuela adjoins Colombia, which since the election of right-wing President Uribe in 2002 has pursued a markedly different agenda from some of its left-wing neighbours. The Colombian and Venezuelan presidents accuse one another of hosting armed groups hostile to the other. Since 2002 relations between the two countries have in general become progressively worse. This situation, in combination with the potential course of Venezuelan regional foreign policy as a whole, is currently Latin America's most serious challenge to regional security.

A purely ideological reading of the security situation would, however, be incomplete. Although Venezuela leads the populist left in Latin America, the region demonstrates no simple link between ideology and unstable international relations. Instead, the region suffers most from slow democratic decay and the impact of this on regional security. In many countries, democracy is not marching forward, but creeping back, and the flashpoint of the continent as a whole is undoubtedly the Andean region, where ideological tensions are strongest, but the quality of governance is also weakest.

On the one hand, the Colombian political system has thus far been unable wholly to outgrow its entrenched association with paramilitarism and political violence. Despite multiple initiatives of the civilian government, some sectors of the security forces, particularly the army, continue to violate human rights, and the legislative coalition supporting President Uribe has been dogged for the last three years by an evolving investigation into the ties many of its number previously enjoyed with paramilitary groups. On the other hand, the Bolivarian Revolution, both in Venezuela and elsewhere, has involved the progressive use of irregular militia that support the government through violence and exercise unofficial police and intelligence functions. In Venezuela, a wide range of organisations have been promoted by the government and have regularly attacked the opposition, particularly in the unstable aftermath of the failed coup against President Chávez in 2002. In October 2009 Chávez celebrated the legalisation of paramilitary groups, ostensibly for defence against external threats, with the declaration, 'we will all be soldiers now'.[7] In Ecuador in 2007, the newly elected President Rafael Correa was able to push through the dissolution of the old Congress with the assistance of mobs of radical supporters who surrounded and attacked other government institutions at key moments.[8] More recently, Correa has announced the formation of 'civilian defence networks' akin to those in Cuba and Venezuela, and for similar purposes.[9] In what may have been an isolated incident, this trend has reportedly even moved beyond the 'Bolivarian' states to another regime with substantial ties to Chávez: in Argentina, the opposition now claims that the government has begun arming *piqueteros*.[10]

Democracy is being visibly eroded

Such developments have multiple impacts on Latin American international relations. Firstly, the inflammatory rhetoric of populism encourages uninhibited hostility against foreign actors in pursuit of domestic political benefits. Secondly, the emerging radical nationalism of certain militaries and their influence over political leaders clearly deepens international tensions. Thirdly, continued encouragement of irregular forces not only makes violent subversion of other regimes more possible and likely, but also fosters those regimes' perception of risk, making the chances of strategic miscalculation from other disputes more likely.

Democracy is also being visibly eroded through a combination of excessive presidentialism and the desire and ability of several current leaders to remain in power for significant periods of time. In Honduras, President Manuel Zelaya was ejected from office by the armed forces in a coup inspired by his intention to hold a referendum to gauge support for the formation of a Constituent Assembly to draft a new constitution. The extended stalemate between the ousted Zelaya and the de facto regime was resolved late in October 2009 and the potential consequences for regional security were thus successfully contained. In Colombia, Uribe's contemplation of a third term in office, which, despite substantial approval from a majority of his electorate, would require a second amendment to the constitution, reflects this disposition to extend mandates beyond accepted constitutional limits. On the left, the leaders of Venezuela, Ecuador, Bolivia and Nicaragua are all interested in holding on to power for the foreseeable future, either through manipulated re-election or wholesale constitutional reform. These trends have clear consequences for regional stability. Where the leaders of highly presidentialist regimes exercise unmediated control over foreign and defence policy, the potential for abrupt and hostile policy changes is clearly greater. While changes of government would allow new leaders to begin new relationships, and the democratic process itself might generate more moderate foreign-policy programmes if these were desired by electorates, the current situation will generate an ossification and a personalisation of conflict. In particular, it is hard to see Uribe and Chávez ever enjoying a constructive relationship – or even the limited modus vivendi that they maintained in the past and which brought both their countries significant economic benefits. The Colombian and Ecuadorian governments showed signs in late 2009 of rapprochement after more than 18 months without diplomatic relations, but this is likely to prove a fragile experiment in economic pragmatism and does not foreshadow a permanently stable relationship between the two leaders. Correa, for his part, had been effectively obliged to tone down his hostility to the Colombian government after continued public emphasis by Bogotá on the sponsorship of his first presidential campaign in 2006 by FARC and Ecuadorian drug traffickers.[11]

Insofar as they represent serious policy challenges for any Latin American government, non-state and transnational threats also have an impact on the region's international relations. Disputes over the nature and origin of these threats, and the lack of accepted norms to govern their management, are serious deficiencies. Over the last three decades drug trafficking and the related crimes of weapons and ammunition trafficking and money laundering have been major drivers of insecurity in the Andean region. Colombia, Peru and Bolivia produce almost all of the world's cocaine. While coastal and terrestrial trafficking corridors through Central America and Mexico to the United States have long been established, recently new channels to Europe have been opened via Venezuela, Brazil and from there through

West Africa. Unfortunately, extensive counter-narcotics programmes have not been successful in reducing the availability of illegal drugs in consumer countries.

Beyond violent and illegal actors, humanitarian crises too have created transnational security problems. The flow of refugees southwards across the Colombia–Ecuador border has generated a permanent governance challenge for Ecuador and contributed significantly to diplomatic tensions. When refugees moved into Venezuela from Colombia, Chávez used politically motivated citizenship programmes not only to give refuge to FARC insurgents but also to bolster his own electoral support base.[12]

In the Andean region in general, the absence of any kind of systemic approach to the handling of transnational security threats is striking, despite past attempts to develop one within the institutional framework provided by the Andean Community. The Colombian conflict continues to show how difficult it is for the region to develop any kind of shared response to terrorist issues, as neighbouring governments prefer not to assume the costs of effective counter-insurgency or seek to use the conflict in Colombia to their own strategic advantage. Divergent politics and a lack of useful precedents for the cataloguing of illicit organisations in shared 'lists' on which common action can proceed also complicate this issue. It is in the Andes that the non-state and inter-state security challenges mix most dangerously. Recent security cooperation between Colombia and both Brazil and Peru indicates that like-minded states may be able to craft acceptable common approaches, but it would be best if they could one day do so within an institutional context. Fostering a more common strategic culture on these matters would be a necessary goal of any regional security structure worthy of the name.

Territory and resources

South America is increasingly plagued by the politics of energy disputes and natural-resource controversies. Nationalisation policies affect neighbouring countries, not just foreign oil companies, and regional energy suppliers are keen to use their resources as a diplomatic weapon. The existence of energy resources in poorly governed areas or in environmentally sensitive areas can inspire disquiet among indigenous and environmentally conscious political groups. The presence of natural resources across national boundaries naturally excites controversies over international frontiers. Historical disputes over boundary definitions persist, and anxieties over past territorial losses are still fresh and intense. Natural-resource requirements revive or amplify territorial differences. The disagreement between Venezuela and Colombia over the western shore of the Gulf of Venezuela was largely settled in 1941 in terms of the land border, but was re-kindled when technological developments permitted the exploration of the sea floor and the discovery of oil along the uncertainly demarcated maritime border.[13] Bolivia's bitter argument with Chile over direct access to the Pacific has driven La Paz to use its energy assets as a bargaining chip with Santiago in this long-simmering border dispute, heightening diplomatic tensions. The dispute between Chile and Peru over 37,900km^2 of maritime territory is exacerbated by competition for the rich fishing grounds that this territory contains. Any visitor to the Southern Cone would be forgiven for thinking that the War of the Pacific involving Chile, Peru and Bolivia ended in 1993, not 1883, so raw are the nerves that guide the statements of political leaders on border disputes, and so intense the suspicion that every military modernisation plan of a neighbouring country has as its sole objective the recovery of lost land.

Military conflict over such disagreements is in most cases exceptionally unlikely. The only instance of this in recent years in Latin America has been the 'Cenepa' War between Ecuador and Peru in 1995 that effectively ended a long-term territorial dispute. However, a rapid land snatch or consolidation of control over contested territory remains feasible and could not be remedied by the current toothless range of regional security institutions. Territorial disputes may also be used as pretexts for aggression by leaders with expansionist political projects of a nationalist or other ideological nature, or who see military conflict as serving their short-term domestic political interests. Such was the case with the Argentine military regime when it seized the British Falkland Islands in 1982. However, the predominant pattern now is for states to turn to the International Court of Justice (as Peru and Chile have done) for a ruling, though while a decision is pending, grievances voiced by leaders courting popular support still infect diplomatic relations. Territorial disputes are therefore a serious problem for regional security. Without necessarily provoking military conflict, they make bilateral relationships subject to frequent disruption, undermine the regional harmonisation of security and defence objectives in the long term, and can have a malign effect on broader tensions. The presence, for example, of Colombian paramilitaries in the Venezuelan state of Zulia, adjacent to the contested maritime boundary and site of the old terrestrial boundary dispute, has been perceived by Chávez as particularly threatening because of that state's historical propensity to pro-Colombian separatism.

Beyond territory, the energy security of states, particularly in the Southern Cone where states are considerably more dependent on one another than in the Andes for oil, natural gas or both, is also a serious issue. Energy differences sour regional relations hugely, but despite occasional energy summits, these tensions are not resolved. There is much energy devoted to energy politics but little serious debate about energy integration. Yet formulating policies on energy security is important precisely because differences easily assume a strategic dimension.

Energy differences sour regional relations hugely

The desirability of energy integration is by no means a given in Latin America. Two economic models now vie for supremacy: regional integration, particularly through the Common Market of the South (Mercosur) that brings together Argentina, Brazil, Paraguay and Uruguay as full members, involving lowered barriers to intra-regional trade and foreign direct investment; and the emerging model promoted by Chávez through the Bolivarian Alliance for the Americas (ALBA), bringing together Bolivia, Cuba, Ecuador, Honduras, Nicaragua, Venezuela and three Caribbean states,[14] that exists to promote Venezuelan regional hegemony and involves the barter of state-owned resources, particularly energy, directly between governments.

The difficulties of developing sound energy economics and politics is shown in the example of Bolivia and Brazil. By early 2006, Petrobras, the Brazilian state energy company, had made substantial investments in Bolivian gas fields, to the extent that approximately half of Brazil's gas was supplied by Bolivia. However, Bolivian President Evo Morales chose to join an ALBA-associated trade agreement in April of that year, which was anticipated to bring substantial Venezuelan largesse, and soon afterwards announced plans for the nationalisation of Bolivia's natural-gas reserves and industry, including the stakes held by Petrobras. A diplomatic rift ensued, and Brazil began preparing for autonomy from Bolivian gas imports, but later in the year renegotiations took place that allowed Petrobras to continue operating in the country. The impact of the Brazil–Bolivia dispute was cushioned by both Lula's careful diplomacy with Morales and Bolivia's acute infrastructural weakness, which prevented it from independently extracting and delivering the necessary volumes of gas after it had issued the nationalisation decree, but the tension at the time was significant. The obvious influence of Venezuelan President Chávez and Venezuelan resources in Morales's original decision to nationalise his gas reserves also generated tensions between Brazil and Venezuela.

Energy-security vulnerabilities are additionally driven by competition for limited resources. Chile can supply with its own resources only 5% of the oil and 20% of the natural gas it needs, and has largely been dependent on Argentine imports of natural gas. In 2002, however, economic crisis and domestic energy shortages drove the Argentine government to cut off gas supplies to Chile. Similarly, Bolivian gas has also generated tensions not just between Bolivia and Brazil but also between Brazil and Argentina as its two main consumers. As the dispute between Bolivia and Brazil unfolded, Brazil also saw the stability of gas imports from Bolivia threatened by rising demand from Argentina, and in particular Argentina's agreement to pay Bolivia more for its gas. These tensions were mitigated in 2008 and 2009 by falling Brazilian demand for natural gas, the increasing role of liquefied natural gas production and imports across the region, and in the long term by Brazil's discovery of its own gas reserves. However, given the scale of the resource challenges that South America will face over the coming decades, these kinds of disputes could become typical.

Lastly, energy-security problems are in some cases caused by the deliberate use of export restrictions as a policy weapon, usually as part of a wider conflict. This has occurred with Bolivia and Chile. Because of its grievance over Chile's refusal to grant it access to the Pacific, Bolivia has steadily refused to export any of its natural gas at all to Chile. In 2003, moreover, the Bolivian government, in response to domestic discontent, withdrew a planned gas plant on the coast of Chile that had been intended to supply the United States. The next year a referendum was passed in which Bolivians were invited to vote in favour of using natural gas as a negotiating tool to get Chile to grant access to the sea. In the same way, Peru also withheld natural gas from Chile prior to the arrival in office of the second Alan García administration, also for reasons of territorial grievance.

Outside powers

Many of the current crop of Latin American leaders spent their formative years under the shadow of frequent US intervention, and this history goes some way to explaining the extreme political sensitivity of the US–Colombia agreement. Conversely, the nascent relationships of other Latin American countries, particularly Venezuela, with foreign powers such as Russia and Iran are viewed suspiciously in Washington. Extra-regional powers often behave according to clear geopolitical calculations, which are primarily but not entirely resource oriented. Yet, diplomatic, economic and military interests of outside powers in Latin America do not yet pose the sort of geopolitical challenge that should be a priority for defence policy or the sizing of armed forces. The need for the region to defend against an external threat, or to preserve its integrity against the competitive diplomacy of two or more mutually hostile great powers, is not there. Cold War thinking about Latin American international relations is inappropriate, for now.

This is most obvious in the case of the United States, the relevance of which as a determinant of change within Latin America is in secular decline. The United States under President Barack Obama, consumed with greater foreign-policy priorities and economic distress at home, can devote only limited attention to Latin America and does not see playing arbiter between competing foreign-policy or security visions in the region as a desirable ambition where its strategic interests are not threatened. It is inclined to be, in foreign-policy terms, a 'third-way' actor in Latin America: respectful of desires for Latin American emancipation from a heavily burdened past with America, but willing to strike strong bilateral relationships where these are sought. In terms of security, its most important relationships continue to be with Colombia and Mexico. With Colombia, it is locked in an extended counter-narcotics and counter-insurgency war and sees its relationship with the country, straddling both oceans and the gateway to South America, as of obvious geopolitical significance. In Mexico, the United States sees narcotics-related violence along its southern border escalating to an alarming level not seen since the heyday of Colombian narco-terrorism two decades previously. Discussion of the country as a partially failed state has begun, presenting the United States with both a harsh security problem and a considerable immigration challenge – to which Washington has responded with a package of counter-narcotics assistance similar in some respects to that given to Colombia. Within this framework, Obama has made some modest changes, but the perceived importance of these relationships has not diminished. Strategically, Brazil is becoming the most important regional partner and the United States, building on already strong ties, clearly wishes to establish a relationship with the South American giant that recognises Brazil's growing role, not least in global forums such as the G20. Politically, with Obama anxious to mark a break with the past, the United States' relationship with Cuba is a key priority for improvement. In itself of limited strategic importance, such a development has the potential to unlock significant political capital both among US constituencies and across Latin America. In practice, however, despite positive signals and the lifting of some minor restrictions, a wholesale policy change remains legally tied to democratic reform and human-rights compliance, and so the trade embargo continues.

The only exception to this panorama of constructive involvement or relaxed indifference is Venezuela, despite Obama's disposition to publicly signal re-engagement.[15] While the United States is at pains not to be unnecessarily embroiled in Latin American political disputes, in the Venezuelan case an enduring strategic concern persists owing to the importance of that country's hydrocarbon resources and Chávez's highly vocal hostility to the United States. Particularly troubling are his authoritarian tendencies at home, his continued dalliance with FARC insurgents in Colombia, his aspirations to ideological leadership and petro-hegemony in Latin America, and his enthusiastic development internationally of economic, military and intelligence cooperation with Russia, China and Iran. All of this presents a limited but real challenge to US interests in Latin America. On the other hand, Chávez's apparent fears of US-sponsored destabilisation of his regime are not currently realistic, given the general direction of Obama's Latin American policy. At present, US strategy is one of cautious containment, promoting Brazilian regional leadership, ensuring Colombian continuity, watching and waiting while the Venezuelan economy suffers, and, without the excessive noise that would complicate Obama's approach to other Latin American governments, making sure that the ties of the Chávez government to proscribed terrorist organisations and drug-trafficking interests are widely known.[16]

In this context, the return of Russia and especially the new interests in Latin America of Asian states inevitably create a new foreign-policy dynamic for Latin American states previously animated largely by the form and substance of US engagement.

Chávez has made nine official visits to Russia

Russia has recently re-engaged with the region after almost 20 years of post-Soviet absence. In late 2008, Russian President Dmitry Medvedev visited Peru, Brazil, Venezuela and Cuba and Foreign Minister Sergei Lavrov both Colombia and Ecuador, while high-level delegations from Argentina, Brazil, Venezuela, Colombia, Mexico, Cuba and Nicaragua have also visited Moscow. Chávez has made nine official visits to Russia in the last decade. Russia took part in the Asia-Pacific Economic Cooperation (APEC) summit in Peru in 2008 and in 2009 hosted a BRIC summit with leaders from Brazil, India and China. The national foreign-policy concept signed by Medvedev in 2008 identified Latin America as a priority and emphasised interest in 'strategic partnership' with Brazil.[17] In this, Russia has been able to capitalise on the economic interests of Latin American states, particularly Brazil, but also, particularly in the case of Venezuela and other ALBA member states, on their desire to oppose US interests and upgrade their military arsenals.

For its part, Moscow's interest is primarily driven by the pursuit of energy resources. The Russian state-controlled energy company Gazprom recently signed agreements with Bolivia to develop its gas reserves and is now accelerating the development of operations in other countries of the region. In Venezuela, Gazprom has also secured a 25-year agreement to extract heavy crude as part of a consortium with four other leading Russian oil companies and in partnership with the Venezuelan state-owned oil company PDVSA. However, Russia is also using the region both to compete for influence with the United States and retaliate for its political engagement elsewhere, especially in Georgia, where the George W. Bush administration's support for a government despised by Russia had angered Moscow. Wishing to signal that if the United States operates freely in its neighbourhood, Russia can do the same in Washington's 'near abroad', Russia's diplomacy is aimed at showing that it too can garner friends in distant places. In late 2008, therefore, and in gestures that had more symbolic than military importance, Russian strategic bombers landed in Venezuela and Russian warships conducted exercises with the Venezuelan Navy and traversed the Panama Canal for the first time in 64 years before visiting Cuba and Nicaragua. Russia has also engaged in a sustained campaign for the recognition of South Ossetia and Abkhazia and even sent an Abkhaz delegation to Latin America to lobby, succeeding first with Nicaragua in September 2008 and then in Venezuela a year later. Russian leaders might reasonably hope that the ALBA alliance as a whole will recognise these mini-states, with Ecuador the most likely to do so in return for securing Russian military hardware on credit.

The same broad principles on greater engagement hold true for China. Like Russia, it has so far focused heavily on Latin American natural resources, principally as part of its international campaign to secure maximum access to energy it needs to fuel its growth. Despite relatively low levels of direct investment – Chinese President Hu Jintao's 2004 prediction of US$100 billion of investment in Latin America in the following ten years does not look likely to be met – this focus has been principally manifested since 1999 in rapidly expanding trade ties, without ideological differentiation and across all Latin America. China has also cooperated with Brazil on satellite technology. These economic relationships are not without their challenges – China's focus on primary resources is capable of retarding the diversification of some Latin American economies, and the nature of its support for state industries in some countries could arguaby deprive those countries of serious privatisation options – but in general they are viewed in extremely positive terms by Latin American governments and private sectors. Like Russia, however, China has also developed relationships of more strategic import with the ALBA nations, in particular Venezuela, and has direct military-to-military relations with them. Nevertheless, there is little evidence that China's military diplomacy is yet strategically problematic or that serious attempts are being made, at least by the Chinese themselves, to transfer arms to illegal buyers. Moreover, the reduction in tension between China and Taiwan has resulted in both announcing a diplomatic freeze by which each would avoid engaging in further competition for diplomatic recognition internationally, a decision that has helpful implications for Latin America given that it was in the past such an important theatre for the political competition between Beijing and Taipei.

India, too, is more active in Latin America. In the Caribbean, it takes advantage of ethnic links to build political relationships. In South America, it is also fiercely interested in energy and natural-resources exploitation. On balance, a greater amount of Indian investment is led by private companies rather than the state alone. Jindal's $2.1bn investment in the Bolivian iron-ore industry is the biggest from the private sector in India, while India's Reliance has been involved in oil concessions in both Peru and Colombia while importing crude from Mexico, Venezuela, Brazil and Ecuador. India's BRIC status reinforces a natural South–South tendency in its diplomacy. Yet the reluctance of India to sell arms within Asia has inspired it to sell in Latin America. India signed its first defence export agreement with Ecuador in 2008 for the sale of advanced light helicopters and, with Russia, is marketing its supersonic cruise missile in the region. Like Brazil, India is hopeful of one day gaining a permanent seat on the United Nations Security Council, and the nature of its diplomacy in Latin America can be also be seen as related to that ambition.

The outside powers newly interested in Latin America need, no less than the United States, to be sensitive to how their involvement is perceived locally. Their engagement is seen positively insofar as states in the region have been able to diversify their trade, investment and diplomatic relations as US dominance has lessened, its original plan for the creation of a pan-American free-trade area having failed and fragmented into a handful of agreements with individual countries. Several Latin American countries have made integration with Asia via APEC and the Latin American Pacific Rim Initiative a foreign-policy priority – Mexico, Peru and Chile are already members of APEC, and Colombia, Ecuador and Panama have all expressed interest in joining. The big power of South America, Brazil, has seized on the concept of a territorial power, enjoys its emerging-market status encapsulated in the BRIC acronym, and wants to shape the regional agenda more ambitiously, with an eye to gaining global recognition as a key player. More controversially, Venezuela's relationships with countries such as Russia, Iran and China are not just a way of ruffling the feathers of the US hawk but, as for some of Venezuela's allies, are an increasingly important source of investment and military resources. Since 2005 Chávez has spent $6.6bn of funds or credit on Russian weapons, mostly for offensive conventional warfare, procuring 92 T-72 tanks, the S-300 air-defence system, 53 MI-28 helicopters and 24 SU-30MKV fighter aircraft.

These trends inevitably mean that the involvement of foreign powers could also provoke conflict, because foreign-policy projects compete for prominence and wider acceptance, particular relationships are loaded with ideological and historical significance, and the friendships that some states enjoy with foreign powers are perceived by other states in the region as potentially altering the strategic and particularly military balance. Extra-regional relationships do no more than potentially augment existing tensions, but are significant conflict multipliers nonetheless.

In thinking about regional security arrangements in Latin America, it will be important to find ways for those frameworks to acknowledge the growing role of outside powers in the region and legitimise unthreatening extra-regional arrangements arrived at by Latin American states exercising their sovereign will. No summit was called when Venezuela conducted naval exercises with Russia; one was thought necessary when Colombia offered facilities to the United States. The rub will be in defining 'unthreatening', but that can only come once Latin American powers agree properly to consult about the full range of security issues through a regional security structure in a disciplined and organised manner.

The future regional security agenda for South America

In terms of regional security, much has improved in recent years: it is excellent that Brazil and Argentina have put aside their prior interest in developing nuclear weapons; that Argentina and Chile have come to an accommodation over their border; and that intense diplomatic, military and economic exchanges between most of the members of Mercosur do much to allay tensions. However, some old security problems persist, others of a newer generation have arisen, and no single foreign power will assume responsibility for maintaining and enforcing its own vision of order, as the United States once did. There is now both an opportunity and a need for South America to cater effectively to its own security.

How might it do so? Regional security institutions are an important part of the answer, but only a part, as many factors of insecurity are domestic and individual governments and national policymakers must ultimately bear responsibility for these. Furthermore, in Europe, Asia, the Middle East and Africa, various forms of the same security problems suffered in Latin America persist, sometimes much more severely, and where regional institutions exist in these areas to manage these problems, they do not always, or even often, function effectively. In South America itself, it would be naive automatically to accord too much importance to Unasur as an institution; the region has been acquiring and testing institutional formulae for collective security for at least 60 years. Sometimes these have had a negative impact, sometimes limited positive impact, and very often no significant impact at all. Nevertheless, although any such institution must necessarily be an imperfect answer to regional security problems, the Unasur project does have some significance. Good national governance should ideally have a positive impact on international relations from beneath, but multilateral institutions must work to do so from above. South America suffers from a volatile mix of domestic instability and democratic lacunae, transnational security problems that from their very nature disrespect national borders and generate conflict wherever they fail to elicit cooperation, conflicts of interest between governments over territory and resources, and the lucrative but potentially problematic geopolitical influence of a range of extra-regional powers. Unasur should seek to mitigate all of these.

Experiences elsewhere suggest some key targets for the institution to meet. Where containment of conflict has been effective, it has been because efforts in regional political reconciliation have been successful, there is an acceptable level of transparency on military and strategic goals of the key countries, outside powers have played a constructive role with sufficient regional consent, the larger regional powers adopt greater regional responsibility for the enforcement of agreed norms, and institutions exist that can provide legitimacy to conflict-resolution measures taken either individually or collectively. Progress along each of these fronts is necessary for South America to achieve a higher level of security confidence. In achieving this progress, the region will wish to note the increasing interest of a variety of outside powers in South American affairs, and its own need to engage more fully with the outside world, while acknowledging that the only impetus for improving the regional security outlook can come from initiatives taken by key powers within the region.

External models need to be carefully chosen and adapted, and are not those usually suggested. NATO is an irrelevant model, principally because there is no external threat to Latin America remotely similar to the threat posed to North America and Western Europe by the Soviet Union during the Cold War. The European Union may appear a compelling example, but its emergence was possible because of an extraordinary process of political reconciliation that the EU reinforced but did not in itself create. That political reconciliation, crucially between France and Germany, was solidified through membership in NATO and common policies towards the clear external threat both faced. These parallels simply do not exist in Latin America. Slightly more relevant to Latin America is the Asian experience of the last 40 years and its varied experimentation with the apparatus of regional security mechanisms.

NATO is an irrelevant model

In Asia, as in Latin America, the proliferation of regional organisations and security forums is often itself an indication of insecurity. The

Asia-Pacific is replete with overlapping security architectures: ASEAN, the ASEAN Regional Forum, the ASEAN+3 arrangements, and the East Asia Summit all offer numerous opportunities for dialogue and confidence building. Actual dispute settlement is a much more ad hoc affair, and true defence consultations are elusive.[18] Delicate territorial disputes in the South China Sea cannot easily be mediated through any existing formal regional security institution. No Asian security institution has been able to assist in building confidence across the Taiwan Strait, seen by China as a resolutely internal matter. The proliferation dilemmas of North Korea have been handled through the Six-Party Talks involving key outside powers, yet converting this into the basis of an East Asian security structure is an ever-receding goal.

ASEAN is perhaps the most successful regional organisation after the EU. However, even after 40 years, its members find it difficult to cooperate on defence. The key problem remains the lack of a deep political accommodation between the members. There are still suspicions and even enmities deriving from historical, ethnic and religious factors, not to mention extraordinarily diverse political systems and a paucity of shared values. Efforts at confidence building through these formal institutional arrangements take time, and true defence cooperation will only take place when the political accommodation is strong enough to permit it. Conflict resolution has been very difficult through ASEAN, though under the chairmanship of Singapore this year, the group was able to get Thailand and Cambodia to take reasonable approaches towards the resolution of their border dispute.

There is one unique feature of the geopolitics of South America that might permit the creation of a more effective regional security architecture. In Asia, a very small country, Singapore, has provided a good deal of the intellectual and diplomatic energy behind the modernisation of ASEAN and its efforts to engage the larger East Asian powers. The comfortable relationship between Chile and Brazil offers the prospect of a small country of the Southern Cone, in tandem with the continent's largest power, framing more productive security arrangements that could have wider regional acceptance. Indeed, as Brazil is viewed with less suspicion in its own region than is China in Asia or Russia in Europe, the prospects for congenial great-power leadership in South America to advance security cooperation are good. However uncomfortable such ambitions of leadership appear, they are what the continent needs to accelerate security cooperation and avoid the inevitable tendency to craft good communiqué language that has little practical result.

The Santiago Declaration of March 2009 that in effect inaugurated the South American Defence Council was a good start, containing as it did a four-part plan of action in the fields of defence policy, military cooperation, the defence industry and training.[19] However, the organisation can go much further in addressing the broader range of issues affecting the region. There are two essential conditions for this to happen. The first is that the institution be able to enforce, through a range of potential sanctions, the important principles of its evolving charter and operating practices. Such collective action would require stronger cooperation than now exists between member states, but the norms of the Defence Council need to be seen to be enforceable if they are to be respected.

The second condition is a serious, far-reaching and long-term agenda. Although Unasur and the Defence Council gained relevance largely in response to the 2008 Andean crisis, it would be fair to state that, so far, Unasur has largely been a forum for war by other means between Venezuela, Ecuador and Colombia, with the other member states important less as facilitators of dialogue and conflict resolution or stakeholders than as actual or potential allies of one side or the other. The agenda cannot be dominated in the long term by the single-issue concerns of the most vocal governments, in a process in which both what is discussed, and how, is determined by the alliances and persuasive power enjoyed by the parties to a particular dispute at a particular time. Indeed, if such a trend continues, then Unasur will lose credibility and salience and perhaps ultimately fail. Unasur member states must ultimately seek convergence on the relevant security challenges and the norms that should govern their management. Only in this way will the region move towards a common strategic culture and Unasur's ambitious construction of South America as a 'zone of peace'. If such a process were successful, it could later be extended to Central American states and Mexico. For the immediate future the South American

Defence Council needs directly to address domestic, transnational, regional and international concerns with a specific agenda.

* * *

To avoid the hijacking of Unasur for esoteric diplomatic purposes and its manipulation for short-term ends, the Defence Council should develop a rich and ritualised agenda of activity to foster transparency, build a common strategic culture and elaborate principles for the management of disputes. Emphasis on external security will from time to time be necessary, but should not take permanent precedence over developing better cooperation on continental security dilemmas. In an era when military expenditure is increasing, in some cases simply because improved economic fortunes permit modernisation, in others because the adoption of peacekeeping missions requires adjustments in force structures, and in a few because expansionist policies are perhaps contemplated, the overall impact of a renewed Defence Council agenda must be to shine a clear light on strategic activity. Given the tensions and suspicions that exist, the following agenda would serve that end.

Firstly, the Defence Council should encourage the more regular publication and updating of Defence White Papers. Chile was the first Latin American country to publish a Defence White Paper (in 1996), and the importance of this exercise, since followed by a number of other countries, was underscored when the OAS in 2002 drafted guidelines on developing national-defence policy and doctrine papers. In the current context, Defence White Papers should explain national strategies fully, including the rationale for links of various kinds with outside powers. The South American Defence Council could seek to establish a schedule by which all 12 of its members were to produce Defence White Papers, pressing those who have done so to update them and those who had not yet done so to produce them for the first time. These papers should then be open for discussion at expert-level meetings of the council, where concerns could be addressed. Creating more transparency in the discussion of strategic issues should become a primary activity of the council.

Secondly, the Defence Council should consider placing energy-security and natural-resources questions on its standing formal agenda for all meetings. The aim would be to have defence ministers consult on the risks of interruption of supplies or the use of energy as a diplomatic weapon in inter-state relations. Energy security should be formally introduced into regional security discussions, not left to energy ministers alone to address. This may be controversial, but insofar as energy competition and security are such important realities in the southern hemisphere, and create poisonous political disputes, it is the responsibility of those charged with national security to address these questions head on.

Thirdly, the Defence Council should consider developing norms for how cross-border activities to deal with transnational threats are to be conducted. The Santiago Declaration insisted on territorial sovereignty and the inviolability of frontiers. But, as non-state actors refuse to accept these norms, states have to come to understandings on how to deal with transnational tensions. The council should openly discuss the manner in which sovereign territory is used by non-state actors to threaten other states, and the potential need for 'hot pursuit' of terrorists across state frontiers. International cooperation in poorly governed areas partly occupied by terrorist groups is beginning to take place across the Afghanistan–Pakistan border. It would be right for defence ministers in South America to consider formally under what circumstances such cooperation could take place in their own region.

Fourthly, and relatedly, the South American Defence Council should invite each member state to deposit with Unasur information on the strengths and activities of non-state actors they consider to be involved in illicit transnational activities such as crime, drug trafficking and terrorism. Obligating member states to put forward their assessments of the non-state actors operating on their territories would, in the first instance, foster disputes over the alleged strengths and strategic objectives of these groups. But insisting that these be deposited with a multilateral organisation could take some of the sting out of the bilateral tensions that public discussion of these organisations often inspires.

Fifthly, the Defence Council could encourage or even require the use of satellite technology and other means through which states might efficiently monitor border areas. Cross-border security arrangements could be agreed and the Defence Council charged with monitoring compliance and forcing consultation in the event of breakdowns of important agreements.

Sixthly, the Defence Council could develop a range of potential sanctions that would be applied to make fully enforceable important principles of the council's evolving charter and operating practices. Such collective action would, of course, require stronger cooperation than now exists between member states, but to become respected, the norms of the council need to be seen to be enforceable.

Finally, the Defence Council of Unasur should work to coordinate participation of member states in extra-regional security arrangements consistent with generally declared political aims, such as the Proliferation Security Initiative. States could consider undertaking joint exercises to test their capacities to participate in such international regimes. While each state would naturally wish to reserve the right to join such structures, efforts to agree views on participation in such extra-continental regimes would have the effect of harmonising security perspectives and strategic outlooks. This, in and of itself, would be a useful confidence-building measure within South America.

There is a complex security agenda in Latin America and specifically in South America. Reliance on the established formulas of diplomatic communication and on outdated legal constructs is insufficient. More ambitious goals need to be set for the region's defence and security institutions. The process requires leadership, tact and imagination. This seven-part agenda is hugely ambitious. Real advances along this path will require high levels of political reconciliation among countries with radically differing governing styles. But it is a necessary, if long-term, agenda, because it is related to the true security threats to which South America is subject, and because it offers opportunities for South American states to make a stronger collective contribution to international security. Unasur's Defence Council, armed with a robust agenda, could build a more effective security order in the continent. Perhaps in a few years, some future Unasur summit will make a less interesting televised spectacle, but record more obvious success in building the elements of a more common future strategic culture that permits economic development and growth, within a less charged political environment. Once better established in South America, these processes might be usefully extended to Mexico and the Central American states, thus including all of Latin America in a genuine security community.

Notes

1 Unasur comprises Argentina, Bolivia, Brazil, Chile, Colombia, Ecuador, Guyana, Paraguay, Peru, Suriname, Uruguay and Venezuela.

2 The two countries signed a Defense Cooperation Agreement on 30 October 2009, which 'will facilitate effective bilateral cooperation on security matters in Colombia, including narcotics production and trafficking, terrorism, illicit smuggling of all types, and humanitarian and natural disasters' and 'does not permit the establishment of any U.S. base in Colombia' but instead 'ensures continued U.S. access to specific agreed Colombian facilities' which would remain 'under Colombian control'. The facilities in question are 'three Colombian air force bases, located at Palanquero, Apiay, and Malambo', 'two naval bases and two army installations, and other Colombian military facilities if mutually agreed'. The agreement is stated to imply no increase in US personnel, the limit established in 2004 by the US Congress of 800 military and 600 civilian workers remains in force, and the US claims to have the 'expectation and commitment' that personnel numbers will continue to decline, as in previous years. See US Department of State, 'U.S.–Colombia Defense Cooperation Agreement', 30 October 2009, http://www.state.gov/r/pa/prs/ps/2009/oct/131134.htm.

3 See Simon Romero, 'Venezuela Still Aids Colombia Rebels, New Material Shows', *New York Times*, 2 August 2009, http://www.nytimes.com/2009/08/03/world/americas/03venez.html. FARC's interest in bringing down the presidential plane has been evidenced by the discovery and neutralisation of several recent plots. See 'Capturan a presunto guerrillero que estaría haciendo seguimiento al avión presidencial', *El Tiempo* (Colombia), 27 August 2009, http://www.eltiempo.com/archivo/documento/CMS-5956528#; and 'Capturan a dos presuntos guerrilleros involucrados en planes terroristas en Bogotá', *Caracol Radio* (Colombia), 17 October 2009, http://www.caracol.com.co/nota.aspx?id=896206.

4 This had taken place in 2004. See 'Chávez Attacks "Invasion Plot"', BBC, 13 May 2004, http://news.bbc.co.uk/1/hi/world/americas/3709609.htm.

5 The document describes the 'Global En Route Strategy' of the US Air Force's Air Mobility Command (AMC). It is currently available at http://www.vtv.gov.ve/files/GlobalEnRouteStrategy.pdf.

6 See 'Declaración conjunta de Reunión Extraordinaria del Consejo de jefes y jefas de Estado de la Unión de Naciones Suramericanas', 28 August 2009, available at http://www.comunidadandina.org/unasur/28-8-09bariloche.htm.

7 See 'Chávez legaliza a milicias armadas bajo su control', *Clarín* (Argentina), 24 October 2009, http://www.clarin.com/diario/2009/10/24/um/m-02025930.htm.

8 See 'Evacuado Congreso mientras se enfrentan policías y manifestantes', *La Hora* (Ecuador), 30 January 2007, http://www.lahora.com.ec/frontEnd/main.php?idSeccion=529056.

9 See '"Defensa" a revolución es antigua', *El Universo* (Ecuador), 16 August 2009, http://www.eluniverso.com/2009/08/16/1/1355/40D59652C63D49AB9F2A4FE1C7E257D6.html.

10 See 'Carrió dijo que hay piqueteros armados y el Gobierno la cruzó', *Clarín* (Argentina), 22 October 2009, http://www.clarin.com/diario/2009/10/22/elpais/p-02024287.htm; 'Milagro Sala: una comandante K que controla más de $200 millones', *Clarín* (Argentina), 25 October 2009, http://www.clarin.com/diario/2009/10/25/um/m-02026579.htm.

11 See Maite Rico, 'El dinero perdido de las FARC', *El País*, 1 August 2009, http://www.elpais.com/articulo/internacional/dinero/perdido/FARC/elpepuint/20090801elpepuint_10/Tes.

12 For the use of naturalisation to provide refuge, see for example 'Arrepentidos de las FARC y del ELN revelan cómo Chávez apoya a la guerrilla', *Perfil* (Argentina), 6 April 2008, http://www.diarioperfil.com.ar/edimp/0249/articulo.php?art=6612&ed=0249.

13 This point is made by Jorge Domínguez, 'Boundary Disputes in Latin America', *Peaceworks No. 50*, United States Institute of Peace, September 2003, p. 26.

14 These are Antigua and Barbuda; Dominica; and Saint Vincent and the Grenadines.

15 Most notably, Obama made sure to be photographed meeting Chávez at the 5th Summit of the Americas in April 2009. See 'Chavez Tells Obama: "I Want to be Your Friend"', Reuters, 17 April 2009, http://www.reuters.com/article/GCA-BarackObama/idUKTRE53G60K20090418.

16 See 'Drug Control: U.S. Counternarcotics Cooperation with Venezuela has Declined', United States Government Accountability Office, Report to the Ranking Member, Committee on Foreign Relations, US Senate, July 2009, http://www.gao.gov/new.items/d09806.pdf. Despite the new administration's care not to provoke public frictions, it has made its concern evident regarding certain issues. For instance, US Secretary of State Hillary Clinton recently expressed worry over Venezuelan arms procurement from Russia, provoking a vehement response from Chávez. See 'Clinton "Totally Wrong" in Criticism of Venezuelan Arms Buys: Chavez', AFP, 25 September 2009, available at http://www.theaustralian.news.com.au/story/0,25197,26123855-36235,00.html.

17 For the full text of the Foreign Policy Concept signed in 2008 see 'The

Foreign Policy Concept of the Russian Federation', 12 July 2008, http://eng.kremlin.ru/text/docs/2008/07/204750.shtml.

18 A number of Asian defence ministers have told the IISS that the first time that they ever met each other was at the IISS Shangri-La Dialogue, an informal institution that the IISS established in 2002, bringing together all the defence ministers of the Asia-Pacific and of the key outside powers.

19 Available at http://www.flacso.org/uploads/media/Declaracion_de_Santiago_de_Chile.pdf.

Structuring Middle East Security

Peter Jones

Of all the world's regions, only the Middle East lacks an inclusive mechanism for the promotion of regional cooperation and security.[1] Europe has the Organisation for Security and Cooperation in Europe (OSCE); Asia the Association of Southeast Asian Nations (ASEAN); the Western Hemisphere the Organisation of American States (OAS); Africa the African Union; and so on. Not all of these regional systems are equally effective, of course. But the lack of any such system in the Middle East is striking. Why does the Middle East stand outside this worldwide trend? Is it in the region's interest to try to develop such a system? How could the first steps be taken towards such a goal, given the Middle East's many rivalries and conflicts?

The Middle East is characterised by multiple, sometimes overlapping conflicts, both between and within states. While some of this is due to the Arab–Israeli dispute, many regional security issues are only peripherally related to that problem, if at all. More people have died in the region's other conflicts than in the Arab–Israeli dispute.[2] Moreover, the development, or attempted development, of nuclear, biological or chemical weapons in the region has had as much to do with other regional disputes or imperatives as it has had to do with the Arab–Israeli dispute. Certainly, the only instances of the *use* of such weapons in the region – Iraq's use of chemical weapons against Iran and its own population, and Egypt's use of chemical weapons in Yemen – have had nothing to do with Israel.

Peter Jones is Associate Professor in the Graduate School of Public and International Affairs at the University of Ottawa.

Survival | vol. 51 no. 6 | December 2009–January 2010 | pp. 105–122 DOI 10.1080/00396330903461682

This is not to deny the importance of the Arab–Israeli conflict, particularly in its radicalising effects throughout the region. But any truly regional approach to security and cooperation will have to accept as a starting point that a broader approach will be required. Focusing purely on the Arab–Israeli dispute as the sole security problem of the region does not reflect the Middle East's complex and multidimensional security environment.

The idea of adopting a regional approach to enhanced cooperation and security in the Middle East has generated considerable interest over the years. One of the first regional leaders to take up the idea was President Hosni Mubarak of Egypt, who raised the possibility in April 1990 in the context of a broader disarmament plan for the Middle East.[3] Prince Hassan bin Talal of Jordan referred several times in the 1990s to the idea of a 'Middle East OSCE'. In 2002, then Crown Prince Abdullah of Saudi Arabia alluded to the need for some sort of Middle East system in the context of his Peace Initiative to the Arab League Summit in Beirut.[4] Most recently, at the IISS Manama Dialogue convened to address these kinds of issues in a major track-two setting, the foreign minister of Bahrain made public statements in favour of

> the establishment of a regional organisation in which all countries in the Middle East and North Africa region are members, without exception … a genuinely Middle Eastern body in which Middle Eastern countries sit down to reach Middle Eastern solutions to Middle Eastern issues.[5]

Complementing these official regional musings, academic and track-two diplomatic efforts have for some years been devoted to exploring this question.[6] These efforts have developed many of the ideas surrounding this issue, and have produced a cadre of regional experts with in-depth knowledge of the possibilities. Though there is little tangible evidence that the ideas generated in these forums have reached the political realm, some argue that attempting to measure the specific impact of such efforts misses the point; it is precisely the development of an 'epistemic community', and the general diffusion of new concepts into the region's discourse, which are the true accomplishments of such activities, though these may be difficult to quantify.[7]

The critical questions

The Middle East does have experience with cooperation and security systems, but this has been limited. The Arab League is the most broadly inclusive system in the Middle East, but it is exclusive of non-Arab states. Moreover, the league's members have, to date, seemed reluctant to imbue it with the necessary capacities and authority to act as a real security mechanism for the region.

There was an attempt made as part of the multilateral track of the Middle East peace process to create an ongoing process for regional security and arms control, known as the Arms Control and Regional Security Working Group (ACRS). ACRS was one of five multilateral working groups created as part of the Madrid peace process. It met in plenary six times between 1992 and 1995, and held numerous working sessions between the plenary meetings. Several notable confidence-building measures were agreed. However, a dispute over the question of how to address Israel's nuclear status led to the group's demise in 1995.

Among its weaknesses, ACRS was never fully representative of the region, as important countries were either excluded (Libya, Iran, Iraq) or chose to stay out of the process (Syria, Lebanon). Moreover, ACRS was intimately tied to the Arab–Israeli peace process, and its underlying conception was that regional security is primarily a function of the Arab–Israeli dispute. This is not necessarily true.[8]

With the end of ACRS, attention turned to the idea of creating a more inclusive and far-reaching cooperation and security framework for the Middle East. This raised numerous complex questions, including:

- What kind of security are we talking about in discussions of a regional system for the Middle East?
- Should the Middle East strive for a region-wide approach, or opt for subregional systems, probably focusing on the Persian Gulf in the first instance?
- What role should be played by outside powers, particularly the United States, in such a system?
- Can a regional cooperation system be launched in the Middle East before the Arab–Israeli dispute is resolved?

To a very large extent, these questions are intertwined and cannot be answered in isolation.

What kind of security?

Given that any regional system that might be created in the Middle East is likely, for the foreseeable future, to be primarily state-centric, the types of security which are most relevant to this debate are 'collective defence' and 'cooperative security' – a term used here not in the sense associated with Woodrow Wilson and the League of Nations, but rather in the sense of states cooperating to establish norms of behaviour and mechanisms to give those norms effect over time.[9] Whether any future regional system is ultimately designed to provide either type of security will depend on the underlying threat perceptions of the Middle Eastern countries that take part.[10] Moreover, the experience of other regions has shown that institutions providing different forms of security can co-exist within a given space, provided their objectives are not mutually contradictory, raising the possibility that both collective and cooperative mechanisms will emerge simultaneously in the Middle East.

CENTO was never particularly robust

If we imagine that the type of regional architecture sought for the Middle East is a collective defence arrangement, this would mean, in practice, an alliance of some sort (even if it is not called that), in which only a certain number of regional countries would band together, probably with the United States, in an attempt to resist a perceived aggressor. This would require a high degree of congruence with respect to the basic consideration of what the threat was, even if regional politics and cultural norms meant that it was never formally identified.

Historically, there has been at least one attempt to create a multilateral organisation of this type in the Middle East, the Central Treaty Organisation (CENTO), sometimes known as the Baghdad Pact. This Cold War alliance against Soviet penetration of the region existed from 1955 to 1979, but was never particularly robust. The Gulf Co-operation Council (GCC), created in 1981, has some elements of a defence alliance and may develop further along those lines. Though the latter does not identify a specific enemy, both CENTO and GCC arrangements contain the idea of collective defence against aggression, though this is expressed far more weakly than it is in, say, the NATO Treaty.

In place of multilateral defence treaties, many Middle Eastern states have traditionally relied on bilateral defence arrangements with outside powers. The United Kingdom was once the primary defence partner for many in the region, until it was replaced by the United States. Often these arrangements are not codified by formal treaties, but by a web of basing agreements, mutual exercise arrangements and other expressions of intent. For the most part, the threat which these bilateral defence arrangements are meant to deter is not formally mentioned, but is quite clear. For the individual GCC states, for example, it was originally Iraq and Iran, and is now Iran.[11]

If, on the other hand, the Middle East were to move toward a more cooperative regional system, one could reasonably expect that a greater number of countries would participate; that the system would be open to all of them, if they decided to join; and that it would not be aimed at countering a specific country, so much as developing a code of conduct and associated dialogue mechanisms to give that code effect. In other words, there would be no unifying desire to counter another country but rather a general agreement that uncertainty and lack of common standards of behaviour were the danger. To the extent that a threat was perceived, it would be more associated with concerns over the possible impact on regional stability of such issues as arms races, demographic pressures, environmental problems and other challenges faced by all of the region's states.[12]

Thus, in the case of such a cooperative security system, the bulk of the discussions, at least initially, would likely focus on fairly traditional issues of state-to-state security. But consideration might also be given to possible mechanisms for the discussion of social, economic and political issues in the region, particularly as they affect regional stability and security. It seems reasonable to expect that any such discussions would be relatively low-key in the first instance, as many regional states are not comfortable with the idea of multilateral dialogue on such issues.

Interestingly, the two types of security are not mutually exclusive. In Europe, the OSCE and NATO co-exist, as did the OSCE's predecessor (the

Conference on Security and Cooperation in Europe) with both NATO and the Warsaw Pact. Thus, member states do not necessarily have to pick and choose among different types of groupings. Members of collective defence arrangements (such as NATO) are also members of cooperative security mechanisms (the OSCE), and maintain that their collective defence arrangements enable them to better fulfil their cooperative security obligations, and vice versa.

Pan-regional or sub-regional?

The 'Middle East' (a term invented by Westerners to describe the region's place in their own worldview, and not by those who live there) is a large and complex region. Though many of its inhabitants share a single language and religion, the cultural and other differences between them are significant. Some have questioned whether it makes sense to speak of the 'Middle East' as requiring one approach to security and cooperation.

Broadly speaking, most analysts accept that there are three distinct sub-regions within the Middle East: the Persian Gulf, the Levant and the Maghreb. Moreover, the boundaries of the Middle East are not entirely agreed. Some studies regard a suitable definition of the Middle East as including the members of the League of Arab States, Iran, Israel and Turkey.[13] While most would accept this intuitively, for the purposes of security, it leaves unanswered some important questions. How, for example, would events in Pakistan and Afghanistan, two countries 'outside' the Middle East, but whose security decisions affect many of its members, be factored in?

Initial proposals and studies, including the Mubarak plan and ACRS, took the view that a pan-regional approach should be adopted in the first instance. Though some of these did note that there should also be sub-regional systems, they assumed that the pan-regional approach would have a degree of primacy in setting the region's norms regarding cooperation.

Despite much discussion and study, however, this approach failed to generate any sustained traction in the period leading to the US invasion of Iraq in 2003. There are at least three reasons for this. Firstly, as noted, a truly pan-regional approach was never actually tried. Each of the 'visions' that informed the various approaches (the Arab League, the peace process, ACRS) was, to some extent, exclusionary in terms of how it defined the region and its members.[14]

Secondly, it is doubtful that many regional leaders ever really accepted the notion of a genuine discussion of regional cooperation and security. Some took the view that the ongoing Arab–Israeli dispute made inclusive pan-regional discussion impossible. The Iranian revolutionary government was not accepted by some of its neighbours, in part because of its aggressive actions to 'export' its ideology in the immediate period after the 1979 Islamic Revolution. Turkey exhibited a degree of ambivalence about its status as a 'Middle Eastern' country.

Thirdly, it seems that regional leaders across the Middle East have avoided real discussion of these issues because of a fear that any move toward cooperation might require a diminution of sovereignty, which many Middle Eastern governments cling to in an absolute sense. Some regional leaders have also seemed uncomfortable with the thought that any discussions would raise a variety of sensitive social, demographic and political issues that they are reluctant to air in what would be a relatively open forum.

The Arab–Israeli issue could not simply be taken off the table

In the wake of the US invasion of Iraq, a number of authors, many of them Americans, began to argue that a sub-regional approach, focused on the Persian Gulf, should be considered.[15] Most proponents of this idea took the view that such an approach could work because it would exclude the Arab–Israeli dispute from discussion by simply cutting Israel out of the debate. It was quickly shown, however, that such an apparently simple course of action would not necessarily yield early or dramatic results. It turned out that the Arab–Israeli issue could not simply be taken off the table, with key countries arguing that even a Persian Gulf approach to security must take account of Israel in some way.[16] Moreover, Arab analysts outside of the Persian Gulf sub-region argued that their countries should also be included in any deliberations, given that they make contributions to that area and their national interests are bound up in it.[17]

Interestingly, there were considerable differences of view among those proposing a Persian Gulf sub-regional approach as to what kind of security should be striven for. Some of those who were most keen on a Persian Gulf system in the wake of the American invasion of Iraq supported collective defence arrangements between the United States and certain Gulf countries, which would exclude Iran.[18] Others advanced the idea of an inclusive, cooperative sub-regional security system.[19] Thus, even within the supposedly more 'simple' sub-regional approach, there are still considerable differences of view. It is hardly surprising that progress has been far slower than anticipated by those who were early proponents of this scheme.

One interesting question that has largely been lost in this debate is whether it is even necessary to choose between a pan-regional or a sub-regional approach, rather than pursuing both options simultaneously. Michael Yaffe, writing in the immediate aftermath of the US invasion of Iraq, and perhaps trying to generate policy impetus in Washington, went so far as to declare that 'pan-Middle East strategies have a single major problem: they don't work'.[20] Instead, he proposed that efforts be concentrated on a Persian Gulf-based collective defence system involving the United States and select regional countries, one which might, in time, be replicated in the other sub-regions of the Middle East, and possibly tied together into a pan-regional network.

But how realistic was this view? Are Middle Eastern countries likely to rely solely on an interlocking series of sub-regional collective security arrangements with the United States as the only basis of regional stability? The unpopularity of the United States across the Middle East gives reason for doubt.[21]

It seems more reasonable to suggest that there are some issues best dealt with on a sub-regional basis, while others require a more pan-regional approach. A group of regional experts, myself among them, who met several times in the late 1990s under the auspices of the Stockholm International Peace Research Institute (SIPRI) went over this ground in considerable detail. The group's final report, in a section entitled 'The role of sub-regions and the relationships between bilateral, sub-regional and global security arrangements', concluded:

> the creation of a region-wide security regime should be undertaken in a manner which is synergistic with bilateral, multilateral or sub-regional approaches to security issues. This could best be accomplished by establishing a broad set of principles (for regional conduct) which would be relevant to all levels of discourse in the region and then taking a functional approach as to which issues should be dealt with at which levels and in what manner. Some issues, such as those related to weapons of mass destruction, will require a regional approach. Others may best be dealt with sub-regionally.[22]

The fundamental mechanism by which a sufficiently flexible system could be achieved was identified by the SIPRI process as the 'geometry variable'. This is the notion that, within the framework of an overall set of regional principles, progress on different issues can be made at different rates of speed and in different forums, and even by different constellations of actors, as appropriate to the issue at hand. Some approaches will be primarily collective; some will be primarily cooperative; some will be sub-regional; some will be pan-regional. What is required, however, is an overarching set of norms to bind the whole together.

Absent such norms, there is the risk that the system will devolve into a disjointed set of sub-regional dialogues proceeding in very different directions. While this may not be a problem in such areas as environmental cooperation, where the questions facing each sub-region will in most cases be quite different, it would be a significant problem in those areas where region-wide agreements will eventually be necessary, such as the Arab–Israeli dispute, nuclear-, biological- or chemical-weapons proliferation, and international terrorism.

The role of outside powers

Another unresolved question concerns the proper role of states outside the region. Indeed, should outside powers have *any* role? These are questions that have given rise to some strong opinions. Hardliners in the Iranian government, for example, argue that all outside forces must leave the region before any new approach to security and cooperation can be advanced.

Some Western analysts, on the other hand, believe that future approaches to regional security will require an intimate network of collective defence arrangements between outside powers, particularly the United States, and selected regional states.[23]

Between these two extremes lie more subtle approaches. It seems clear that any regional security architecture in the Middle East will have several components. For example, while the overarching system may be based on notions of cooperative security, there will likely be some collective defence arrangements within it, involving defence 'understandings' between the United States and certain regional countries. (The recent musings of US Secretary of State Hillary Clinton about a possible defence umbrella for the GCC states in response to Iranian nuclear ambitions may be a case in point.[24]) This is not necessarily unusual: other regions feature both approaches simultaneously, without having to choose between them.

It also seems likely that outside powers will play different roles in each level of any Middle Eastern security architecture according to the needs and desires of those involved. It is, for example, likely that the United States (probably with some involvement of the United Kingdom and France as well) will be the principle outside power involved in those issues pertaining to defence, on both the pan-regional and sub-regional levels. Europe is likely to be heavily involved in issues related to economic cooperation. China will also play an increasing role here.

Broadly speaking, there are two categories of outside powers with a potential role to play in any Middle Eastern security system. Firstly, there are those that are relevant across the Middle East and to all of its sub-regions. It would be logical to expect that these countries (or international bodies) would take part in many, if not all, of the deliberations of any regional or sub-regional bodies. It will be up to Middle Eastern states to decide which countries qualify for this role. The overlapping memberships of the G8, the permanent members of the UN Security Council and the Middle East Quartet may be the most likely candidates.

A second category of outside powers would be those countries that have a role to play on a functional basis, given the issue at hand, or those that are particularly relevant to a given sub-regional dynamic. One could thus imagine that states such as India and Pakistan, though they would not be part of the regional system, could have a role to play in any discussion of, for example, a regional Weapons of Mass Destruction Free Zone,[25] perhaps in the field of guarantees to respect the zone. More broadly, states that border Middle Eastern sub-regions such as the Persian Gulf and North Africa could be invited to play a role in such areas as economic and environmental cooperation.

ASEAN provides an example of the type of system this flexible approach to outsider participation could take, in which regional states make up the inner core of the system, with various other countries and international bodies becoming involved in regional affairs on a functional basis. Ideally, the states of the Middle East would lead in the creation of any such system, setting the procedural and substantive parameters of the system and having first say in its operation and evolution. Outside powers would be present in a supportive role, and to ensure that their concerns about regional developments were given proper due.

But this may be too ambitious, at least at first. Several Middle Eastern states do not yet recognise each other. It will be difficult for them to come together in a sufficiently collegial manner to permit the degree of unanimity required to play the leading role in any regional system. Thus, we may expect that at least some outside powers will also play a facilitative role in the creation and early operation of a regional system. The trick will be for the region's states to avail themselves of this assistance without surrendering leadership over their future.

The Arab–Israeli peace process

A final question concerns the possibility of constructing a regional cooperation and security system without first resolving the Arab–Israeli dispute. In an ideal world, this problem would not have to be faced: the peace process would be finished and two states, Israel and Palestine, would exist side-by-side in peace and harmony. But this is not likely to happen for some time, if ever.

As noted above, the Arab–Israeli dispute is far from the only conflict in the Middle East, nor is it the most deadly. But it does occupy a special place in the region's political and social life. The Middle Eastern public is particularly attuned to this conflict, and it plays a significant role in the radicalisation of youth across the region. The development of a cooperative security system is thus tied to the Arab–Israeli dispute in practice, even if the issues are quite different. But this should not mean that the dispute has to be fully resolved before progress can be made on the wider system.

One key may lie in the notion that a new approach to regional security could assist the peace process indirectly. The growing importance of Hamas in the Israeli–Palestinian dispute, for example, may cause some of Israel's neighbours, notably Egypt, to wonder if a process of ongoing discussion and cooperation on security matters might be helpful in containing possible threats to stability. Such cooperation can go on quietly, behind the scenes – no doubt it already does on the level of the security services. But there is an argument to be made that a more diplomatic process could complement secret talks by contributing to the development of regional norms that would support the goal of enhancing moderate forces and strengthening states as the primary actors on the regional stage. More broadly, by demonstrating that a new and more cooperative future is possible in the region, a more formal security system could make the difficult compromises required to make peace in the Arab–Israeli dispute seem less intractable.

A new approach to regional security could assist the peace process indirectly

It is worth noting that in no other region did the central dispute characterising the area need to be resolved before a more cooperative approach to security dialogue could be developed. This is not to equate the Arab–Israeli dispute with any other, though residents of the Middle East sometimes underestimate the gravity and bitterness of the Franco-German and later Cold War rivalries in Europe when they argue that their own rivalries cannot be so easily overcome. But it is clear that other regions have found ways to at least begin a dialogue over new approaches to cooperation, even as they have been locked in serious, and in some cases deadly, conflicts.

In Europe, the divisions of Germany and Berlin, the occupation of Eastern Europe, the existence of huge peacetime armies and the deployment of thousands of nuclear weapons were not used as a pretext to refuse engagement over regional stability; these factors made such engagement more complex, but also convinced leaders and peoples that it was vitally necessary. In Asia, the conflicts and pressures of decolonisation and the Cold War were not used as a pretext to refuse to engage in the process which would eventually lead to ASEAN; they made regional leaders more determined to do so. Other regions have had similar experiences.

This is not to equate the Middle East with Europe, Asia, or any other region. Each region is different in important ways. But it is significant that other regions have experienced war, occupation, proliferation and a host of other ills, and yet have managed to begin a process of dialogue and cooperation regardless. For too long some Middle Eastern leaders have used the pretext of the Arab–Israeli dispute to avoid uncomfortable decisions and discussions over wider questions and to mollify those within their own populations who have preached intolerance. The inability of regional leaders to move beyond the Arab–Israeli dispute and begin to develop the new regional structures which are required to deal with the political, security, economic, social and environmental challenges they now face is weakening their ability to deal with these problems and is strengthening those who seek to overthrow the existing regional order.

Looking ahead

Without question, the creation of a regional security system in the Middle East will be a complex affair. There are different conceptions of the basic notions of security in play; the question of the proper relationship between regional and sub-regional approaches requires much deliberation; the role of outside powers remains vexing; and the ongoing Arab–Israeli conflict is seen, at least by some, as rendering progress impossible for the time being. One way forward may be to accept that no single system is going to emerge – no single approach or regional security system can possibly address the many questions in play. Rather, it might be best to conceive of the road ahead as involving discussion of a 'system of systems'.

Where appropriate, some Middle Eastern countries, along with certain outside powers, may seek to create collective defence arrangements. But this does not mean that an inclusive, cooperative security system cannot also be explored. The two have co-existed in other regions and indeed enhanced each other. Similarly, there is no reason to think that pan-regional and sub-regional dialogues could not be developed simultaneously, each stressing different issues. Above all, it will be important to avoid 'either–or' approaches when considering the region's security future.

The key may lie in recognising that the development of such systems in all regions of the world has been a long-term, evolutionary process. No regional cooperation system was born fully formed. A patient, long-term view is required, as is a degree of flexibility. It may well be, in the first instance, that not all countries of the region will be prepared to participate in official discussions until the Middle East peace process is completed. Perhaps only a few regional countries will take part in any official track at the beginning of the process, and the issues discussed might be relatively uncontroversial ones.

However, a broader cross-section of regional states may be willing to participate in a structured, but unofficial, process addressing a wider range of issues. This would require the creation of an ongoing track-two process dedicated to the discussion of regional cooperation and security issues, but one that enjoyed close links to official diplomacy.[26] Such a system might draw lessons from the experience of the Asia-Pacific region, where a standing unofficial process exists to complement and support the official one. Though not without its difficulties, this process permits regional countries to explore ideas that are too sensitive for the official process, in a low-key, relatively low-risk environment.[27]

The advantage of such a system for the Middle East would lie in its ability to assist the regional states in transcending the 'recognition barrier' that is so tied up with the Arab–Israeli process. The logic is that, while it is practically impossible for many regional states to meet with Israelis in official settings, the same is not necessarily true of unofficial settings. The trick is to imbue unofficial efforts with sufficient structure and 'connectivity' to the official track that it is capable of fostering useful, policy-relevant discussions of critical issues. Such a track could not make or enforce decisions. Only official meetings can do that. But it would serve at least as a forum where some discussion on matters of mutual interest could take place until political developments in the region progress to the point that an official process could be developed.

A longer-term vision is thus required. Policymakers need to have a broad sense of where the region needs to go, even if the map to get there is not yet fully drawn. A regional security 'system of systems' is not going to spring up overnight. It may, in the first instance, feature small steps to institutionalise dialogue over small issues. It may begin on both the track-one and track-two levels simultaneously. The details will have to be discussed and agreed, of course. What is required now is high-level recognition that this type of regional arrangement is a necessary component of the Middle East's response to what has happened in Iraq and to wider regional trends, and a willingness to begin the long process of its creation. The Middle East desperately requires some rules of behaviour for its states and a mechanism to allow for ongoing dialogue over security issues. As the experience of other regions has shown, individual conflicts, no matter how serious, need not stand in the way of regional institutional development. Indeed, in other parts of the world, the creation of cooperative systems was seen as critical in managing, and ultimately helping to resolve, the central dispute.

Notes

1 The term 'Middle East' as used in this essay is intended to convey the sense meant by the larger term 'Middle East and North Africa' (MENA).

2 Although exact numbers are necessarily speculative, losses from the Arab–Israeli conflict are in the 60–70,000 range since 1948. The Algerian Civil War cost some 150–200,000 dead, the Yemen Civil War some 125,000 and the Iran–Iraq War some 500,000.

3 See *Letter dated 19 April 1990 from the Permanent Representative of Egypt addressed to the President of the Conference on Disarmament*, Conference on Disarmament document CD/989, 20 April, 1990.

4 The Saudi peace plan was advanced at the Arab League Summit in March 2002 and has since been adopted, with minor modifications, by the Arab League. It was re-endorsed at the Arab League Summit in Riyadh in 2007. See 'Text: Arab Peace Plan of 2002', http://news.bbc.co.uk/1/hi/world/middle_east/1844214.stm.

5 See Sheikh Khalid Bin Ahmed Bin Mohamed Al Khalifa, keynote address to the 5th IISS Regional Security Summit, Manama, Bahrain, 12 December 2008, http://www.iiss.org/

conferences/the-iiss-regional-security-summit/manama-dialogue-2008/plenary-sessions-and-speeches/opening-remarks-and-keynote-address/keynote-address-sh-khalid-bin-ahmed-bin-mohamed-al-khalifa/.

6 Among the principal texts are Peter Jones, *Towards a Regional Security Regime for the Middle East; Issues and Options* (Stockholm: SIPRI, 1998), available at http://books.sipri.org/files/misc/SIPRI98Jones.pdf (hereafter cited as the *SIPRI Report*); Shai Feldman and Abdullah Toukan, *Bridging the Gap: A Future Security Architecture for the Middle East* (Lanham, MD: Rowman and Littlefield, 1997); and the collection of essays in the special issue on 'Building Regional Security in the Middle East: International, Regional and Domestic Influences', *Journal of Strategic Studies*, vol. 26, no. 3, September 2003.

7 For more on how track-two efforts can contribute to the consideration of regional security matters, see Peter Jones, 'Filling a Critical Gap, or Just Wasting Time: Track Two Diplomacy and Regional Security in the Middle East', *Disarmament Forum*, no. 2, 2008, http://www.unidir.org/bdd/fiche-article.php?ref_article=2726; Dalia Dassa Kaye, *Talking to the Enemy: Track Two Diplomacy in the Middle East and South Asia* (Santa Monica, CA: RAND Corporation, 2007); Dalia Dassa Kaye, 'Track Two Diplomacy and Regional Security in the Middle East', *International Negotiation: A Journal of Theory and Practice*, vol. 6, no. 1, 2001, pp. 44–77.

8 For more on the ACRS, see Bruce Jentleson, *The Middle East Arms Control and Security Talks: Progress, Problems and Prospects*, IGCC Policy Paper no. 2 (Los Angeles, CA: University of California, 1996); Peter Jones, 'Arms Control in the Middle East: Is It Time to Renew ACRS?', *Disarmament Forum*, no. 2, 2005, http://www.unidir.org/bdd/fiche-article.php?ref_article=2278.

9 For more on this conception of cooperative security see Janne Nolan, *Global Engagement: Cooperation and Security in the 21st Century* (Washington DC: The Brookings Institution Press, 1994).

10 See Peter Jones, 'Is a Common Threat Perception a Necessary Precondition for the Creation of a Regional Security and Co-operation System?', *Conflict INFOCUS*, no. 21, October 2007, pp. 3–5, http://www.rccp-jid.org/infocus/infocus_21.pdf.

11 Some GCC states have also had concerns about each other.

12 See Jones, *SIPRI Report*.

13 See, for example, J. Prawitz and J.F. Leonard, *A Zone Free of Weapons of Mass Destruction in the Middle East* (Geneva: UNIDIR, 1996).

14 For a thoughtful discussion of the question of defining the Middle East region as a function of who is excluded, see Saad Eddin Ibrahim, 'Future Visions of the Arab Middle East', *Security Dialogue*, vol. 27, no. 4, December 1996, pp. 425–36.

15 For examples see Flynt Leverett, 'The Middle East: Thinking Big', *The American Prospect*, 21 February 2005, http://www.prospect.org/cs/articles?article=the_middle_east_thinking_big; Michael Yaffe, 'The Gulf and a New Middle East Security System', *Middle East Policy Journal*,

vol. 11, no. 3, Fall 2004, http://www.mepc.org/journal_vol11/0409_yaffe.asp; Fariborz Mokhtari, 'Security in the Persian Gulf: Is a Security Framework Possible?', *American Foreign Policy Interests*, February 2004; James A. Russell, 'Searching for a Post-Saddam Regional Security Architecture', *MERIA Journal*, vol. 7, no. 1, March 2003, http://meria.idc.ac.il/journal/2003/issue1/jv7n1a3.html; Kenneth M. Pollack, 'Securing the Gulf', *Foreign Affairs*, vol. 82, no. 4, July–August 2003, http://www.foreignaffairs.com/articles/58993/kenneth-m-pollack/securing-the-gulf; Joseph McMillan, Richard Sokolsky and Andrew Winner, 'Toward a New Regional Security Architecture', *Washington Quarterly*, vol. 26, no. 3, Summer 2003, pp. 161–75; Andrew Rathmell, Theodore Karasik and David Gompert, *A New Persian Gulf Security System* (Santa Monica, CA: RAND Corporation, 2003).

16 Prince Saud Al Faisal, Minister of Foreign Affairs, Saudi Arabia, 'Towards a New Framework for Regional Security', IISS Gulf Security Dialogue: The Gulf Dialogue, Bahrain, 5 December 2004.

17 See, for example, Mohamed Kadry Said, 'Potential Egyptian Contribution to a Security Framework in the Gulf', *Middle East Policy Journal*, vol. 11, no. 3, Fall 2003, http://www.mepc.org/journal_vol11/0409_said.asp.

18 See, for example, Yaffe, 'The Gulf and a New Middle East Security System'.

19 See, for example, The Stanley Foundation, *The Future of Gulf Security: Project Report* (Muscatine, IA: The Stanley Foundation, November 2007); and Leverett, 'The Middle East: Thinking Big'.

20 Yaffe, 'The Gulf and a New Middle East Security System'.

21 A point noted even in the immediate aftermath of the US-led invasion and occupation of Iraq. See, for example, Riad Kahwaji, 'U.S.–Arab Cooperation in the Gulf: Are Both Sides Working From the Same Script?'; and Volker Perthes, 'America's "Greater Middle East" and Europe: Key Issues for Dialogue', *Middle East Policy Journal*, vol. 11, no. 3, Fall 2003, http://www.mepc.org/journal_vol11/0409_perthes.asp.

22 Jones, *SIPRI Report*, p. 22. A list of participants in the SIPRI process may be found on pp. 51–3.

23 Yaffe, 'The Gulf and a New Middle East Security System'.

24 Mark Landler and David E. Sanger, 'Clinton Speaks of Shielding Mideast from Iran', *New York Times*, 22 July 2009, http://www.nytimes.com/2009/07/23/world/asia/23diplo.html.

25 Vilmos Cserveny et al., *Building a Weapons of Mass Destruction Free Zone in the Middle East*, UNIDIR/2004/24 (Geneva: UNIDIR, 2004).

26 This approach is sometimes call 'track-1.5' diplomacy. For more on this and the origins of the term, see Jeffrey Mapendere, 'Track One and Half Diplomacy and the Complementarity of Tracks', *Culture of Peace Online Journal*, vol. 2, no. 1, 2006, pp. 66–81. Susan Allen Nan has defined 'track one and a half' as 'diplomatic initiatives that are facilitated by unofficial bodies, but directly involve officials from the conflict in question'.

'Track One-and-a-Half Diplomacy: Contributions to Georgia–South Ossetian Peacemaking', in Ronald J. Fisher, *Paving the Way: Contributions of Interactive Conflict Resolution to Peacemaking* (New York: Lexington, 2005), pp. 161–74.

27 A thoughtful analysis of the accomplishments and limitations of track-two diplomacy on regional security in the Asia-Pacific region may be found in Desmond Ball, Anthony Milner and Brendan Taylor, 'Track Two Security Dialogue in the Asia-Pacific: Reflections and Future Directions', *Asian Security*, vol. 2, no. 3, December 2006, p. 182. The authors acknowledge that their analysis builds on Brian Job, 'Track 2 Diplomacy: Ideational Contribution to the Evolving Asia Security Order', in Muthiah Alagappa (ed.), *Asian Security Order: Instrumental and Normative Features* (Stanford, CA: Stanford University Press, 2002), pp. 241–79. For more on the idea of Asian track-two meetings as a possible model for such dialogues in the Middle East see: Dalia Dassa Kaye, *Talking to the Enemy*, p. 120; and Peter Jones, 'Track II Diplomacy and the Gulf Weapons of Mass Destruction Free Zone', *Security and Terrorism Research Bulletin*, Gulf Research Center, no. 1, October 2005, http://www.grc.ae/bulletin_WMD_Free_Zone.pdf.

China and the United States: Between Cold and Warm Peace

Rosemary Foot

Since the beginning of 2009, top American and Chinese officials have repeatedly stressed that the two countries are 'in the same boat' and need to work together to weather the storm of the several crises, especially economic, that are buffeting the world.[1] But a successful voyage requires a single designated captain; orders, given harshly or kindly, are expected to be obeyed; and there has to be agreement on the rules of navigation. Ending up on the rocks is always a possibility, which leads to hedging behaviour. And if you do reach the shore successfully, any grievances suppressed while you all breasted the waves may come spilling out into the open.

The boat metaphor captures reasonably well issues of cooperation and competition contained within the Sino-American relationship. In the last few months, the two nations have often been spoken of as equals or co-dependents, especially as a result of the global economic crisis. On the other hand, underlying much of this commentary has been a sense that, over the longer term, we are witnessing a transition of power from the United States to China, which might well involve intense rivalry and potentially even war. China's rise raises questions about America's ability to adjust to Beijing's enhanced influence; about how China will use its newfound strength; and about whether its military modernisation will set off an arms race in Asia, with all the attendant concerns associated with a security dilemma. The Asia-Pacific region has enjoyed inter-state peace since 1979, but the strategic

Rosemary Foot is Professor of International Relations and John Swire Senior Research Fellow at St Antony's College, Oxford University. With her co-author, Andrew Walter, Foot is working on a book, *China, the United States and Global Order*, forthcoming from Cambridge University Press.

Survival | vol. 51 no. 6 | December 2009–January 2010 | pp. 123–146 DOI 10.1080/00396330903461708

architecture has been unsettled by China's growing influence and ability to project power. Many question whether China's growing strength should be compared with the US position at the end of the nineteenth century or, more ominously, with the rise of Germany and Japan during the same period.

One new feature of the debate is the acceptance that cooperation between the United States and China is vital to global and regional order in many issue areas. Yet sustained cooperation between Beijing and Washington will be difficult to maintain. Four factors account for much of that difficulty: the conviction, in both countries, of national 'exceptionalism'; the two countries' differing political systems; the historically resonant problem of China's rise and the attendant transition of global power (which may be an impending reality or may be more a matter of perception); and long-standing mutual strategic distrust. The task of analysis becomes one of defining which of these factors are structural and which are more susceptible to diplomatic negotiation. The purpose of such negotiation is to manage more successfully a relationship comprising both partnership and rivalry, the better to cope cooperatively with serious global challenges, of which three of the most urgent are the global economic crisis, climate change and the proliferation of nuclear weapons.

The global economic crisis

The United States and China are the world's two largest economies in purchasing power parity terms.[2] They are both engines of growth for a world economy that has not fractured in the way some had predicted. Were the global economy to be mired in recession for several years, many millions more people would be condemned to poverty and there would be little hope of achieving the Millennium Development Goals.[3]

In the United States, the administration of President Barack Obama has stressed that China is part of the solution to the global economic crisis, not part of the problem, leading US Secretary of State Hillary Clinton in Beijing in February 2009 to aver that the United States and China were 'truly going to rise or fall together'.[4] US Treasury Secretary Timothy Geithner's revelation in May 2009 that he had talked to his 'counterparts in China over the past few months much more than I've talked to my counterparts from any other country' was an indication of how central China's economic position and policies have become in Washington's thinking.[5]

China's stimulus package of some 4 trillion renminbi, together with its earlier steps of eliminating quotas for lending and reducing interest rates, was described by one of the leading US analysts of China's role in the global economy as representing 'the gold standard in terms of [a] response to the global economic crisis'. Nicholas Lardy, quoting International Monetary Fund findings, stated that Beijing was doing more than any other economy, including the United States, to stimulate demand.[6] China's growth rate soon recovered, although not to its previous double-digit levels, and one well-known economist from China has suggested that a rate of 7–9% can be sustained for another 10–20 years given the persistence of factors that favour such growth.[7]

Thus China is critical to global economic recovery. It is also critical to the United States in that, according to estimates, it holds more than half of its $2tr in currency reserves in US treasury bonds. Clinton urged the Chinese to keep on buying. However, there remains a palpable fear in the United States that the Chinese might decide that they no longer wish to continue to do so, given Beijing's doubts about the wisdom of US fiscal policies and the associated risk of rising inflation. As Prime Minister Wen Jiabao put it in March 2009, 'we have lent a huge amount of money to the US. Of course we are concerned about the safety of our assets. To be honest, I am definitely a little worried.'[8] When the head of China's Central Bank, Zhou Xiaochuan, referred the same month to the need to replace the US dollar as the world's reserve currency, his statement thus took on added resonance.[9]

Clinton urged the Chinese to keep on buying

Fears about major shifts in Chinese economic policies, however, are overstated. Chinese leaders also realise the relationship with the United States is one of interdependence, not simply US dependence. Beijing understands that if it cuts back too swiftly or steeply on its purchase of US bonds, or diversifies too quickly out of US dollars, the value of its assets will plummet. With the United States a major purchaser of its goods and with the Chinese economy still dependent significantly on exports and foreign investment to continue high growth rates, Beijing retains an interest in helping get the United States back on its economic feet. The Chinese government estimates that its needs to grow at least 8% per annum to avoid excess unemployment and social unrest.[10] This constrains it in terms of the extra pressure it might contemplate placing on the US economic position and pushes the two countries towards a coordinated stance, even if evident unease underlies that cooperation.

Climate change

The United Nations' Intergovernmental Panel on Climate Change's Fourth Assessment Report in 2007 concluded that 'warming of the climate system is unequivocal, as is now evident from observations of increases in global average air and ocean temperatures, widespread melting of snow and ice and rising global average sea level'. In March 2009, a gathering of scientists in Copenhagen concluded that matters are deteriorating at a rate that matches the worst-case scenario predictions of that 2007 report, with sea levels rising at twice the speed projected in that 2007 document.[11]

Changes in temperature are already having a negative impact on human security in many parts of the world and will further distort patterns of economic development. A series of official Chinese documents and policy statements acknowledge that fact. Beijing's October 2008 White Paper entitled 'China's Policies and Actions for Addressing Climate Change' outlines the widespread problems climate change poses for the country, stating that China is 'most susceptible to the adverse effects of climate change, mainly in the fields of agriculture, livestock breeding, forestry, natural ecosystems, water resources, and coastal zones'.[12] The US Department of Defense and US intelligence agencies have elevated the discussion of global warming to a security issue, and are working on ways to incorporate that new thinking into the next US national security strategy.[13]

At the same time, the United States and China are in many respects at the heart of the problem: they are the world's two largest energy consumers and the two largest producers of greenhouse gases, together accounting for over 40% of all global emissions.[14] According to one 2009 report, whereas the United States has been responsible for approximately 29% of energy-related carbon-dioxide (CO_2) emissions since 1850 (and China for only 8% over the same period), some estimates show China's annual emissions in 2007 to have been 14% higher than those of America, and growing four to six times as fast.[15] Whereas China's per capita emissions are only a quarter of America's, they are nevertheless above the world average.[16]

The American and Chinese positions have also been significantly (and for the most part negatively) influenced over the past two decades by the stances the other has taken in climate-change negotiations. Each side has been reluctant to play a substantive if differentiated role in strengthening its commitment to reducing CO_2 emissions unless the other also accepts that it too must play its part. Particularly during the George W. Bush administration, but also under previous administrations, the arguments that tended to dominate in the United States with regard to Beijing were three-fold.[17] Firstly, there was the matter of effectiveness: some in the United States argued that without China's agreement to reduce its own absolute level of emissions any efforts that the United States made would be rendered meaningless. Secondly, others asserted that any US effort to control emissions would lead manufacturers to move operations to states like China where controls were fewer, with a consequent negative impact on US employment rates.[18] Thirdly, there were those who stated that unilateral efforts on America's part would reduce its negotiating leverage with China.

> *China is suspicious of US motives*

China's reluctance to participate more actively has also partially been built on suspicions of US motives and the potentially negative outcomes associated with American policy stances. Firstly, China has long refused to move beyond some voluntary national constraints on the grounds of equity, since the industrialised world and especially the United States have been the chief culprits in creating the problem of global warming. To give up this argument would not only mean acceptance of this lack of fairness, but also serve to reduce the pressure on the United States to adopt mandatory emissions targets. Moreover, Beijing argues that, for it to become at least a middle-income country by 2030, its aim since the reform era, it has to be allowed to continue to grow and thus to emit. Chinese also often voice suspicions that the US government's real aim in calling for China's participation in post-Kyoto emissions targets is to increase its economic costs and thus constrain its rise. Finally, Beijing has sometimes suspected that any US attempt to deal with China on climate-change issues on a bilateral basis, outside the Kyoto framework, is part of an attempt to break down solidarity within the developing world, solidarity from which China has benefited and which has been important in keeping attention directed away from China and on to the United States, particularly after the George W. Bush administration withdrew from the Kyoto process.[19]

However, climate-change negotiations have shown that these perceptions are in flux. Obama has made a commitment to mandatory abatement targets. The Chinese chief spokesperson on climate change, Xie Zhenhua, has described climate change as a more serious issue for China even than the global economic crisis. And Beijing has published national targets to improve the efficiency of its energy use, and to increase its use of renewable fuels and of hydro and nuclear power. At the UN climate summit in September 2009, President Hu Jintao added carbon to the mix: 'We will endeavour to cut carbon dioxide emissions per unit of GDP by [an unspecified] notable margin by 2020 from the 2005 levels'.[20] Were there to be positive outcomes to a bilateral US–China dialogue on climate change and energy use, leading to a real and productive partnership, this could have a major beneficial impact on the capacity to strike climate-change deals elsewhere. Conversely, 'if either fails to act, the mitigation strategies adopted by the rest of the world will fall far short of averting disaster for large parts of the world'.[21]

Nuclear non-proliferation

The behaviour of the United States and China, as two leading nuclear-weapons states, in reference to non-proliferation is an important factor in the debate about how to strengthen the damaged nuclear non-proliferation regime. The two countries have worked cooperatively to roll back the North Korean nuclear-weapons programme but have been less in step over the putative Iranian programme. Both have signed, but neither has ratified, the Comprehensive Test-Ban Treaty, but both say ratification is a near-term goal.

Both state that they will work to negotiate a global Fissile Material Cut-Off Treaty. There are real opportunities for the two governments to accede to the test-ban treaty in the next year or so, which will increase the pressure on other states, such as India, Pakistan and Israel, to do so as well. If they were to work together cooperatively on these issues, new life could be breathed into the nuclear non-proliferation norm, perhaps increasing global pressure on North Korea and Iran to reverse or limit their nuclear programmes.

Then there is the matter of nuclear disarmament. Already, Obama has made some progress in this area, with the signature of an interim agreement with the Russian government, under START II, to reduce the number of nuclear warheads to between 1,500 and 1,675 within seven years, and to place limits on delivery vehicles, dropping numbers from the currently permitted 1,600 to a range between 500 and 1,100. Undoubtedly, Russian–American success in finalising this agreement, due for completion in December 2009, will put additional pressure on China to enter into nuclear-disarmament negotiations. This is important because, while China is far behind the United States and Russia in terms of the numbers of its warheads, it has been modernising and improving the quality of its nuclear arsenal.[22]

Obstacles to cooperation: exceptionalism

Applied to the United States, the concept of exceptionalism is well understood.[23] It is based on a self-perception that America 'differs qualitatively from other developed nations because of its unique origins, national credo, historical evolution, and distinctive political and religious institutions'.[24] One consequence can be that the United States assumes 'its national values and practices are universally valid and its policy positions are moral and proper, not just expedient'.[25] This gives it a right, or more accurately a duty, many administrations have believed, to enforce and interpret the rules of global order that others are expected to obey.

But the Chinese also have exceptionalist tendencies based on their long civilisation, the concept of honour embedded in the idea of tribute, and a strong Han cultural identity. Imperial tradition dictated the prime goals of the emperor to be 'to preside over a stable and harmonious order' and to overawe all others when they beheld the fruits of this enviable order – in the economy, the arts and philosophy.[26] This sense of uniqueness, of a capacity to awe others with the glories of Sinic culture, makes partnership and equality that much more difficult to contemplate. It reinforces the sense of victimhood and of being wronged that China developed as a result of the actions of a predatory West in the nineteenth and early twentieth centuries. These perceptions underpin some of China's sensitivity to diplomatic and public criticism. International image, perhaps one should call it respect, matters to China in a way that, arguably, is not as true of many other countries.

The drawbacks of this exceptionalist framing in both societies are many: it means that both have tended to see their actions in world politics as uniquely virtuous, which makes accepting the validity of the other's point of view difficult. The United States, in particular, as a consequence of its overwhelming power, has more readily been able to act on this exceptionalist premise in the post-war era. It has perceived itself as the 'custodian' of the rules of global order in this period,[27] and has been more able than China to put its interpretations of those rules into operation. More recently, Washington has recognised a need to give greater ground to the perspectives of others, but it remains hard for the United States to interpret its actions as others do. China, for its part, has become more insistent on removing aspects of the current global order that it perceives as unjust.

Political systems

Depictions of China and the United States tend to pit an authoritarian one-party state with well-developed means of surveillance and repression against a participatory electoral democracy where citizens are active in enforcing constitutional rights and where interest groups and civil society have many points of access to the political process. These depictions are accurate enough, as far as they go, but probably don't capture the real problems that differing political systems pose to Sino-American cooperation.

It is not that China has undertaken no political reforms. It has established a norm of term limits and age limits for top office holders, and it has sanctioned a debate on increasing inner-party democracy, and on methods of rooting out corruption. The leadership has been more responsive to public attitudes (often expressed via street protests or over the Internet); and a culture of non-governmental organisations is thriving, although very few have managed to carve out a space relatively independent of state control. The Chinese Communist Party tries to legitimate its rule by arguing that its form of democracy is designed to give primacy to beneficial economic outcomes over political process, and that it will protect China's honour in international negotiations. But the way it has dealt with minority issues in Tibet and Xinjiang, as well as human-rights activists and other social critics, are reminders that its rule can be harsh and unyielding.

Neither Beijing nor Washington much likes what it sees in terms of the other's polity, and irritants and misperceptions arising from the domestic sphere will remain prominent in the relationship. However, beyond those differences in values are questions relating to the decentralisation of power in the two systems. Decentralisation can sometimes mean that implementation of some of the bilateral agreements they reach, or which involve both in crucial global-order questions, is particularly challenging. In the United States, diffusion of power among the different branches of government can result in outcomes unexpected by those overseas governments less familiar with its political system. Examples include the Kyoto Protocol and the Comprehensive Test-Ban Treaty. The Clinton administration signed both accords, but was unable to muster the 67 votes in the Senate necessary to ratify them.

China's political system is, paradoxically, both authoritarian and highly decentralised, with a large proportion of governmental officials working at local level. In addition, the workings of the market and the transfer of resources to the localities has meant that implementation of policy is often in hands far from the centre. There are five levels of government to negotiate, which exerts enormous demands on the central government as it tries to keep local-level incentives and interests in line with those policy preferences expressed in Beijing.[28] Environmental policy is one area where it has been difficult to establish local support for directives from the centre. For example, from 2002 to 2004 some 70,000 violations of environmental laws were reported to the centre, but only 500 were addressed. In most cases, the explanation was that 'local governments ... insisted that local firms violate environmental laws in order to increase production and employment and that those same governments then protected the firms involved from higher level retribution'.[29]

If partnership depends on predictability, reciprocity and living up to commitments in order to build trust, then the domestic systems are to some degree impediments to that end.

Power: transitions and perceptions

Some theorists of international relations have argued that the danger of war is at its height when a power transition is about to take place. When a dissatisfied rising power catches up with and begins to overtake the dominant state in the system, that contender is deemed likely to spark a conflict.[30] The rise of Germany from the end of the nineteenth century is often cited as the prime example, both because of Germany's increasing material resources and its sense of dissatisfaction with its position in the global hierarchy.

The United States has long been the preponderant power in the global system and has played a central role in shaping the post-1945 institutional and behavioural order. Few expect a shift in the distribution of power in China's favour to be an easy adjustment for America, which has long enjoyed great strategic latitude in political and military action.

Some power indicators suggest that this transition is well under way. The United States' share of world trade and global GDP has declined from 16% and 30% respectively in 1999 to 11% and 23% in 2008, with China's relative increases largely responsible for that decline. China's GDP in 2009, in PPP terms, makes it a relatively close second to the United States and nearly twice the size of Japan. Whereas China enjoyed growth rates of some 10% between 2000 and 2007, the United States managed only about a quarter of that.[31] Beijing's economic strategy has given it the largest foreign-exchange reserves, some $2tr, in the world at a time the United States holds the largest debt. China is the world's most rapidly developing economy and is now seen as a key driver of the world economy. Some contend, in addition, that Beijing's soft power has risen, particularly at a time US policies were eroding America's own.[32]

And then there are China's steadily rising defence budgets. Whenever another double-digit increase in China's military expenditure is announced, the reaction in parts of the US government, and beyond, is that China is 'catching up' to the point where it now has the second-largest defence budget in the world. Sino-American naval clashes in the South China Sea and Beijing's commitment to the development of a blue-water navy provide concrete grounds for this perspective.

This view of change in the distribution of global power is further reinforced in part by the perceived diminished importance of other actors, including the European Union and Japan. These actors are seen as relatively passive in terms of their foreign policies and strategically dependent on Washington. Russia has leverage in some areas, but it lacks China's economic importance. India, though also of rapidly increasingly importance, is still far from matching China's impact on the United States and the rest of the world.

China is much weaker than gross figures imply

Chinese officials and other commentators also tend to send contradictory messages in relation to their country's power, and this reinforces the sense that China is dissatisfied with its global status. At times of great strategic uncertainty, it becomes even more important to send signals that are clear and consistent, but China is often unclear. For example, China states that it is or aims to be a 'responsible great power', but it is also a member of the developing world and much weaker than the gross figures imply, depending on methods of calculation.

Beijing often states that it cannot be expected to do more in terms of the provision of global public goods because it has many material and social burdens to satisfy at home, and because it has not been given its rightful status in global institutions such as the International Monetary Fund. But attempts to give China a greater role and set of responsibilities, while welcome at one level, also spur in others a sense that they are responsibilities it is not yet able to bear.

Although these contradictory messages reflect in some respects the reality that is China – a nation of 400 million living in reasonable comfort and 900m living in conditions we associate with the developing world – they also reinforce the perception of China's discomfort with the global order and that there is great uncertainty in Beijing born of a lack of a domestic consensus behind its current and future strategy.

Mutual strategic distrust

Mistrust has been a long-standing feature in the US–China relationship and will continue into the future. Many Chinese elites express a sense of vulnerability with respect to the United States, based on a belief that Washington will not allow China to continue rising.[33] Various scenarios are envisioned: that the United States will seek to deny China access to energy and other resources that it needs to continue on its path to wealth and power, or that Washington will place obstacles in the way of completing its historical project of reunification with Taiwan. Wang Jisi has noted that some in China view its resurgence as futile unless this reunification is completed.[34] Climate change is another lens through which we can view this distrust, given the Chinese argument that the main US goal has been to increase its costs via adoption of new technologies, and to form a wedge between it and other members of the G77 negotiating coalition.

The United States for its part perceives in China's military modernisation and in some of its political actions a project potentially to deny the American military free access to the seas and to the bases of its Asian allies that are so important to its global military presence. Some in the United States also believe that China seeks to deny Washington membership in Asia-Pacific regional groupings where matters of import to the United States often are discussed. As US Deputy Secretary of State James Steinberg put it in September 2009:

> China must reassure the rest of the world that its development and growing global role will not come at the expense of security and well-being of others ... While China, like any nation, has the right to provide for its security, its capabilities and its actions also heighten its responsibility to reassure others that this buildup does not present a threat.[35]

Unproductive partners and inevitable rivals?

A focus on these four negative factors requires us to consider whether the inevitable outcome is rivalry, and possibly deadly rivalry, or whether we can be more sanguine. The first two – exceptionalism and decentralised political systems – are important constraints on developing a close partnership and will always render negotiations and their outcomes difficult to sustain without constant attention. Exceptionalism can perhaps be ameliorated over the next few years because of the advent of a new US administration; Obama may be less subject to exceptionalist sentiments than many of his predecessors. As he put it in April 2009 in response to a question on the topic, his pride in the Amercan nation did not prevent him from 'recognizing that we're not always going to be right, or that other people may have good ideas, or that in order for us to work collectively, all parties have to compromise ... and that includes us'.[36] These are unusual statements for a US president, and in many ways have already influenced the way his administration has approached China, stressing elements of co-stewardship and partnership. Recent US treatment of China suggests a more realistic appraisal that its growing power requires acknowledging it is more of an equal than a secondary state requiring tutelage. This US attitude could, in turn, help to satisfy China that its worth and place have been recognised.[37]

China's military budget is one-eighth of America's

The power-transition arguments can be criticised for a lack of clarity about what to measure and for the inconsistency of the underlying argument.[38] Moreover, some aspects of the argument are over-blown: power-transition ideas tend to exaggerate the threat that China is said to pose to US interests and to global order, as well as China's overall strength. For example, Chinese defence spending has certainly been rising sharply (between 1998 and 2007, China's military budget has been estimated to have increased by 202%[39]), but spending in 2008 was still about one-eighth that of the United States. Although Chinese figures are widely believed in the United States, especially in the Defense Department, to understate the real expenditure by a factor of two to three, and the International Institute for Strategic Studies in London points out how notoriously difficult it is to calculate the true levels of Chinese defence expenditure,[40] we have, for several years now, lived in a world where the US defence budget outstrips those of the next 20 countries combined. In 2009 SIPRI calculated US military spending as being at 41.5% of the world total.[41]

Similarly, China remains well behind both Russia and the United States in numbers of nuclear weapons. Whereas the United States has about 2,700 operational and 2,500 reserve warheads, compared with a Russian deployment of approximately 4,800 warheads, China is estimated to have about 200.[42] Thus, it is reasonable to expect China to be cautious about entering into nuclear-disarmament negotiations, and reasonable to accept its argument that it will not ratify the Comprehensive Test-Ban Treaty unless and until the US Senate does so.

America's proportion of global GDP at 23%, too, although down by 7 percentage points over eight years earlier, is not out of line with its position at many other times since 1945. The choice of year for the comparison matters a great deal. There are, moreover, real differences in whether the size of the Chinese economy is measured in terms of purchasing power parity or market exchange rates. PPP figures exaggerate China's true economic size, are difficult to construct and are open to significant error. The choice of per capita or gross figures is also important when considering a hugely populous state such as China.

There are other power indicators perhaps more appropriate to measuring economic competitiveness, such as levels of productivity, or numbers of Internet hosts, or demographic features. China's rank on the Human Development Index (which makes reference to longevity, educational attainment and quality of life) is 94th out of 179 countries. Using such indicators, China's rise looks far more modest.[43]

Beyond such doubts about the metrics used for determining power transition is the larger understanding of what power is and how it is used. Robert Dahl's oft-cited definition is that power is the ability of A to make B do what it would otherwise not do.[44] Power matters in this formulation because if you are the powerful one, the assumption is that you can produce the outcomes you desire. There is widespread agreement, however, that this definition is incomplete. Many now accept that power is not located simply in the ability to convert material resources into desired outcomes, and criticise the notion that there is, on a reliable and regular basis, a direct relationship between power as resources and its conversion into particular outcomes. Power resides in many different locales in the global system: in regional and global institutions (via norms, rules and law), and in actors other than states (transnational and domestic advocacy groups, social movements, multinational firms and terrorist groups, to name a few of the most important). There are many examples where entities of these kinds have constrained the political choices of even powerful state actors, prompting them to move along paths they otherwise would probably not have taken.

Both the United States and China reside within a dense network of global institutions that impose some constraints on and raise expectations about their behaviour, which carries costs if those expectations are not met. This is especially so for a state such as China that is a newcomer in certain respects to the modern global system and thus, and because of its resurgence, is under intense global scrutiny.

The US government has, in the past, acknowledged that China is to some degree restrained or shaped by the rules of the system. Then US Deputy Secretary of State Robert Zoellick's speech in 2005 on China as the 'responsible stake-holder' acknowledged the extent to which China had become integrated within the international system of collective beliefs and rules that we associate with post-1945 global order:

> The China of today is simply not the Soviet Union of the late 1940s; it does not seek to spread radical, anti-American ideologies. While not yet democratic, it does not see itself in a twilight conflict against democracy around the globe. While at times mercantilist, it does not see itself in a death struggle with capitalism. And most importantly, China does not believe that its future depends on overturning the fundamental order of the international system. In fact, quite the reverse: Chinese leaders have decided that their success depends on being networked with the modern world.[45]

Indeed, many Chinese statements confirm the belief that integration into international society has been beneficial to China, including statements contained in Beijing's January 2009 Defence White Paper.

Zoellick's conclusions reflect the important social aspect of power. Power is a social phenomenon that rests not simply on compulsion but also on changing the collective beliefs of others about the way the world works. While individual policy stances of China may suggest a desire to reform aspects of the global order, or to alter the range of issues that make it onto the international agenda, Beijing is not presenting a well-developed, radical alternative vision to the current system. It is often a cautious and conservative force, but it would be difficult to argue that it has been especially disruptive where US interests have been strongly engaged. If there were to be a fundamental clash of ideas and convictions on issues of importance to both parties, and neither side were willing to give way, conflict would probably result. In its absence, peaceful coexistence becomes possible.[46]

The primacy of the US dollar may come to an end

Nor does East Asian public opinion suggest that China is about to supplant the United States as the preferred partner of choice, even with shifts in relative power and a widespread belief that China has the greatest economic influence in Asia.[47] Not only does this suggest that Beijing's soft power is not particularly influential in its own region, there are also underlying fears that China might become a military threat in the future.[48] This latter sentiment means that America's military presence is desired by several regional states that continue to see Washington as an important pillar of the security order. Many of the smaller or weaker countries, too, prefer to see a range of states involved in security deliberations in the Asia-Pacific to expand their room for diplomatic manoeuvre and reduce the direct impact of any one state's overwhelmingly powerful presence.[49]

This critique is not meant to imply that some significant changes are not in train, and these changes do, of course, relate to China's growing power. China is present in many more global arenas, influencing outcomes particularly in the economic and political fields. It is attempting to shift the orientation of its own economy, to reduce its dependence on Western consumer markets by promoting south–south trade and investment. It will try to diversify its international reserves and investments, while shortening the maturity structure of its enormous holdings of US treasuries. Indeed the primacy of the US dollar may come to an end, albeit not for a long while yet. The Brazil–Russia–India–China (BRIC) Summit communiqué in June 2009, for example, called for a 'more diversified international monetary system', but this was not exactly a ringing endorsement for an immediate or even medium-term shift away from the dollar.[50] China is more assertive within bodies such as the UN Security Council. It is beginning to have, in addition, a military impact within its own region and even had a military presence far from its shores in 2009, when it sent ships to the coast of Somalia to engage in anti-piracy operations.

This is not, however, a power transition in which China has supplanted the United States as a global actor, or has challenged the structures of meaning that Washington has had such a large role in shaping. The uncertainties of the Chinese economic and political system diminish the attractiveness of holding its non-convertible currency as reserve assets, or of establishing it as a fully fledged security partner. We are in the middle of an adjustment period for the United States and other previously central major states, rather than a clear power transition, a difference that is important to recognise.

The future of global order requires that areas of common interest be built upon so that changes in material power come to be viewed not as threats but as sources of productive power to achieve goals associated with the global commons. This requires, above all, dealing with mutual strategic distrust.

Between cold and warm peace

International-relations scholar Charles Kupchan argues that to transform a 'cold peace (stability based on competition and mutual deterrence)' into a 'warm peace (stability based on cooperation and mutual reassurance)' requires certain demanding conditions be met: strategic restraint and mutual accommodation has to be sustained for the parties to view each other as ' benign polities'. Above all, they must reach a consensus on key elements of international order: 'a new hierarchy, basic rules concerning trade and the use of force, procedures for managing territorial change, and mutual recognition of spheres of influence'.[51]

Some of the basic rules concerning trade do seem to have been agreed via participation in the World Trade Organisation even if the dispute-resolution mechanism has to be used. Participation in institutional arrangements across a wide range of issues has already helped build some areas of constraint in the relationship. Aspects of hierarchy are also under negotiation, as seen in the rise of the Group of Twenty Finance Ministers and Central Bank Governors (G20), prospective alterations in voting rights in bodies such as the International Monetary Fund, and in ways of dealing with each other bilaterally, with more frequent, sustained and institutionalised high-level meetings.[52]

Issues involving the use of force and procedures for managing territorial change in US–China relations have centred on the Taiwan question, an issue that appears to have stabilised but remains an underlying sore. However, as China's military reach increases, new points of contention could arise in the bilateral relationship or between China and America's Asian allies.

While the idea of spheres of influence seems outmoded, anti-democratic and inappropriate in a globalised world, the question remains of how far China would like to go to reduce US influence in the Asia-Pacific and how willing Washington is to tolerate China's presence in regions such as Latin America, where previously it had not been particularly visible. Above all, there is the troubling military dimension to the relationship. The Pentagon, in particular, is concerned about China's military modernisation and strategic intent. It finds Chinese military strategy opaque and Beijing resistant to becoming more transparent about its military plans and development. China, on the other hand, views calls for transparency with great suspicion, as designed to expose its weaknesses. Pentagon exaggeration of Chinese power, in Beijing's view, is designed to stoke fears of a 'China threat'.

The stand-off between the Chinese and American navies in the South China sea in March 2009, when Chinese ships harassed a US Navy survey ship, the USNS *Impeccable*, exemplifies an area where 'rules of the game' urgently need to be established. Neither side chose to make too much of this confrontation as such, and it has already been a subject of discussion between Chinese Foreign Minister Yang Jiechi and US National Security Adviser General James L. Jones.[53] This was undoubtedly only one of several such instances of confrontation which neither side has chosen to publicise. But were American or Chinese blood to be shed as a result of clashes like these, it could derail any domestic or bilateral consensus that exists on the need for cooperation over critical global-order issues. The larger symbolic importance of these naval clashes is that this most critical of state-to-state relationships remains stuck for now, and for the near future, somewhere between a cold and warm peace, or between cooperation and rivalry.

On this issue and other important issues policy choices are there to be made, and navigational rules – literally as well as figuratively – have to be agreed in areas where they do not yet exist. The Obama administration has made a useful beginning in its recognition that 'strategic reassurance' is a key to stabilising ties, although this has to be recognised as a need for both sides.[54] Were that recognition to be acted upon, it would enable movement towards the warmer end of the continuum. Exaggerating the extent of China's resurgence and the challenge it poses to global norms, or neglecting areas of the relationship that might generate potentially dangerous competition, will lead to less positive outcomes.

Acknowledgements

Earlier versions of this paper were presented at St Antony's College, Oxford, and at a conference on 'The Future of Sino-American Relations and the Korean Peninsula' organised by the Korean Association of International Studies, 11 September 2009, Seoul, Republic of Korea. The author acknowledges with thanks the organisers' permission to publish this paper as given in Seoul, as well as the helpful comments of the discussant and audiences at both venues.

Notes

1 As US Secretary of State Hillary Clinton put it in remarks at the Asia Society in New York on 13 February 2009: 'An ancient Chinese story tells of warring feudal states, whose soldiers find themselves on a boat together crossing a wide river in a storm. Instead of fighting one another, they work together and survive. Now, from this story comes a Chinese aphorism that says, "When you are in a common boat, you need to cross the river peacefully together." The wisdom of that aphorism must continue to guide us today.' Chinese Foreign Minister Yang Jiechi, in a speech given at the Center for Strategic and International Studies in Washington DC on 13 March 2009, put it thus: 'At a time when the international financial crisis continues to spread and develop, the primary common interest of China and the United States is to weather the storm together like passengers in the same boat and support each other to get through the tough times and emerge from the crisis victorious.'

2 For an explanation of purchasing power parity, see http://www.oecd.org/std/ppp.

3 The Asian Development Bank's pessimistic assessment in April 2009 was that 'more than 60 million individuals who would have been lifted above the extreme income poverty line of $1.25 per day had the region's high growth continued in 2009 will remain mired in poverty instead'. See *Global Economic Crisis: Challenge for Developing Asia and the ADB's Response*, Asian Development Bank Report, April 2009, p. 6.

4 Quoted in Bonnie Glaser, 'U.S.–China Relations: A Good Beginning is Half Way to Success', *Comparative Connections*, vol. 11, no. 1, April 2009.

5 David Leonhardt, 'The China Puzzle', *New York Times Magazine*, 17 May 2009, http://www.nytimes/com/2009/05/17/magazine/17china-t.html. Geithner also revealed that during the April G20 meetings he had travelled to the hotel suite of Vice Premier Wang Qishan to further their discussions. At the beginning of June 2009, Geithner was in Beijing, where he met President Hu Jintao, Prime Minister Wen Jiabao and other high-ranking officials. During a speech at Peking University he stated: 'China and the United States individually and together are so important in the global economy and financial system that what we do has a direct impact on the stability and strength of the international economic system.' See David Barboza, 'In China, Geithner Backs Cooperation', *New York Times*, 1 June 2009, http://www.nytimes.com/2009/06/01/world/asia/01china.html.

6 Nicholas R. Lardy, 'China's Role in the Origins of and Response to the Global Recession', transcript of testimony at the hearing before the US–China Economic and Security Review Commission, 17 February 2009, http://www.piie.com/publications/papers/print.cfm/doc=pub&ResearchID=1165. China's stimulus package is supposed to contribute to 3% of GDP.

7 Fan Gang, 'China's Capacity of Managing Impacts of Global Crisis and Potentials for Further Growth', lecture given at Oxford Forum on China and the World Economy, 18 May 2009, Oxford. Fan was referring to items such as low labour costs, the high savings rate, urbanisation and globalisation effects, among other factors.

8 Michael Wines, 'China "Worried" about safety of U.S. Treasuries', *New York Times*, 14 March 2009, http://www.nytimes.com/2009/03/14/business/worldbusiness/14china.html.

9 See Zhou Xiaochuan, 'Reform the International Monetary System', 23 March 2009, http://www.pbc.gov.cn/english/detail.asp?col=6500&ID=178.

10 However, even as Chinese growth rates have returned to something close to 8%, one report from China noted that one-third of China's recent university graduates cannot find work. Aliza Rosenbaum, 'China Preserves Jobs while Pushing up Oil Price', *International Herald Tribune*, 12 August 2009.

11 Intergovernmental Panel on Climate Change (IPCC), *Climate Change 2007: Synthesis Report* (Geneva: IPCC, 2007), Summary for Policymakers, p. 2; International Scientific Congress on Climate Change: Global Risks, Challenges

and Decisions, Copenhagen, 10–12 March 2009, 'Key Messages from the Congress', 12 March 2009, http://climatecongress.ku.dk/newsroom/congress_key_messages/.

12 'China's Policies and Actions for Addressing Climate Change', 29 October 2008, http://english.gov.cn/2008-10.29/content_1134544.htm.

13 'Predictions of Mayhem as the Globe gets Warmer', *International Herald Tribune*, 10 August 2009.

14 Kenneth Lieberthal and David Sandalow, *Overcoming Obstacles to U.S.–China Cooperation on Climate Change* (Washington DC: Brookings Institution, 2009).

15 *A Roadmap for U.S.–China Cooperation on Energy and Climate Change* (New York: Pew Center/Asia Society, 2009), p. 18. This study was co-chaired by Steven Chu before he became Obama's energy secretary. Both governments are now making more serious attempts to address the problem, the Obama administration by committing the federal government to the post-Kyoto process and promising mandatory reductions in the country's emissions targets of 80% by 2050. (He is, however, meeting a great deal of domestic resistance.) China, while it continues to rule out mandatory targets for itself or to make absolute cuts in emissions, has agreed a number of national targets designed to cut the rate of *increase* in its CO_2 emissions. Its 11th five-year plan (2006–10) announced energy-intensity goals that included reducing its per unit GDP energy use by 20% by 2010 over that of 2005; adopting the target of renewable fuels for 10% of its total energy consumption by 2010, rising to 15% by 2020; and increasing its take-up of hydro and nuclear power.

16 Karl Hallding, Guoyi Han and Marie Olsson, *A Balancing Act: China's Role in Climate Change* (Stockholm: Commission for Sustainable Development, April 2009), p. 96.

17 This and the next paragraph rely substantially on Lieberthal and Sandalow, *Overcoming Obstacles;* Michael P. Vandenbergh, 'Climate Change: The China Problem', *Southern California Law Review*, vol. 81, July 2008, pp. 905–58; and Zhang Zhongxiang, 'China, the United States and Technological Cooperation on Climate Control', *Environmental Science and Policy*, vol. 10, nos 7–8, November–December 2007, pp. 622–8.

18 US Energy Secretary Steven Chu made headlines when he suggested in March 2009 that carbon tariffs on goods entering the US market might be used to create a level playing field where countries have not applied a cost to carbon. See Trevor Houser, 'Why Carbon Tariffs are a Bad Idea – For Now', *The Argument*, ForeignPolicy.com, 26 March 2009, http://experts.foreignpolicy.com/posts/2009/03/26/why_carbon_tariffs_are_a_bad_idea_for_now.

19 Todd Stern and William Antholis argued in 2007 that developing countries 'must be treated differentially' with the poorest among them exempted from climate-change commitments, but the more advanced, including China, committing to actual 'targets, albeit less stringent than those of the industrialized countries, or policy undertakings by sector'. See

Todd Stern and William Antholis, 'A Changing Climate: The Road Ahead for the United States', *Washington Quarterly*, vol. 31, no. 1, Winter 2007–08, p. 184. Todd Stern has since become the US State Department's climate-change envoy.

20 'UN Climate Summit: Key Quotes', BBC News, 22 September 2009, http://newsvote.bbc.co.uk/mpapps/pagetools/print/news.bbc.co.uk/1/hi/sci.tech/82693.

21 William Chandler, 'Breaking the Suicide Pact: U.S.–China Cooperation on Climate Change', Carnegie Endowment Policy Brief 57 (Washington DC: Carnegie Endowment for International Peace, 2008).

22 Christopher P. Twomey, 'Chinese–U.S. Strategic Affairs: Dangerous Dynamism', *Arms Control Today*, vol. 39, no. 1, January–February 2009, pp. 17–20.

23 For two recent expositions see Michael Ignatieff (ed.), *American Exceptionalism and Human Rights* (Princeton, NJ: Princeton University Press, 2005); and Rosemary Foot, 'Exceptionalism Again: the Bush Administration, the "Global War on Terror" and Human Rights', *Law and History Review*, vol. 26, no. 3, Fall 2008, pp. 707–25.

24 Harold Hongju Koh, 'America's Jekyll-and-Hyde Exceptionalism', in Ignatieff, *American Exceptionalism*, p. 112.

25 Edward C. Luck, 'American Exceptionalism and International Organization: Lessons from the 1990s', in Rosemary Foot, Neil MacFarlane and Michael Mastanduno (eds), *US Hegemony and International Organizations* (Oxford: Oxford University Press, 2003), p. 27.

26 Vivienne Shue, 'Legitimacy Crisis in China?', in Peter Hays Gries and Stanley Rosen (eds), *State and Society in 21st-Century China: Crisis, Contention, and Legitimation* (New York: RoutledgeCurzon, 2004), p. 31.

27 W. Michael Reisman, 'The United States and International Institutions', *Survival*, vol. 41, no. 4, Winter 1999–2000, pp. 71–2.

28 Lieberthal and Sandalow, *Overcoming Obstacles*, p. 33.

29 *Ibid.*, p. 77, n. 40.

30 A.F.K. Organski and Jacek Kugler, *The War Ledger* (Chicago, IL: University of Chicago Press, 1980.) See also John J. Mearsheimer, *The Tragedy of Great Power Politics* (New York: W.W. Norton, 2001) where he reverses the source of danger: 'The emergence of a potential hegemon, however, makes the other great powers especially fearful, and they will search hard for ways to correct the imbalance of power and will be inclined to pursue riskier policies toward that end. The reason is simple: when one state is threatening to dominate the rest, the long-term value of remaining at peace declines and threatened states will be more willing to take chances to improve their security' (p. 345).

31 Jonathan Broder, 'Power Playing with Others', *CQ Weekly*, 20 April 2009.

32 Joshua Kurlantzick, *Charm Offensive: How China's Soft Power is Transforming the World* (New Haven, CT: Yale University Press, 2007); and Yu Xintian, 'Soft Power Enhancement and China's External Strategy', *China International Studies*, no. 12, Fall 2008, pp. 20–35.

33 Rosemary Foot, 'Chinese Strategies in a US-Hegemonic Global Order: Accommodating and Hedging', *International Affairs,* vol. 82, no. 1, January 2006, p. 83.

34 Wang Jisi, 'China's Changing Role in Asia', in Kokobun Ryosei and Wang Jisi (eds), *The Rise of China and a Changing East Asian Order* (Tokyo: Japan Center for International Exchange, 2004), p. 14.

35 James B. Steinberg, 'Keynote Address at the Center for a New American Security', Washington DC, 24 September 2009.

36 Broder, 'Power Playing with Others', p. 898.

37 That the Obama administration uses the language of partnership and equality with China may reflect not just China's growing power, but also a deeper set of beliefs given that the administration has approached other states in a similar manner.

38 For one excellent critique see Steve Chan, *China, the U.S. and the Power-Transition Theory: A Critique* (London: Routledge, 2008).

39 *SIPRI Yearbook 2008* (Oxford: Oxford University Press, 2008), p. 177.

40 *The Military Balance 2009* (Abindgon: Routledge for the IISS, 2009), pp. 365, 375.

41 *SIPRI Yearbook 2009* (Oxford: Oxford University Press, 2009), Summary, section 5, Military Expenditure, p. 11.

42 *SIPRI Yearbook 2009,* Table 8.1, p. 346.

43 Chan, *China, the U.S. and the Power-Transition Theory,* introduces some of these additional measures.

44 Robert Dahl, *Who Governs? Democracy and Power in an American City* (New Haven, CT: Yale University Press, 1961).

45 Robert Zoellick, 'Whither China: From Membership to Responsibility', remarks to the National Committee on US–China Relations, US Department of State, 25 November 2005, http://www.state.gov/s/d/former/zoellick/rem/53682.htm.

46 For a fuller exposition of ideas akin to these see Yuen Foong Khong, 'Negotiating "Order" During Power Transitions', in Charles A. Kupchan et al., *Power in Transition: The Peaceful Change of International Order* (Tokyo: The United Nations University Press, 2001), p. 34.

47 See the Chicago Council on Global Affairs report 'Soft Power in Asia: Results of a 2008 Multinational Survey of Public Opinion', based on more than 6,000 interviews in China, Vietnam, Japan, South Korea, Indonesia and the United States in January and February 2008 (before the unrest in Tibet).

48 See also the results of a PIPA study of 22 countries in 2005 which revealed that an average of 59% of the 22,953 respondents concluded that a militarily more powerful China would generate negative reactions, http://www.pipa.org/onlineReports/China/China_Mar05/.

49 Evelyn Goh, 'Great Powers and Hierarchical Order in Southeast Asia: Analyzing Regional Security Strategies', *International Security,* vol. 32, no. 3, Winter 2007–08, pp. 113–57; David M. Lampton, *The Three Faces of Chinese Power* (Berkeley, CA: University of California Press, 2008), esp. ch. 5.

50 For a useful analysis of the BRIC summit, see 'Quarter Defined by

Differences', *Financial Times*, 16 June 2009, p. 8.

51 Charles A. Kupchan, 'Introduction: Explaining Peaceful Power Transition' in Kupchan et al., *Power in Transition*, pp. 7–9. He adds also the condition of legitimation, whereby the parties 'forge a consensus not just on rules, but on the values that underlie those rules' (p .9). This is a particularly demanding condition to meet.

52 For example, the Bush–Hu era's strategic economic dialogue and high-level political dialogue has been maintained in the Hu–Obama era, even if under a slightly different name.

53 Peter Baker, 'Obama Calls for Military Dialogue with China', *New York Times*, http://www.nytimes.com/2009/03/12/washington/12web-china.html.

54 Steinberg, 'Keynote Address', 24 September 2009.

Mekong Dams and the Perils of Peace

Richard Cronin

Less than two decades after the end of a long and bloody conflict, a new kind of danger is looming over the six countries that share the watershed of the 4,880-kilometre-long Mekong – a river that at the height of the conflict earned the name 'River of Terror and Hope'.[1] Peace has brought a new peril to more than 60 million people (mostly in Cambodia, Laos and Vietnam) reliant on traditional farming and fishing, and ultimately to the stability and peace of the Mekong region as a whole. This time, however, the danger is not about ideology or territory, but water: who controls it, how it should be used, and for whose benefit. China's economic development and geopolitical objectives pose the most important, but by no means the only, threat to human security and regional stability. To varying degrees the former war-torn countries are also pursuing short-sighted, environmentally unsustainable development policies, sometimes in conjunction with Chinese ambitions for regional economic integration.

The 795,000km² Mekong basin, about the size of the Danube basin in central and eastern Europe, comprises a large portion of five Southeast Asian countries (Cambodia, Laos, Thailand, Vietnam and Myanmar) and China's Yunnan Province. The river rises in the Tibetan Plateau and plunges some 4,000m through the high gorges of Yunnan Province before slowing and broadening in the Golden Triangle area where the borders of

Richard Cronin is a Senior Associate and Director of the Southeast Asia Program at the Stimson Center in Washington DC. He is the co-producer of a documentary video 'Mekong Tipping Point' and co-editor (with Amit Pandya) of *Exploiting Natural Resources: Growth, Instability, and Conflict in the Middle East and Asia* (Stimson Center, 2009).

Survival | vol. 51 no. 6 | December 2009–January 2010 | pp. 147–160 DOI 10.1080/00396330903461716

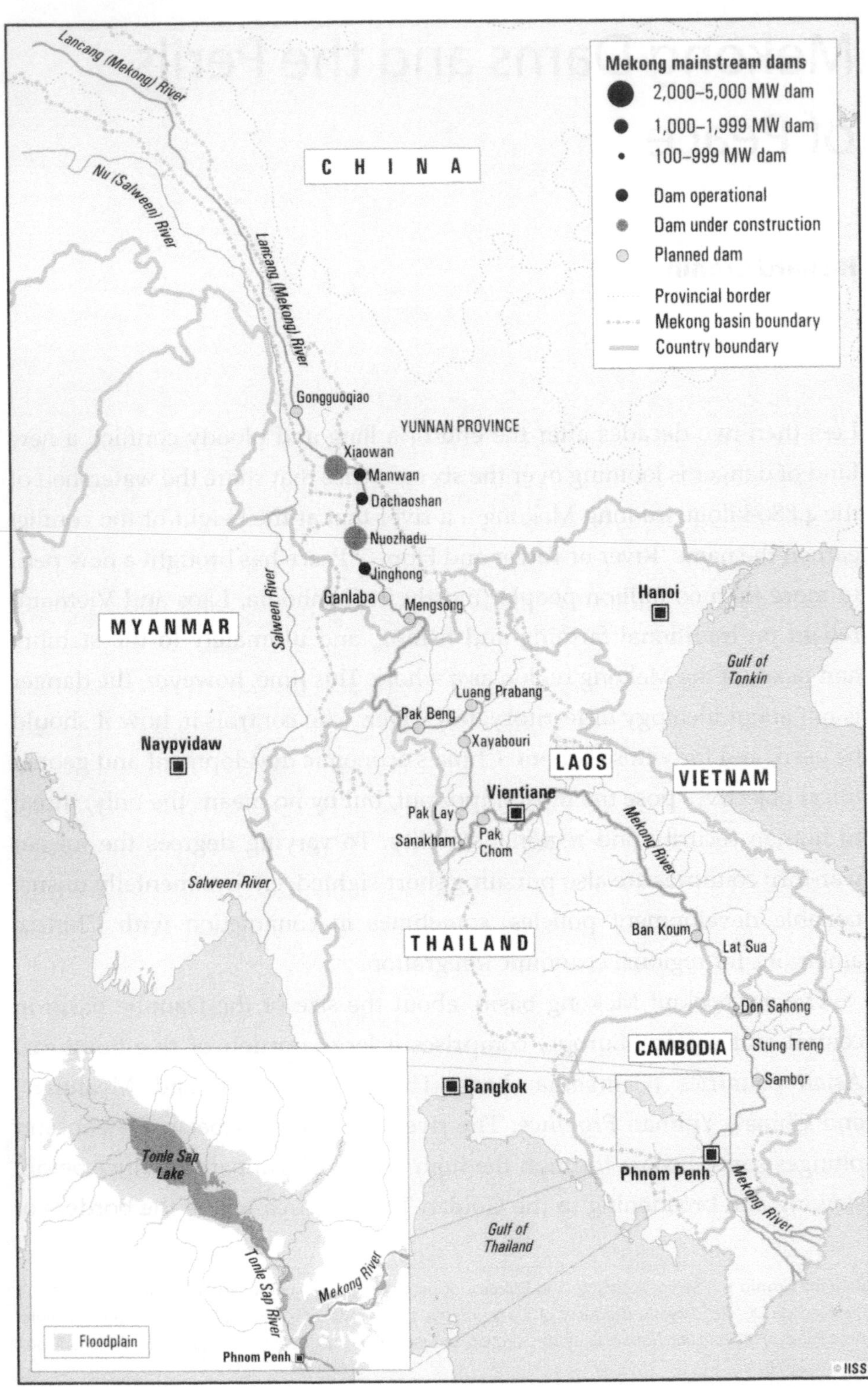
Mekong mainstream dams
2,000–5,000 MW dam
1,000–1,999 MW dam
100–999 MW dam
Dam operational
Dam under construction
Planned dam
Provincial border
Mekong basin boundary
Country boundary
Lancang (Mekong) River
Nu (Salween) River
CHINA
YUNNAN PROVINCE
Gongguoqiao
Xiaowan
Manwan
Dachaoshan
Nuozhadu
Jinghong
Ganlaba
Mengsong
Salween River
MYANMAR
Naypyidaw
Hanoi
Gulf of Tonkin
Luang Prabang
Pak Beng
Xayabouri
LAOS
VIETNAM
Vientiane
Pak Lay
Sanakham
Pak Chom
Mekong River
Ban Koum
Lat Sua
THAILAND
Don Sahong
CAMBODIA
Stung Treng
Sambor
Bangkok
Phnom Penh
Gulf of Thailand
Tonle Sap Lake
Tonle Sap River
Floodplain
© IISS

Laos, Myanmar and Thailand converge. The river forms much of the Laos–Thailand border before bifurcating Cambodia, dividing into nine branches that form Vietnam's Mekong Delta and emptying into the South China Sea.

The Mekong is the 12th-longest river in the world, with the 8th-largest annual discharge. But its most important characteristic, ecologically and sociologically, The most important ecological and sociological characteristic of the Mekong is not its length, discharge or the area that it drains, but the ratio of 30 or more between its wet and dry season flows. Seasonal extremes are moderated by Cambodia's Tonle Sap ('Great Lake') lake–river system that connects to the Mekong at Phnom Penh. As the wet-season flood builds, the river reverses direction and the lake expands several-fold, becoming a flood buffer and giant seasonal nursery for migratory fish and other aquatic life. For about three months after the floods subside the lake empties back into the Mekong, bringing with it the world's richest concentration of freshwater migratory fish both in numbers and species, and providing part of the Mekong Delta enough water to produce a third rice harvest.

The buffering role of Tonle Sap and the importance of its seasonal wetlands led to a 1995 treaty signed by Cambodia, Laos, Thailand and Vietnam creating the Mekong River Commission. The commission commits the countries to maintain an 'acceptable natural reverse flow' into Tonle Sap.[2] A cascade of eight or more massive hydropower dams under construction in Yunnan and 11 or more dams proposed for the mainstream and its tributaries by Laos and Cambodia raise serious questions about the future viability of the buffer.

Beijing has put great store in the massive energy potential of the upper half of the river in Yunnan Province and Tibet, as the development of hydropower is the key to its 50-year 'Go West' infrastructure-development project launched in 2000, Beijing's most ambitious and highest-priority national endeavour.[3] But for the downstream Southeast Asian countries, the hoped-for 'peace dividend' in Southeast Asia is being put in jeopardy by the short-sighted pursuit by all the countries in the basin of an outdated and wasteful development paradigm.

To many Southeast Asians, China's 'Go West' strategy resonates ominously with the perceptions of the Mekong basin by developers, investors and even the Asian Development Bank as 'Asia's Last Frontier'.[4] In parallel with China's push to develop the region's hydropower potential, the bank is providing leadership and billions of dollars in financial support to developing the region's overland and power connectivity under a 1992 initiative called the Greater Mekong Subregion.

River at risk

Large dams alter the natural hydrology of rivers in unpredictable ways, and hold back soil-renewing silt, while the 'hungry water' below them scours river banks and stream beds, destroying fish habitat and wiping away fields and villages. The cascade of dams under construction in China's Yunnan Province and the half-dozen proposed dams in northern Laos are particularly threatening because of their large storage capacity and impact on the river's natural hydrology and seasonal inflows, the key to its natural bounty. Along with proposed dams in Cambodia, they also threaten to advance the expected date of sea-level rise in the Mekong Delta.

The upper part of the river, which the Chinese call the Lancang Jiang, comprises 44% of the long river's total length and 90% of its fall of nearly 5,000m from source to ocean (Figure 1). Although Chinese territory accounts for only about one-fourth of the Mekong's catchment area and contributes only about 13% of the total annual flow at the point the river reaches the

Figure 1. Altitude profile of the Mekong River

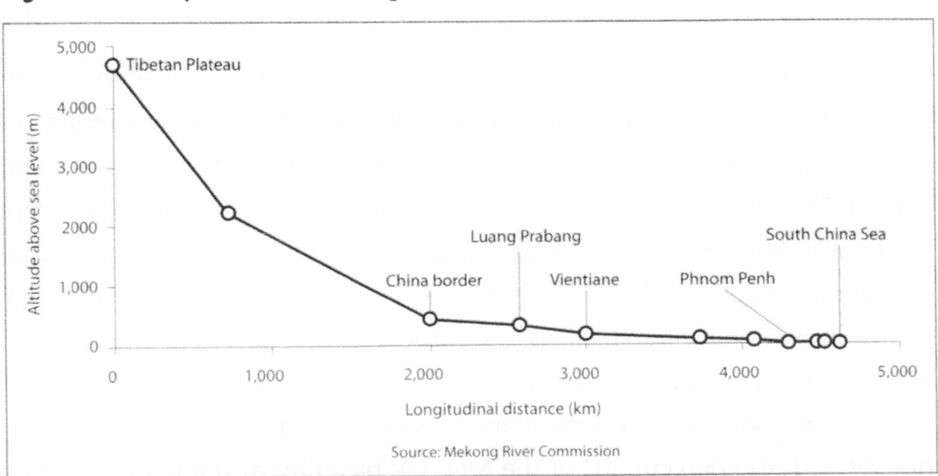

Source: Mekong River Commission

The names given the river by those who live with it reflect its character. To the Tibetans where it emerges it is Dza Chu ('Water of Stone'), the Chinese call it Lancang Jiang ('Turbulent River'), the Lao and northern Thai call it Ma Mekong ('Mother of Waters'), while to the Vietnamese it is the Cuu Long ('Nine-tailed Dragon').

South China Sea, summer glacier and snow melt on the Tibetan Plateau accounts for as much as 40–70% of the dry-season flow. The Upper Mekong also contributes as much as half of the vital sediment that annually replenishes farmers' fields and rebuilds the Mekong Delta during the monsoon floods.

The first three dams in the Lancang cascade, two of which are already operational, have active storage of about one billion cubic meters of water each. These dams and reservoirs are very large by any standard, but they are dwarfed by the 292m-high Xiaowan Dam, whose 15bn m^3 reservoir is now ready to be filled and the 254m-high Nuozhadu, whose reservoir will hold nearly 22bn m^3 of water.[5]

Xiaowan alone is big enough to regulate the river – that is, to control a substantial amount of its flow by opening and closing the sluice gates. Both Xiaowan and Nuozhadu will act as cistern dams to keep downstream dams in Yunnan and those planned for the lower Mekong in Laos and Cambodia running during periods of drought and to support year-round navigation by sizeable commercial boats of up to 400 deadweight tonnes when fully loaded. China plans to put as much as 40% more water in the river during the dry season and to reduce the monsoon flow by 17%, depending on circumstances.[6]

While hydrological engineers and developers speak of increasing the availability of water for the dry season as a boon to their downstream neighbours, biologists and other natural scientists warn that the impact of the Yunnan cascade will destroy the very characteristics that make the Mekong the most productive freshwater river basin in the world, after the Amazon.

Proposals for upstream dams seriously threaten the Mekong Delta, already under severe stress from climate change, human factors and saltwater intrusion. The delta is Vietnam's rice bowl, producing 40% of the country's crop. Annual floods replenish the soil naturally, reducing the need for financially and environmentally costly fertilisers, and allowing farmers in the delta to cultivate three crops per year. The delta is also a fast-growing hub of industrial and other economic activity, and the annual flood pulse helps to purge pollutants that accumulate during the dry season. Vietnam has no stretch of the mainstream that can generate hydropower and only stands to lose from upstream development that alters water and sediment flows and the river's fisheries.

As if these impacts were not enough, 11 smaller dams are planned on the Lower Mekong, nine by Laos and two by Cambodia, and Thailand is contemplating diverting water from the Mekong to its relatively parched northeast. The southernmost of these dams, especially at the Sambor Rapids and the Laos Don Sahong Dam at Khone Falls, would pose an immediate and absolute barrier to the spawning migration of a large variety of fish species. These migratory fisheries constitute the majority of the commercial catch, which makes up 80% of the animal protein in the diets of over 60m people, particularly in the densely populated lowlands of Cambodia and Vietnam's delta region. Besides playing a largely non-replaceable role at the subsistence level, the fisheries also make a huge contribution to local and national economies. The estimated first-sale value of the highly migratory Lower Mekong wild-fish catch has been conservatively estimated at $2.4–3bn, with an ultimate value as the catch moves through the economy of several times that.[7] About half of the dams planned in Laos and Cambodia involve engineering and development agreements with Chinese state-owned companies and would be financed by Chinese banks and official development assistance.

Vietnam only stands to lose

The track record of numerous dams on the Mekong's tributaries does not provide any basis for optimism about mitigating the effects of mainstream dams either in Yunnan or on the Lower Mekong. To date, no relocation effort has left the majority of the people displaced better off than before, and there have been no successful attempts to move Southeast Asian fish around a dam by constructing fish ladders. A fish ladder built for Thailand's Pak Mun dam, the first such effort in Southeast Asia, was a failure.[8] The most serious relocation effort to date, at Laos's highly controversial Nam Theun

2 Dam supported by the Asian Development Bank and the World Bank (a private project on a major Mekong tributary intended to supply power to Thailand), reportedly has encountered major and perhaps insurmountable difficulties.[9] Moreover, many existing dams are silting up much faster than the 50–100 years originally anticipated, cutting into operating efficiency and requiring expensive dredging operations. In fact, China reportedly sped up the construction of the Xiaowan dam because the Manwan Dam was already silting up twice as fast as anticipated. Unless the flushing action of the Xiaowan dam can clear the silt build-up, the Manwan Dam may become inoperable in as few as 20 years. There is a very real possibility that mainstream dams may silt up well before the anticipated longer-term impacts of climate change. The rapid shrinking of the winter snow cap and retreat of glaciers on the Tibetan Plateau has led to predictions that the Upper Mekong flow will be sharply reduced. Some models suggest a of shifting rainfall patterns in which the decrease in flow from the Tibetan Plateau may be offset by increased rainfall in the Lower Mekong, a development that would not help China's Yunnan Cascade.[10]

Development for whom?

The concept of the Mekong as an undeveloped frontier is a chimera, one that lives only in the mind's eye of those, both domestic and foreign, who covet its last remaining stands of tropical forest, its mineral wealth and, most of all, its water. And beyond the value of the timber, much of the rapid deforestation (both legal and illegal) now taking place in the Lower Mekong countries of Myanmar, Cambodia, Laos and Vietnam is being carried out to make way for dams and monoculture plantations.

It is not in China's interest to turn the Mekong into an environmental and ecological disaster, but for Beijing several factors outweigh the economic and political risks (to the extent those risks are even understood by decision-makers) of turning the Mekong into a Southeast Asian equivalent of the Yangtze or Yellow rivers, both of which have become so degraded and polluted that they can barely support life. Firstly, China has a seemingly insatiable hunger for energy, and the eight-dam Lancang cascade is designed to produce 15,600MW, nearly as much as the Three Gorges project, which has a current installed capacity of 18,300MW. Secondly, despite growing recognition of the human and environmental costs of past infrastructure projects, China continues to suffer from a mindset strongly biased towards harnessing nature for development. Thirdly, China remains committed to incorporating the natural resources of the Mekong basin into its manufacturing supply chain to expand its political and economic influence. China, moreover, is by no means monolithic. Its giant state-owned hydropower companies, utilities and banks have significant political clout and are equal to ministries in the country's political and bureaucratic hierarchy. These companies pursue commercial opportunities with weak and corrupt governments in the Lower Mekong with little or no restraint.

An air of secrecy surrounds the Yunnan cascade

The real cost will be borne by the poorest part of the population, and a lack of coordination and transparency will undermine even the marginal value of these projects and increase regional tensions. An air of secrecy surrounds the Yunnan cascade and most of the Lower Mekong dam proposals. There is little discussion of the future cascade as a whole or how the dams will be operated. On the Lower Mekong, Chinese, Thai and other companies, both private and semi-public, are pursuing dams on a project-by-project basis, with no sign of coordination. Local communities remain woefully under-informed about projects that will have drastic impacts on their lives, from outright displacement and physical relocation to destruction of dry-season subsistence gardens and traditional fishing grounds.

Dams have a legitimate place in the trade-off between development and the environment, but only after both long-term costs and benefits are fully assessed, which almost never happens. The plans by China, Laos, Thailand and Cambodia to harness the Mekong's mainstream are prime examples of the kind of development that benefits those who finance and build the dams, and distant urban areas that gain additional electricity, at huge cost to those who lose their land, fisheries and related livelihoods. None of the current proposals or projects for mainstream dams could pass even the most cursory environmental-impact assessment.

Finally, many of the dams will provide electricity in support of mining operations that will create serious downstream pollution problems. Because of poor governance, even top political leaders and senior officials in some cases are not aware of these environmentally destructive mining activities.

America returns

The US government and foreign-policy community have largely ignored the Mekong basin in the more than three decades since the last helicopter lifted off the roof of the American embassy in Saigon. Concern both within and outside Southeast Asia about the threats posed by Beijing's emerging regional hegemony and the impact of short-sighted and potentially catastrophic efforts to harness the energy potential of the Mekong River have been sufficient to cause the United States to emerge from its post-Vietnam geopolitical torpor. At the ASEAN Ministerial Meeting in Phuket, Thailand in July 2009, US Secretary of State Hillary Clinton declared that 'the United States is back in Southeast Asia', a region she described as 'vital to global progress, peace and prosperity'.

Although China's efforts to regulate the flow of the Mekong is not driven by a desire for the ability to withhold water from its downstream neighbours (which would be impossible over an extended period in any event), the Yunnan cascade does give China short-term leverage if it chooses to put pressure on downstream countries. US concerns have been heightened by the global financial and economic crisis that began in mid 2008, which has increased the disparity in economic power between China and the Mekong countries of Southeast Asia.

The United States has a historical opportunity to make a positive difference to the future of the river and those who depend on it for their sustenance. In addition to its stake in human security, food security and regional peace and stability, the United States has other interests with global ramifications, particularly the impact of climate change and anticipated sea-level rise. The administration of President Barack Obama has shown itself alive to the human-, environmental- and regional-security threats posed by environmental degradation and China's growing regional hegemony and has deftly re-engaged with Southeast Asia at several levels, with emphasis on the Mekong.

Although Washington had begun a policy shift towards re-engagement with Southeast Asia during President George W. Bush's second term, the Obama administration's initiatives reflect a significant difference in concept and approach. The indicators of a qualitative US policy shift include deeper engagement with ASEAN as an organisation, cautious but positive engagement with the Burmese regime, and most importantly a carefully crafted Mekong Initiative that Clinton brought to the Phuket meeting. The centrepiece of this initiative was the signing of a Letter of Intent for a new Mississippi–Mekong 'sister river' agreement with the Mekong River Commission secretariat. The initiative will be the first significant involvement by the United States with the commission since it was established in 1995.[11]

The geopolitical implications of renewed US engagement have not been lost on the four commission countries, and certainly not on China, which has viewed the American Mekong initiative with surprise and concern. The details of US re-engagement with Southeast Asia remain to be worked out, but they include the sharing of US expertise and best practice in fields such as climate-change adaptation, management of floods and droughts, hydropower and impact assessment of other hydrological interventions, water consumption and food security, the management of water resources and other concerns of mutual interest.

In the longer term the Obama administration can use the economic crisis and the need to rebalance the global financial system to promote a new development paradigm. The focus should be on smaller-scale projects more suited to the real needs of the majority of the population, and on economic-growth models which better protect the environment and share more equitably the benefits of development both internally and across national boundaries.

Promoting change in Beijing

China may see revived US involvement in the Mekong region as a meddlesome complication, but its leaders would do better to consider why the

American initiative has received such a positive response in a region they increasingly see as their backyard. A real risk for China that its leaders seem slow to appreciate is the potential for backlash if the Yunnan cascade and the activities of Chinese commercial dam developers in Laos and Cambodia turn the Mekong into another Yangtze or Yellow River.

Modifying China's plans for the Yunnan cascade may still be possible. In May 2009 Premier Wen Jiabao, an engineer by training but no fan of mega-dams, suspended the construction of the first of a planned cascade of 13 dams on the Nu River (which becomes the Salween in Myanmar), the longest undammed river in Southeast Asia. Wen had suspended work on an earlier version of the cascade in 2004 until a more credible review of its environmental impact could be carried out. Reportedly, Wen's 2009 action was in response both to international and local criticism of the impact on an environmentally sensitive region and because of opposition from ethnic minorities on both sides of the Yunnan–Myanmar border who have recently been involved in open fighting against both Chinese and Burmese forces.

Beijing has also shown more concern recently about the downstream impact of the Yunnan cascade. The Obama administration has several levers with which it can promote reconsideration by Beijing of its plans for Yunnan and encourage Chinese leaders to give more thought to the potential for a serious backlash from the impact of proposed dams to be built by Chinese companies in Laos and Cambodia. Firstly, US engagement with the Mekong River Commission has already caused some Chinese officials privately to rethink China's position on membership of the commission and on accepting the obligations under the 1995 treaty for notification, transparency and consultation about projects with significant downstream impact. Secondly, the Obama administration can deepen its engagement with Vietnam, the biggest downstream victim of upstream dams, and continue to develop closer cooperation with Thailand, still the main market for electricity produced in Laos. The United States is also well positioned to offer technical assistance to the commission countries for calculating the full environmental and socioeconomic impact of mainstream dams, assisting with better cost–benefit analysis, and investigating alternative solutions for obtaining the desired energy resources. Finally, because of the significant geopolitical impact of China's activities in the Mekong region, the United States should take up the issue by broadening the agenda of the newly established US–China Strategic and Economic Dialogue, in which discussion of strategic issues has thus far been lacking.[12]

* * *

To avoid the perils of peace in the Mekong basin, the larger powers in the region, inter-governmental organisations, aid donors and the United States all have critical roles. In particular, cooperative and equitable involvement by China and Thailand is critical, and is an area where Washington may have considerable leverage. Non-governmental organisations, development banks and international agencies should be encouraged to pursue new methods and tools to apprise leaders in Yunnan and Beijing (and, to a lesser extent, Bangkok) of the very real risk of policy blowback from their plans for the Mekong.

Notes

1 'Mekong: River of Terror and Hope', *National Geographic*, vol. 134, no. 6, December 1968.

2 Agreement on the Cooperation for the Sustainable Development of the Mekong River Basin, chap. 3, art. 6, 'Maintenance of Flows on the Mainstream'. Mekong River Commission, 1995 Mekong Agreement and Procedural Rules, http://www.mrcmekong.org/agreement_95/agreement_95.htm#chap3.

3 Soon after the programme was launched, China began spending more on infrastructure development in the west than either its central or coastal regions. Hongyi Harry Lai, 'China's Western Development Program: Its Rationale, Implications and Impact', *Modern China*, vol. 28, 2002, p. 432, http://www.case.edu/affil/tibet/tibetanNomads/documents/ChinasWesternDevelopmentProgram_000.pdf.

4 Asian Development Bank, 'Asia's "Last Frontier" Becoming More Connected and Competitive', news release, 8 December 2004, http://www.adb.org/media/Articles/2004/6445_gms_frontier/.

5 The gross active storage of Xiaowan and Nuozhadu, which act as cisterns to the entire cascade, are respectively 14,560 and 22,400 (some sources say 22,700) billion cubic meters. Three other dams already operating have large reservoirs by any standard, but at about 1bn m^3 each they are regarded as providing only 'seasonal storage', which in several dry sea-

sons has been inadequate to maintain full power output. John Dore and Yu Xiaogang, 'Yunnan Hydropower Expansion: Update on China's Energy Industry Reforms and the Nu, Lancang and Jinsha Hydropower Dams', working paper, Chiang Mai's Unit for Social & Environmental Research and Green Watershed, Kunming, People's Republic of China, March 2004, Table 7 (Lancang), http://www.sea-user.org/download_pubdoc.php?doc=2586; M. Quang and P.E. Nguyen, 'Hydrologic Impacts of China's Upper Mekong Dams on the Lower Mekong River', 28 June 2003, http://www.mekongriver.org/publish/qghydrochdam.htm.

6 Michael Richardson, 'Water Management for the Mekong Basin', *Japan Times*, 12 September 2008, http://search.japantimes.co.jp/cgi-bin/e020080912a1.html. Actual releases would depend on the level of the reservoir and the river and power demand.

7 Chris Barlow, Eric Baran, Ashley S. Halls and Mrigesh Kshatriya, 'How Much of the Mekong Fish Catch is at Risk from Mainstream Dam Development?', *Catch and Culture*, vol. 14, no. 3, December 2008, http://www.mrcmekong.org/Catch-Culture/vol14_3Dec08/Mekong-fish-catch.htm; Gary Lee and Natalia Scurrah, Australian Mekong Resource Centre, 'What do MRC Studies Tell us about the Implications of Mekong Mainstream Dams for Fisheries?', *Mekong Brief*, no. 9, November 2008, http://www.mekong.es.usyd.edu.au/events/past/Conference_Nov2008/AMRC fisheries Brief 9 Final (Engl).pdf.

8 'Pak Mun Villagers Still Upset with Governor's Vagueness on Opening Dam Gates', *Prachathai*, 2 November 2009.

9 8th International Advisory Group for the NT2 Hydropower Dam, *The World Bank Approaches to Social, Environmental, Governance, and Financial Issues in the Nam Theun 2 Hhydropower Project, Lao PDR, April 2008: Sustainability of Livelihood*, http://siteresources.worldbank.org/INTLAOPRD/Resources/293582-1092106399982/492430-1092106479653/iag_nt2_8th_mission_report.pdf.

10 United Nations Environmental Programme/Asian Institute of Technology, *Freshwater Under Threat: South East Asia*, http://www.roap.unep.org/publications/SEA_Water_report.pdf, p. 15.

11 Tran Dinh Thanh Lam, 'Southeast Asia: River Deal May Help Dam Debate in Mekong Region', http://ipsnews.net/news.asp?idnews=48106.

12 Previously known as the Strategic Economic Dialogue, which focused only on high-level financial and trade issues, the addition of the 'and' opened up the meeting to the participation of the secretary of state and her Chinese counterpart. To date, the dialogue has been preoccupied with the global economic and financial crisis and climate change, but the scope of dialogue includes regional and international issues. US Department of the Treasury, 'Joint Press Release on the First Round of the U.S.–China Strategic and Economic Dialogue', 28 July 2009, TG-242, http://www.ustreas.gov/press/releases/tg242.htm.

Pakistan's War Within

C. Christine Fair and Seth G. Jones

Since the Obama administration took office in January the United States has, rightly or wrongly, viewed Afghanistan and Pakistan as a single theatre of operations. Key to this strategy is the defeat of Islamist militants and insurgent groups in the Federally Administered Tribal Areas (FATA) and other parts of Pakistan, including the North-West Frontier Province (NWFP).[1] But Washington cannot fight the war in Pakistan; it must rely on Islamabad. Can the Pakistanis succeed?

Since the US-led invasion of Afghanistan in the wake of the 11 September 2001 terrorist attacks, Pakistan's efforts have been viewed by many in the West as desultory and ineffective. It has had difficulty holding territory and securing the population, despite some recent improvement (as evidenced by the operations in Swat in 2009). The renewed offensive against Islamist forces in FATA in October 2009 has raised hopes that Islamabad is now taking the threat seriously, but it is not clear that it has learned the lessons of failure from previous campaigns.

After 11 September, Washington encouraged Pakistan to conduct operations against militants by offering massive financial assistance (over $2 billion per year).[2] US security assistance included reimbursements through

---

C. Christine Fair is an assistant professor at Georgetown University and a senior fellow with the Counter Terrorism Center at West Point. She is the author of *The Madrassah Challenge: Militancy and Religious Education in Pakistan* (Washington DC: USIP, 2009) and co-editor (with Sumit Ganguly) of *Treading on Hallowed Ground: Counterinsurgency Operations in Sacred Spaces* (New York: OUP, 2008). **Seth G. Jones** most recently served as Plans Officer and Advisor to the Commanding General, US Special Operations Forces, in Afghanistan, and is the author of *In the Graveyard of Empires: America's War in Afghanistan* (New York and London: W.W. Norton, 2009). The views represent those of the authors and not their employers.

Survival | vol. 51 no. 6 | December 2009–January 2010 | pp. 161–188 DOI 10.1080/00396330903465204

coalition support funds, military aid (such as the provision of helicopters and air-assault training), and counter-narcotics programmes. Washington also provided aid through the Department of State, CIA, Department of Justice and other government agencies to support counter-terrorism, internal security and development programmes.[3] In the past two years, however, American officials and commentators have questioned the terms and outcomes of this assistance, noting Pakistan's uneven commitment to the 'war on terror' and continued support for the Afghan Taliban and anti-India militant groups.[4]

Many, albeit not all, of Pakistan's hurdles are doctrinal. The army does not claim to conduct population-centric counter-insurgency operations, but rather to engage in low-intensity conflict.[5] The difference has important operational consequences. Pakistan prefers to retain its conventional focus against India and hesitates to adopt a counter-insurgency orientation, viewing operations against internal threats as residing at the lower end of a conventional-conflict spectrum.[6]

Several factors account for the varied outcomes of operations Pakistani security forces have prosecuted against foreign and indigenous Islamist, criminal and insurgent groups in FATA and other parts of Pakistan, including NWFP, since 2001. Firstly, Pakistan has inadequate capacity to clear and hold areas and to win and sustain the support of locals. This likely stems from Islamabad's hesitance to embrace counter-insurgency doctrinally and operationally. Consequently, operations have caused significant local devastation and displacement of populations in Bajaur and Swat, in particular. Secondly, the security agencies, which are not monolithic, have been willing to conduct operations against groups that have threatened Pakistan, but not those that advance what they see as Pakistan's interests in Afghanistan and India. This policy of sustaining the 'good jihadis' has strained Pakistan's social fabric and endangered the state when erstwhile proxies have turned on it. Thirdly, domestic politics have influenced army decision-making. Public-opinion polls indicate that many Pakistanis have been wary of army operations against fellow citizens, and some have accused the government of conducting them at Washington's behest.[7] Fourthly, Pakistani civilian and military institutions have failed to integrate economic, social and political instruments into their operations. In Swat, for example, Pakistani security forces cleared key territory in 2007, 2008 and 2009, but the government did little to deal with grievances among the local population and there was no civil–military plan to contend with the humanitarian crisis precipitated by the operations.

Analysis of how Pakistan's forces are structured and their roles, strengths and weaknesses in key operations undertaken since 2001 may inform US engagement with the Pakistani security establishment and may identify key areas for additional training and policy attention. Such analysis may also inform the debate within and outside Washington about Pakistan's less-than-successful prosecution of its 'war on terror' and whether Pakistan's myriad shortcomings should be attributed to malfeasance, a genuine lack of capacity, or both. It may also be of value to Pakistan-based analysts; it is well known that Pakistan's armed forces neither engage in robust post-operation assessment nor institutionalise lessons that may emerge from such assessments.

Pakistan's forces

Pakistan has employed several kinds of forces in its major operations: the army, the Frontier Corps, and the Frontier Constabulary and Frontier Police.

The Pakistani army has an organisational strength of approximately 550,000 active-duty personnel and another 500,000 reservists. It has nine corps headquarters in addition to the Army Strategic Forces Command, sometimes called Pakistan's 'tenth corps', which commands all the country's land-based strategic assets.[8] The army is a conventional force primarily geared towards a conflict with India, a configuration which it prefers. In the early months of General Ashfaq Kiyani's tenure as chief of army staff from the end of 2007, US officials were optimistic that Pakistan would formally adopt a counter-insurgency strategy. Since then, Kiyani has frequently said that the army will not become a counter-insurgency force; rather, the bulk of the army will remain deployed along the Indian border.[9]

The Frontier Corps is a federal paramilitary force that belongs to the Ministry of Interior but is under the operational control of the military. It comprises two separate forces, FC NWFP (under operational command of XI Corps, with security duties for FATA and NWFP and headquartered in Peshawar) and FC Baluchistan (under operational command of XII Corps and headquartered in Quetta), with separate inspectors-general controlling each and a combined strength of 80,000. While the former force is overwhelmingly Pashtun, the cadres of the latter are not exclusively ethnically Baluch.[10] One reason the army has been averse to conducting operations in FATA and NWFP is the hostility of residents to what appears to be its Punjabi-dominated ethnic composition. Due to this image as a 'Punjabi force', many in FATA view it as a foreign force working with the United States against them.

Over the last several years some have argued that the FC NWFP should be the force of choice for operations in the tribal areas. At first blush this has some appeal, since its cadres are recruited locally and have local knowledge, language skills and a refined sense of the human terrain. But since at least 2004 there have been consistent reports that sympathetic elements of the Frontier Corps have been helping the Taliban.[11]

More fundamentally, the Frontier Corps has generally not been trained and equipped to be a serious counter-insurgency force. It lacks emergency medical-evacuation capabilities and other logistical capacities, and has a long history of distrusting the army to provide this sort of support. Proponents of using the corps in counter-insurgency contend that its inability to effectively conduct such operations derives from its lack of organisational capacity and the lack of support it receives from the army. US special-operations forces have launched a 'train-the-trainer' programme for the corps.

The Frontier Constabulary is a policing organisation raised to provide law and order in the settled areas outside FATA, as well as border-protection duties along the Pakistan–Afghanistan border. It currently also performs static security duties in Islamabad and throughout Punjab. It has faced the brunt of the violence in settled Pashtun areas such as Swat. Frontier Constabulary outposts have been targeted systematically by insurgents, who have also targeted police installations throughout Pakistan. Citizens generally avoid going near these outposts, fearing attack. (Frontier Corps outposts in FATA have also sustained insurgent assaults.) Frontier

Constabulary personnel are generally ill prepared for this fight because they are poorly trained and inadequately equipped, with outdated arms and little, if any, effective personal-protection equipment. They have been killed in large numbers or simply deserted.[12]

The North-West Frontier Province also has a provincial police force, the Frontier Police. Like all Pakistan's police forces, it is in dire need of better training and equipment, increases in personnel strength, and compensation reform.[13] To bolster morale and willingness to engage the enemy, the Frontier Police have established what are effectively life-insurance benefits for the families of slain police officers.[14] Like the Frontier Corps and Frontier Constabulary, the police have been a focus for insurgents who have, for example, violently taken over police stations in Swat and Buner and set up their own police operations. In spring 2009, when Mullah Fazlullah of the insurgent group Tehrik-e-Nifaze-Shariat-e-Mohammadi told the police in Swat to leave their jobs or face punishment, 700 of 1,700 officers deserted their posts.[15]

The key campaigns

Pakistani forces have conducted at least four major campaigns, alongside and subsuming numerous smaller operations, since 2001. As this article goes to press, it is in the middle of a fifth campaign which is being praised in some quarters as showing renewed seriousness. It is too soon to judge its real effectiveness, however, and it is not analysed in this article. The most important campaigns since 2001 include support for the US-led *Operation Enduring Freedom* (2001–02); *Operation Al Mizan* (2002–06); *Operation Zalzala* (2008); and operations *Sher Dil, Rah-e-Raq* and *Rah-e-Rast* (2007–09).

Operation Enduring Freedom (2001–02)

After the 11 September 2001 terrorist attacks, the US-led *Operation Enduring Freedom* aimed to overthrow the Taliban regime in Afghanistan and capture or kill senior members of the Taliban and al-Qaeda. Because of Pakistan's strategic location and its historical involvement in Afghanistan, Washington pressured Islamabad to assist US war efforts.[16] Prior to this, Pakistani security forces had limited experience or success in waging sustained

Operation Sher Dil, 2008
Miles 10
Km 20
Kit Kot
Torghundai
Alizai
Khar
Loe Sam
Nawagai
Mohman Gat
Lakai Sar
Yousaf Khel
Lakarai Sar
Bohai Dag
Kkazana Sar
AFGHANISTAN
Toratigga Sar
Ghalani
Kabul River
Highway
PAKISTAN
Peshawar
Miles 50
Km 100
Malakand Division
Hazara Division
CHITRAL
NORTHERN AREAS
SWAT
UPPER DIR
NORTH-WEST FRONTIER PROVINCE
KOHISTAN
LOWER DIR
Mingora
SHANGLA
BATTAGRAM
BAJAUR
AFGHANISTAN
MALAKAND
Kabul
MOHMAND
BUNER
MANSEHRA
MARDAN
CHARSADDA
ABBOTTABAD
KHYBER
SWABI
Peshawar
HARIPUR
FEDERALLY ADMINISTERED TRIBAL AREAS
NOWSHERA
PESHAWAR
Islamabad
KURRAM
ORAKZAI
HANGU
KOHAT
PUNJAB
KARAK
NORTH WAZIRISTAN
PAKISTAN
BANNU
LAKKI MARWAT
Shakai
Sararogha Fort
Spinkai
Wana
SOUTH WAZIRISTAN
TANK
DERA ISMAIL KHAN
BALOCHISTAN
© IISS
Operation Kalosha II, 2004
Miles 5
Km 10
PAKISTAN
Karikot
AFGHANISTAN
Dzha Ghundai
Wana
Kalosha
Shin Warsak

operations on these territories, despite considerable experience fomenting low-intensity conflicts in India and Afghanistan.

Pakistan made two extremely important contributions to *Operation Enduring Freedom*. Firstly, it granted over-flight and landing rights for US military and intelligence units, allowed access to some Pakistani ports and bases, provided intelligence and immigration information, facilitated logistical supply to military forces in Afghanistan, and (temporarily) broke diplomatic relations with and cut off most logistical support to the Taliban.[17] Secondly, Pakistan deployed units from the regular army, Special Services Group,[18] Frontier Corps and Inter-Services Intelligence (ISI) directorate to the Afghanistan–Pakistan border to conduct operations along infiltration routes from Afghanistan. The regular army employed two infantry brigades for border and internal-security operations for much of 2001 and 2002 and it established two quick-reaction forces from the Special Services Group in Kohat and Wana to provide local Pakistani commanders the ability to deploy troops quickly. In addition, approximately 4,000 Frontier Corps forces were used to conduct operations in the Federally Administered Tribal Areas.[19]

In December 2001, Pakistan employed a mixture of forces in Khyber and Kurram tribal agencies to support US operations at Tora Bora.[20] In March 2002, Pakistan increased force levels in North and South Waziristan to target militants during US-led *Operation Anaconda* in the Shah-i-Kot Valley of Paktia Province in Afghanistan.[21] Throughout 2002, Frontier Corps forces raided weapons caches in South Waziristan; the regular army assaulted al-Qaeda operatives during *Operation Kazha Punga* in South Waziristan; regular army troops entered areas in Khyber and Kurram Agencies to pursue al-Qaeda fighters fleeing Afghanistan; and Pakistani military, police and intelligence forces conducted operations against insurgents in Balochistan Province.[22]

Pakistan played a major role in capturing many senior al-Qaeda operatives and foreign fighters, including Abu Zubaydah, Ramzi bin al-Shibh and Sharib Ahmad.[23] It remanded many of these to the US government, which temporarily billeted them in secret prisons in Kandahar, Bagram and elsewhere. In most cases, Pakistan retained captured Afghans or Pakistanis.[24]

US officials widely praised Pakistani contributions in this period. But Pakistan's role was limited: Washington did not ask Islamabad to target all, or even most, militant groups and leaders operating in and from Pakistan, including senior Afghan Taliban figures and allies such as Jalaluddin Haqqani and Gulbuddin Hekmatyar. Rather, Washington sought Pakistani assistance primarily in capturing or killing al-Qaeda and foreign fighters, which Pakistan saw as in its own interest.[25] *Operation Enduring Freedom* was partially successful in its primary objectives of overthrowing the Taliban regime and capturing some al-Qaeda fighters crossing the border. But the United States and Pakistan failed to capture some key al-Qaeda figures, including Osama bin Laden and Ayman al-Zawahiri, who crossed into Pakistan.

Operation Al Mizan (2002–06)

Among the militants who fled into Pakistan after the collapse of the Taliban regime in Afghanistan were al-Qaeda leaders involved in the 11 September terrorist attacks. These terrorists and their allies attacked Pakistani military and paramilitary installations and US firebases on the Afghanistan–Pakistan border.[26] Washington pressured Pakistan to launch an offensive against the foreign fighters ensconced in FATA. *Operation Al Mizan* comprised several smaller operations, such as *Operation Kalosha II*, which took place in South Waziristan.

Pakistan employed between 70,000 and 80,000 forces in FATA. Between 2002 and 2006, Pakistan conducted nearly two dozen major operations against insurgents,[27] and pursued political means such as requesting South Waziristan's political administration to identify locals harbouring foreign fighters through *jirga*s (tribal assemblies) and consultations with tribal leaders. Pakistan also obtained useful information from local informants, which enabled identification of over 70 Ahmedzai Wazir tribesmen who were supporting foreign fighters.[28]

A number of smaller operations were critical. For example, in early 2004, Pakistan's intelligence services collected reports of al-Qaeda activities in the Wana Valley. In March, partly in response to the ambush of Frontier Corps personnel in the area, Pakistani forces launched *Operation Kalosha II*. The army conducted a major 13-day cordon-and-search operation across a 36km^2 area west of Wana that had come under the command of several militants, including Nek Mohammad Wazir, Noor-ul-Islam, Haji Mohammad Sharif, Maulvi Abbas and Maulvi Abdul Aziz, who were suspected of harbouring foreign fighters.[29] During the operation Pakistan employed the Frontier Corps and XI Corps, based out of Peshawar, under the command of Lieutenant-General Muhammad Safdar Hussain. On 16 March, Frontier Corps forces surrounded three fortress-like houses in Kalosha village, 15km west of Wana, belonging to Nek Mohammad, Haji Mohammad Sharif and Noor-ul-Islam. Fighters from the Ahmadzai Wazir tribe in turn besieged the Frontier Corps' outer cordon. By the end of the day, 15 Frontier Corps soldiers and one Pakistani army soldier had been killed and 14 others taken hostage. Roughly a dozen army trucks, as well as pickup trucks, armoured personnel carriers and light artillery, were also immobilised, destroyed or burned. Pakistani forces also faced tough resistance in the villages of Dzha Ghundai, Shin Warsak and Karikot. The cordon around Kalosha and the surrounding villages failed to impair the mobility of the militants, some of whom dispersed through a network of tunnels. The operation initially involved 700 troops, but by 19 March roughly 7,000 army and Frontier Corps soldiers were fighting at several locations south and west of Wana. On 26 March, General Hussain declared victory: 'We have accomplished the mission that was given to us'.[30]

The cordon failed to impair their mobility

Operation Kalosha II was successful in that it eliminated several local and foreign fighters, disrupted a major al-Qaeda command and control centre, and captured a network of tunnels containing sophisticated electronic equipment and supplies. But it also triggered attacks against nearby Pakistan army and Frontier Corps bases.[31] Some locals were also deeply upset at Pakistan's destructive tactics: the army demolished a number of houses and used private residences as fortifications and barracks.[32] As one local lamented, 'the army took away everything from my house: jewellery, clothes, toiletries, even pillow covers and shoe polish'.[33]

Another important operation took place in June 2004, when 10,000 army troops, along with US-trained Special Operations Task Force (a helicopter-mobile battalion from Special Services Group) and Frontier Corps forces, attacked what was reported to be a force of more than 200 Chechens and

Uzbeks, some Arabs and several hundred local supporters in the Shakai Valley, some 25km north of Wana. Nearly 3,000 soldiers established an outer cordon and the Pakistan Air Force struck at dawn, using precision weapons against nine compounds. Pakistan army forces used indirect artillery fire and precision rocket attacks by helicopter gunships. Helicopters dropped off Special Operations Task Force troops to search the compounds, and infantry troops initiated a simultaneous operation to clear the valley and link up with the task force. Later, an additional force of 3,000 troops was brought into the area to clear more of the valley.[34] Throughout 2004 and 2005, the United States and Pakistan conducted a range of precision strikes against further targets, many of which were in North and South Waziristan.[35]

As casualties mounted, the army pursued 'peace deals' with the local militants.[36] The presence of the Islamist political party, the Jamiat Ulema-e-Islam (JUI), encouraged the government led by Pervez Musharraf to pursue peace deals. While the JUI has long been a political patron of the Taliban and other Deobandi militant groups, it was also a critical member of the clerical political alliance, Mutahidda Majlis-e-Amal (MMA), which did surprisingly well in the October 2002 parliamentary elections. The JUI formed the provincial government in the NWFP and ruled in coalition with Musharraf's party, the Pakistan Muslim League-Q, in Balochistan. The JUI and its allies in the MMA also comprised Musharraf's 'opposition of choice' in the federal parliament. Musharraf's appetite for confronting the militants, which enjoyed the support of elements of the JUI, waned for fear of alienating key leaders of the MMA, whom Musharraf needed to push through his controversial and extra-constitutional policies.

One of the first major efforts to broker a peace settlement, the Shakai Agreement, came in the aftermath of Pakistani operations in Kalosha in March 2004. The government cobbled together a 50-member *jirga* with the help of North-West Frontier Province Governor Syed Iftikhar Hussain Shah and, reportedly, with the assistance of important leaders from the JUI.[37] The Pakistani government demanded the unconditional surrender of foreign militants and their local supporters, as well as the release of Pakistan military personnel and administration staff who were taken hostage in the

Kalosha area on 16 March. During subsequent negotiations, the *jirga* was given three counter-conditions by the insurgents: lifting the army's siege, paying compensation for 83 houses demolished during the fighting, and releasing 163 people arrested during the operation.

The deal that was finally reached included several provisions: Pakistani army troops would not interfere in internal tribal affairs and agreed to stay in their cantonment areas; local insurgents would not attack Pakistani government personnel or infrastructure; and all foreigners would have to register themselves with the government.[38] There were several problems with this deal. It compensated the insurgents for their losses but did not require them to compensate their victims. They were also allowed to keep their arms. Weapons were not 'surrendered', but rather 'offered' to the military as a token, ceremonial gesture. The militants described the deal as a 'reconciliation', which is understood by tribals as the army's tacit acceptance of their opponents as equally powerful and legitimate. By forging this 'reconciliation', the army gave the insurgents previously unearned political legitimacy and permitted them to consolidate their hold over South Waziristan.[39]

> *Locals saw the process as a surrender*

However, the most egregious problem was the way in which the army prosecuted the deal. Final negotiations between Nek Mohammad, Haji Mohammad Sharif and an 18-member group of the *jirga*, which also included local ulema affiliated with the JUI and some elders from the Zalikhel tribe, took place at a Deobandi madrassa not far from Wana.[40] Traditionally, *jirga*s are held in public places, not mosques or madrassas, and religious leaders have had no role in this process.[41] Because the army came to meet Nek Mohammad at this madrassa, locals interpreted the process as a surrender by the army rather than the militants. Nek Mohammad characterised the transaction in exactly this way when he explained that 'I did not go to them, they came to my place. That should make it clear who surrendered to whom.'[42] The deal fortified Nek Mohammad's confidence in his ability to contend with the Pakistani state, and he soon violated the agreement. In June 2004, he was killed by a US missile strike near Wana.[43] In November 2004 the Pakistani government reached a further agreement with Taliban leaders, but that deal lasted only six weeks. Many of the subsequent deals forged by the army with militant groups had similar features to the Shakai Agreement.

During *Operation al Mizan,* Pakistan sought to kill or capture those militants who threatened the Pakistani government. Pakistan's pre-eminent targets were foreign fighters – not Pakistani fighters.[44] President Musharraf had a personal vendetta. In December 2003 al-Qaeda's deputy leader, Ayman al-Zawahiri, issued a fatwa calling for Musharraf's death, and South Waziristan-based militants tried to assassinate him on several occasions.[45] Despite Pakistan's focus on domestic threats, Washington sought to eliminate al-Qaeda leaders and to curb attacks on US firebases. The operation had several successes. It resulted in the capturing or killing of several senior al-Qaeda leaders, such as Khalid Sheikh Mohammed, Abu Faraj al-Libbi, Abu Zubeida and Abu Talha al-Pakistani.

The operation, however, ultimately failed to clear North and South Waziristan of militants. The Taliban and other local groups made significant inroads in usurping the power of tribal chieftains and increasing the importance of mullahs who espoused a Taliban worldview. Pakistan's security competition with India meant that its national-security establishment, including the ISI, had a vested interest in continuing to support some militant groups directed at the Afghanistan and Kashmir fronts. In addition, Pakistani operations were not sustained over time, but rather were marked by sweeps, searches and occasional bloody battles. None of these operations employed sufficient forces to hold territory. The government's initiatives were also hindered by conservative religious parties operating in the tribal areas. These groups considered government efforts against al-Qaeda and other groups an 'American war'.

As a result of the failed peace deals and the mixed success of the military, the local Taliban gradually emerged as a parallel government in the tribal areas, which became a sanctuary for insurgent groups operating in Afghanistan and militants targeting both India and the Pakistani government. The traditional *jirga* was formally banned by the Taliban. In its place, aggrieved parties had to seek intervention by the Taliban representative in their village, who performed the functions of police officer, administrator and judge. The Taliban banned music stores, videos and televisions, and issued edicts that men grow beards. They also continued to target pro-government tribal elders, forcing many to flee.[46]

Operation Zalzala (2008)

After the death of Nek Mohammed, Baitullah Mehsud emerged as a leader of the militants in South Waziristan. In February 2005, the Pakistani government signed a peace deal with Mehsud at Sararogha. As with the Shakai deal, the army agreed to remove troops from Mehsud's territory, compensate the militants for human and material losses, and deploy Frontier Corps personnel to the five forts there. The agreement virtually handed over control of the area to Mehsud.[47] The peace was short-lived: in early 2006, Mehsud began orchestrating a suicide-bombing campaign in Pakistan, which persisted until his death in August 2009.[48] In autumn 2007, Mehsud announced that the various local Taliban groups had united under his leadership and adopted the name Tehrik-e-Taliban Pakistan, or Pakistan Taliban.

In January 2008 Mehsud's men captured Sararogha Fort in South Waziristan and killed many members of the Pakistani security forces.[49] Mehsud declared in a rare public interview that the Pakistani army 'uses the weapons it has against the people and against Muslims. Pakistan should protect Muslims with these weapons and defy enemies with them. However, the army has harmed the people and Muslims with its weapons.'[50]

That same month the Pakistani army launched the three-part *Operation Tri-Star* against the Pakistan Taliban in FATA, with *Operation Zalzala* ('Earthquake') in South Waziristan as a principal component. *Zalzala* aimed to clear several areas held by forces loyal to Mehsud. The goal was not to target groups engaged in attacks in Afghanistan or Kashmir, or even foreign fighters, but to capture or kill key individuals in Mehsud's network who threatened the Pakistani state. One was Qari Hussein Mehsud, believed to be leading a campaign of suicide bombings. Army forces destroyed his house, but failed to capture or kill him.[51] The army dropped leaflets urging locals to vacate the area, and on 24 January launched attacks in several parts of South Waziristan.[52]

Forces loyal to Baitullah Mehsud resisted and engaged in a fairly sophisticated propaganda effort, including uploading videos to YouTube, to discredit the military.[53] Militants also told locals that the army was composed of non-Muslims and was fighting on behalf of the United States.[54] This became an important issue because some clergy would not conduct last rites for slain security-force personnel. Over the next several months, the army cleared most of the village of Spinkai, a Mehsud stronghold, and captured a few other villages and small towns.[55]

By May, the army began to withdraw, claiming victory. The 14th Division was directed to re-open road networks and consolidate tactical outposts into battalion forward operating bases in eastern South Waziristan. The army's apparent intent was to stay in the Mehsud tribal area, continue to dominate key terrain, and retain the capability to redeploy into tactically dominant positions within 48 hours should the security situation dictate.[56]

Operation Zalzala cleared parts of South Waziristan, at least temporarily, and apparently disrupted some planned suicide attacks.[57] The army seized computers, weapons, improvised explosive devices and propaganda material.[58] But the costs were high. According to an investigation led by senior Pakistani military, political, intelligence and tribal officials, security forces destroyed over 4,000 houses in South Waziristan in January alone. In addition, *Operation Zalzala* displaced roughly 200,000 locals, causing significant animosity.[59] In several villages the army applied collective punishment to locals who harboured the Taliban, under the draconian colonial-era Frontier Crimes Regulation that governs FATA. The army used bulldozers and explosives to level Spinkai's bazaar, including petrol stations and even parts of a local hospital.[60]

Success was fleeting

Success was fleeting. Shortly after the army's withdrawal, militants loyal to Baitullah Mehsud re-infiltrated many areas.[61] Qari Hussain Mehsud reactivated the Spinkai Ragzai suicide-training camp, which the army had dismantled.[62] Baitullah Mehsud's network continued throughout the first half of 2009 to attack Pakistani forces, which responded with limited retaliatory strikes.[63] Across Pakistan, there were 2,148 terrorist, insurgent and sectarian attacks in 2008, a 746% increase from 2005.[64] Pakistan's controversial use of collective punishment fostered deep animosity among locals who were loath to support the government's efforts. As one shopkeeper from Spinkai noted, 'hatred against the army will increase if they destroy homes of common people'.[65]

Operations Sher Dil, Rah-e-Haq and Rah-e-Rast (2007–09)

With limited success in the southern parts of FATA, Pakistani security forces began operations against militants elsewhere in the country. There was some cooperation among networks operating in northern parts of FATA and the NWFP, including those led by Faqir Mohammad, Mullah Fazlullah and Sufi Mohammad. Baitullah Mehsud provided some fighters and assistance to the insurgents in Bajaur and Swat as part of his strategy to better coordinate the insurgency through the Pakistan Taliban.

A series of attacks on government agencies, including ISI, Frontier Corps and army personnel, motivated the army to retaliate.[66] By early 2008, insurgent forces in Bajaur Agency led by Qari Zia Rahman among others had pushed government-armed local tribesmen (referred to as *lashkars* or levies) out of their checkpoints at Loe Sam. By June, more than half of the 72 checkpoints in Bajaur had been destroyed, and the civilian government had been disrupted through a major bank robbery and suicide bombings against officials. On 9 September 2008, soon after a security convoy was ambushed by local militants in Loe Sam, army and Frontier Corps units launched *Operation Sher Dil* (Lion Heart).[67]

The primary objective of *Sher Dil* was to target militant groups that threatened Pakistan and to clear and hold Bajaur's population centres and lines of communication. By early December, over 1,000 militants and 63 security personnel had been killed. Pakistani forces found tunnel complexes used for hiding people and storing material such as weapons, ammunition, radio-frequency lists, guerrilla-warfare manuals, propaganda and bomb-making instructions.[68]

The outcome was mixed at best. The operation was heavy handed, relying on aerial bombing, bulldozers and tanks. In the village of Loe Sam, security forces razed virtually every house connected to the extensive tunnel system that had been discovered. Local Taliban and other militants were armed with heavy weapons and reinforced by fighters from Afghanistan, the NWFP and other parts of FATA. As one military official remarked, the militants had 'good weaponry and a better communication system [than ours] … Their tactics are mind-boggling and they have defenses that would take us days to build. It does not look as though we are fighting a rag-tag militia; they are fighting like an organized force.'[69] The fighting caused a significant exodus of locals to Afghanistan and other parts of Pakistan. After completing *Operation Sher Dil*, army and Frontier Corps forces moved to Mohmand Agency to conduct additional operations.

In nearby Swat District in Malakand Division, security forces conducted operations against the Tehrik-e-Nifaze-Shariat-e-Mohammadi (TNSM) militant group.[70] In the first phase of *Operation Rah-e-Haq* in late November 2007, local police led cordon-and-search operations to clear militants operating in the Swat Valley, but the militants gradually re-infiltrated into key cities. The second phase began in July 2008 and continued through the remainder of the year. Fighting was initially heavy in the northern part of the valley, and later spread to southern areas.[71] In January 2009, the army launched a third phase of *Operation Rah-e-Haq*, imposing 'shoot-on-sight' curfews in major cities in Swat. TNSM forces responded by destroying schools and attacking security forces.

The fighting ended in February with an agreement between the government and the TNSM, the Malakand Accord, which institutionalised a disputed form of Islamic law in Malakand Division and part of Hazara Division.[72] By late April 2009, however, militants had begun to occupy shops and government buildings in Mingora, the largest city in Swat, and to move into parts of Swat and neighbouring districts. They also attacked police stations, ambushed Frontier Constabulary personnel, robbed government and NGO offices, destroyed several schools and set up checkpoints along key roads.[73]

In May, Pakistan launched *Operation Rah-e-Rast* to clear areas of Swat and capture or kill key Pakistan Taliban and other militant leaders.[74] Fighting began in Mingora between Special Services Group commandos and about 300 militants positioned in deserted buildings, and continued until a major Pakistani offensive retook much of the city in late May, along with several nearby towns. On 30 May the military announced it had regained control of all of Mingora (though small pockets of resistance remained on the city's outskirts) and had destroyed concrete bunkers and confiscated arms, ammunition and explosives hidden in caves.[75]

The heavy fighting and the military's destructive practices in Swat and nearby districts triggered a flood of internally displaced persons. Refugee organisations estimated that over three million people were displaced because of the fighting.[76] Some went to camps, but most found refuge with host families, rented accommodations or makeshift shelters. Local militants took advantage of the displacement to enlist popular support, provide assistance to internally displaced people, and recruit locals.

Operation Sher Dil involved much better cooperation than previously between the Frontier Corps and the army, and between Pakistan and the United States. Khan regularly briefed US officials on the operations, and the US Agency for International Development's Office of Transition Initiatives provided development assistance, including relief supplies to internally displaced persons and reconstitution assistance. The US military also provided information to Pakistan forces along the Afghanistan–Pakistan border, where they conducted intelligence, surveillance and reconnaissance operations around major passes.

For many Pakistani civilians, however, US assistance was heretical. Maulana Abdul Khaliq Haqqani, chief patron of the Gulshan-i-Uloom madrassa in Miramshah, said he would meet Pakistani or US operations with suicide bombers and remote-controlled bombs, noting that US attacks 'were carried out in the presence of the Pakistan Army; we cannot ignore our army's cooperation with foreign forces in actions that kill innocent people'.[77] In addition, despite support from local tribes, Pakistan was unable to hold on to territory over the long run, and the practice of razing villages and collective punishment contributed to growing frustration with the army.

Popular support?

These operations placed a significant burden on the Pakistani army.[78] In April 2008, one officer explained that he disliked killing Pakistanis and that he had joined the army to kill Indians. In 2007, Musharraf ordered military personnel not to wear their uniforms off base, as they were under active threat from the Pakistan Taliban and suffered substantial, sustained and degrading abuse from the population.[79]

Animosity towards army personnel was likely due in part to Musharraf's increasing unpopularity and to deep popular ambivalence towards the offensives in FATA and the NWFP. According to a survey of nearly 1,000 urban Pakistanis in September 2007, 48% approved of the FATA operations either strongly or somewhat, while 34% disapproved somewhat or strongly.[80] In the same survey, pollsters offered respondents three statements about FATA and asked 'which comes closer to your view?':

> **Statement A**: Pakistan's government should exert control over FATA, even if it means using military force to do so
>
> **Statement B**: The government should not try to exert control over FATA but should try to keep the peace through negotiating deals with local Taliban
>
> **Statement C:** The government should withdraw its forces from FATA and leave the people alone

The plurality (46%) believed Statement B best represented their view. Nearly one in four picked Statement A, only 12% picked Statement C, and 18% declined to answer. This suggests that the least-objectionable aspect to Pakistanis of the government's policy towards FATA has been its deals with the militants. Pakistanis were somewhat more accepting of military action when the target was al-Qaeda. Some 44% of respondents favoured the army entering FATA to pursue and capture al-Qaeda fighters, with 36% opposed. Similarly, 48% of respondents favoured allowing the army to pursue and capture Taliban insurgents who crossed into Pakistan, while 34% opposed the idea. There was strong opposition (80%) to allowing American or other foreign troops to enter Pakistan to pursue and capture al-Qaeda fighters, with 77% opposing such action in pursuit of the Taliban.[81]

Other surveys of rural and urban Pakistanis, conducted at intervals between September 2007 and March 2009, revealed similar popular ambiv-

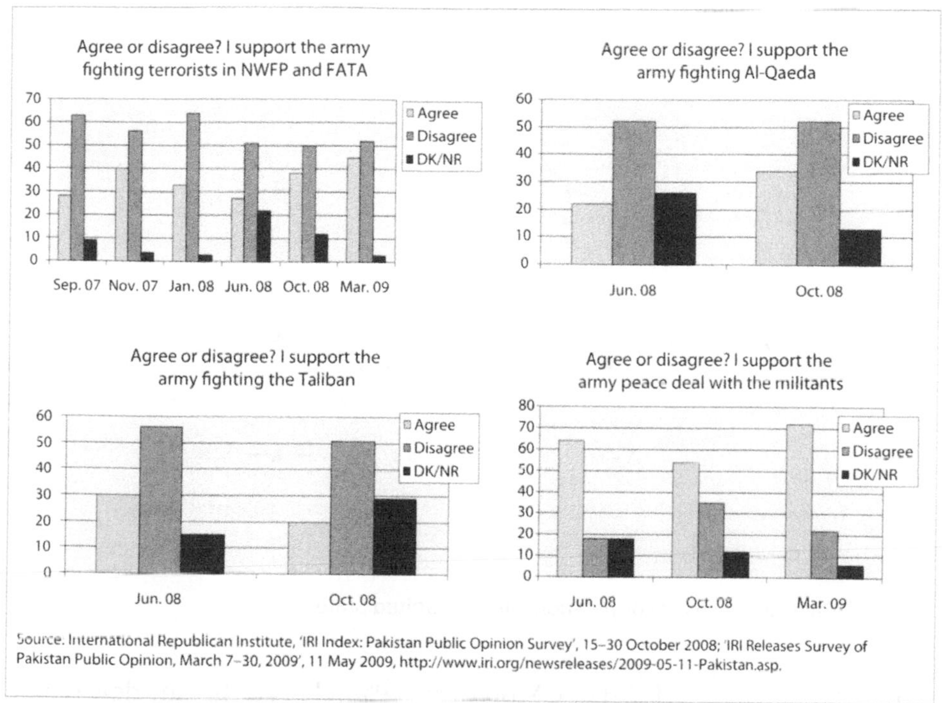

Source. International Republican Institute, 'IRI Index: Pakistan Public Opinion Survey', 15–30 October 2008; 'IRI Releases Survey of Pakistan Public Opinion, March 7–30, 2009', 11 May 2009, http://www.iri.org/newsreleases/2009-05-11-Pakistan.asp.

Figure 1. Pakistani views of military strategies against militant groups

alence about the best way to handle the perceived threats.[82] Respondents were asked whether they agreed with four statements:

- I support the army fighting terrorists in NWFP and FATA
- I support the army fighting al-Qaeda
- I support the army fighting the Taliban
- I support the army peace deal with the militants

The results indicated that most Pakistanis did not support the army fighting in NWFP and FATA as of autumn 2008, although opposition had generally declined since the previous September, and a growing minority supported such fighting. A similar majority opposed fighting al-Qaeda and the Taliban in June and October 2008 (Figure 1).

A majority of Pakistanis generally supported the 'peace deals with extremists', although the strength of this support fluctuated between 52% and 72%. When asked specifically in March 2009 about the Swat deal, 80%

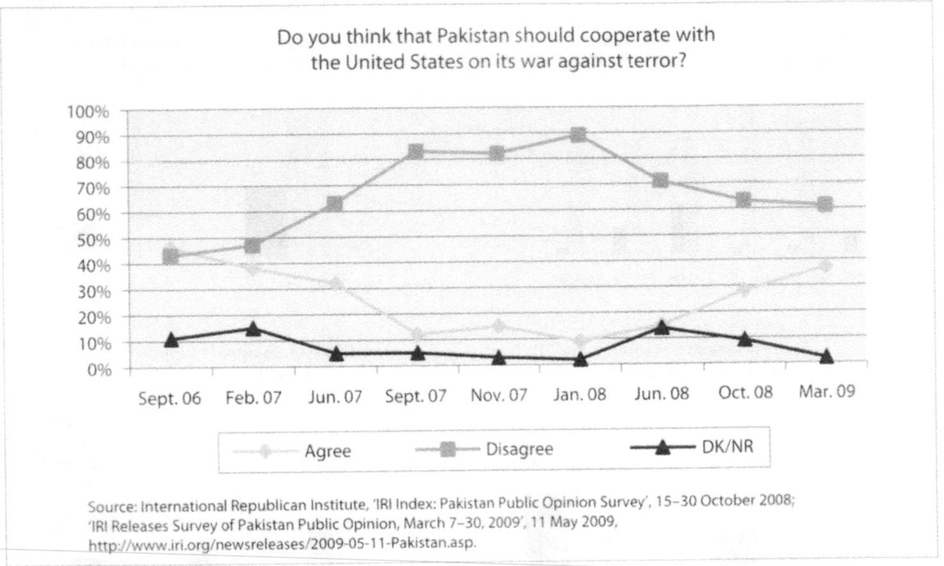

Source: International Republican Institute, 'IRI Index: Pakistan Public Opinion Survey', 15–30 October 2008; 'IRI Releases Survey of Pakistan Public Opinion, March 7–30, 2009', 11 May 2009, http://www.iri.org/newsreleases/2009-05-11-Pakistan.asp.

Figure 2. Pakistani views of cooperation with the United States

supported it while 16% did not. Moreover, 74% believed that the deal would actually bring peace.[83]

Pakistanis show similar ambivalence towards their country's cooperation with the United States, which is widely seen as compelling the Pakistani army to conduct operations against its own citizens. Rejection of cooperation with the United States in its 'war on terror' declined from a high (since the question began to be polled in autumn 2006) of 89% in January 2008 to 63% in October (Figure 2). While Pakistanis generally believe that a wide array of militant groups threaten their nation's security, they remain generally opposed to cooperation with the United States and even to their own army acting against such groups.

While the military component of the government's policy may be unpopular, Pakistanis tend to support political reform in FATA. Only 8% of respondents favoured leaving the colonial-era Frontier Crimes Regulation unchanged, while 46% favoured modifying it slowly over time, and more than one in four favoured abolishing it altogether. The fall of Buner may have mobilised greater public support, but whether this will be enduring remains to be seen.[84] The Pakistani armed forces operate in a challenging social and political environment where there is deep ambivalence about the government's policy of military action and cooperation with the United States, while appeasement of the militants seems quite palatable.

* * *

Prior to 2001, Pakistan had limited experience countering domestic militants. Today, the Pakistani army still prefers to focus on a potential war with India rather than against sub-state actors. Nonetheless, there have been noted improvements since 2001, and throughout 2009 Islamabad has demonstrated increasing resolve to defeat militants challenging the writ of the state. Earlier operations such as *Al Mizan* revealed serious deficiencies in the ability to conduct cordon-and-search operations and to hold territory. In the later operations in Bajaur and Swat, however, the Frontier Corps and army forces showed an improved capability to clear territory and integrate operations with local tribes.

But Pakistani doctrine remains inconsistent with recent population-centric innovations in counter-insurgency warfare. Pakistan's commitment to a conventional orientation and the hardware most appropriate for fighting India has poorly equipped it to deal with the burgeoning domestic threat.

The army has long contended that it is the sole institution that can protect Pakistan. During successive regimes, both military and civilian, Pakistani police and other institutions supporting the rule of law have languished. Moreover, the United States has disproportionately funded the army and Frontier Corps, while paying scant regard to the police and civilian investigatory institutions.[85] Yet the counter-insurgency literature consistently finds that civilian-led rather than army-led approaches ultimately prevail.[86]

Islamabad continues to distinguish among militant groups operating in FATA and the NWFP, and to use the tribal areas for training proxy groups destined for Afghanistan or India. Not only does Pakistan refuse to target some militant organisations, some are even backed by elements in the ISI, Frontier Corps and military. This practice of supporting some proxy organisations and broader religious, political and financial networks has created an environment conducive to militancy and has undermined the ability of the government to maintain law and order.

Pakistan's federal and provincial bureaucracies have failed to provide development and other aid to conflict-afflicted areas, offer adequate assistance to internally displaced persons, or engage in other efforts to secure the support of locals for the government and military operations. This has exacerbated the army's reliance on heavy force and concomitant destruction in places such as South Waziristan, Bajaur and Swat, which has alienated some locals and fostered anger throughout Pakistan.

Finally, the army and government have not been successful in mobilising the country against the militant threat, although there is some evidence that this could be changing following the Taliban's seizure of Buner in the wake of the latest peace deal with militants in Swat in April 2009. Without popular support, military action, long-term holding operations and dedication of national resources are unlikely to be enough to defeat the Pakistan Taliban and other militant groups and rebuild areas affected by conflict.

Notes

1 In March 2009, for example, US President Barack Obama contended that Pakistan's border region had 'become the most dangerous place in the world' for Americans, and General David Petraeus noted that it was 'the headquarters of the al Qaeda senior leadership' who were planning attacks in the West. See Yochi J. Dreazen, 'Al Qaeda's Global Base Is Pakistan, Says Petraeus', *Wall Street Journal*, 11 May 2009. British Prime Minister Gordon Brown warned that 'three-quarters of the most serious plots investigated by the British authorities have links to al-Qaeda in Pakistan'. Sam Coates and Jeremy Page, 'Pakistan "Linked to 75% of All UK Terror Plots", Warns Gordon Brown', *Times*, 15 December 2008.

2 Craig Cohen and Derek Chollet, 'When $10 Billion Is Not Enough', *Washington Quarterly*, vol. 30, no. 2, Spring 2007, pp. 7–19.

3 On US aid to Pakistan see C. Christine Fair and Peter Chalk, *Fortifying Pakistan: The Role of U.S. Internal Security Assistance* (Washington DC: United States Institute of Peace Press, 2006). The Coalition Support Funds, which were technically reimbursements, have been controversial because of poor oversight and Pakistani misuse. Neither Pakistani nor American officials can account for the funds. For several critical reviews, see US Government Accountability Office, 'Combating Terrorism: U.S. Oversight of Pakistan Reimbursement Claims for Coalition Support Funds', GAO-08-932T, 24 June 2008, http://www.gao.gov/products/GAO-08-932T; US Government Accountability Office, 'The United

States Lacks Comprehensive Plan to Destroy the Terrorist Threat and Close the Safe Haven in Pakistan's Federally Administered Tribal Areas', GAO-08-622, April 2008, http://nationalsecurity.oversight.house.gov/documents/20080417120235.pdf; Craig Cohen, *A Perilous Course: U.S. Strategy and Assistance to Pakistan* (Washington DC: CSIS, 2007).

4 Cohen and Chollet, 'When $10 Billion Is Not Enough'; Greg Miller, 'Pakistan Fails to Aim Billions in U.S. Military Aid at al Qaeda', *Los Angeles Times*, 5 November 2007, p. A1; Kathy Gannon, 'Billions in US Aid Never Reached Pakistan Army', *Washington Post*, 4 October 2009, http://www.washingtonpost.com/wp-dyn/content/article/2009/10/04/AR2009100401260.html.

5 In recent months, Pakistani officials have increasingly begun adopting the term 'counter-insurgency' to describe their low-intensity conflict operations. This is likely in response to US focus upon this concept. However, their operational concepts remain consonant with low-intensity conflict even though they have begun to describe these efforts as counter-insurgency.

6 Author discussions with Pakistani senior military officers about their doctrine. In bilateral forums, Pakistani officers will often adopt the language of 'population-centred' counter-insurgency, at least in part because it is expected and in part to defuse accumulating US concerns about Pakistani efficacy, over which the military leadership has become very defensive. See, for example, 'Pak Army Needs No Foreign Training: COAS', *The Nation*, 16 May 2009, http://www.nation.com.pk/pakistan-news-newspaper-daily-english-online/Regional/Islamabad/16-May-2009/Pak-Army-needs-no-foreign-training-COAS.

7 A June 2009 poll (in which one of the authors, CF, collaborated) suggests that, after the fall of Buner, Pakistani opinion appears to have changed. See Clay Ramsay, Steven Kull, Stephen Weber and Evan Lewis, *Pakistani Public Opinion on the Swat Conflict, Afghanistan, and the US* (Washington DC: PIPA, 2009).

8 Each corps has two or three divisions and is commanded by a lieutenant-general. Each division holds three brigades and is commanded by a major-general. A brigade is commanded by a brigadier and has three or more battalions. A battalion has roughly 600 to 900 soldiers under the command of a lieutenant-colonel. See IISS, *The Military Balance 2009* (London: Routledge, 2009); Federation of Atomic Scientists, 'Pakiston [*sic*]: Total Military Force', http://www.fas.org/programs/ssp/man/militarysumfolder/pakistan.html?formAction=297&contentId=165.

9 Ahmed Rashid, 'Pakistan's Worrisome Pullback', *Washington Post*, 6 June 2008, p. A19.

10 See Hassan Abbas, 'Transforming Pakistan's Frontier Corps', *Terrorism Monitor*, vol. 5, no. 6, 30 March 2007.

11 David Kilcullen, *The Accidental Guerrilla: Fighting Small Wars in the Midst of a Big One* (New York: Oxford University Press, 2009), p. 57. For an account from 2004 involving the Tochi Scouts, see M. Ilyas Khan, 'Mixed

Signals', *Herald*, March 2004, pp. 63–5. For recent revelations about Frontier Corps complicity and a recent US attack on Frontier Corps positions firing on US troops in Afghanistan, see Peter Beaumont and Mark Townsend, 'Pakistan Troops "Aid Taliban": New Classified US Documents Reveal that Mass Infiltration of Frontier Corps by Afghan Insurgents is Helping Latest Offensive', *Observer*, 22 June 2008.

12 Author interviews in Pakistan in February and April 2009.

13 Hassan Abbas, *Police and Law Enforcement Reform in Pakistan: Crucial for Counterinsurgency and Counterterrorism Success*, Report of the Institute for Social Policy and Understanding, April 2009, http://belfercenter.ksg.harvard.edu/publication/18976/police_law_enforcement_reform_in_pakistan.html?breadcrumb=/experts/850/hassan_abbas.

14 See Frontier Police, 'Incentive for Martyred Families', http://frontierpolice.gon.pk/PoliceWelfare/index.php.

15 Paul Wiseman and Zafar M. Sheikh, 'Pakistani Police Underfunded, Overwhelmed', *USA Today*, 5 May 2009, http://www.usatoday.com/news/world/2009-05-05-pakistancops_N.htm.

16 These objectives were ironed out during negotiations in September 2001. Washington used both carrots and sticks: it agreed to waive sanctions and provide military and non-military aid, promised to forgive $2 billion of Pakistan's debt, and doled out millions of dollars in 'prize money' for the capture of al-Qaeda members, but also issued a veiled threat of military force if Pakistan did not cooperate. Following blunt messages from US Secretary of State Colin Powell and his deputy Richard Armitage, then President and Chief of Army Staff Pervez Musharraf acknowledged that he 'war-gamed the United States as an adversary'. He concluded that 'our military forces would be destroyed'. See, for example, Cohen and Chollet, 'When $10 Billion is Not Enough'. See also Pervez Musharraf, *In the Line of Fire: A Memoir* (New York: Free Press, 2006), pp. 201–2.

17 Author interview with Wendy Chamberlin, US ambassador to Pakistan, 27 August 2008. See, for example, the negotiations as outlined in Bob Woodward, *Bush at War* (New York: Simon & Schuster, 2002), p. 59. Also see Musharraf, *In the Line of Fire*, pp. 201–7.

18 An elite special-operations force within the army, the Special Services Group, was created in 1956 with active US support.

19 For detailed accounts of Pakistan's assistance, see C. Christine Fair, *The Counterterror Coalitions: Cooperation with Pakistan and India* (Santa Monica, CA: RAND, 2004) and Gary Berntsen and Ralph Pezzullo, *Jawbreaker: The Attack on Bin Laden and Al-Qaeda* (New York: Crown Publishers, 2005), p. 305. Berntsen commanded the CIA team in Afghanistan in late 2001, taking over from Gary Schroen.

20 Rahimullah Yusufzai, 'Fall of the Last Frontier?', *Newsline* (Pakistan), June 2002.

21 On *Operation Anaconda* see, for example, US Air Force, Office of

Lessons Learned (AF/XOL), *Operation Anaconda: An Air Power Perspective* (Washington DC: Headquarters United States Air Force AF/XOL, February 2005); Paul L. Hastert, 'Operation Anaconda: Perception Meets Reality in the Hills of Afghanistan', *Studies in Conflict and Terrorism*, vol. 28, no. 1, January–February 2005, pp. 11–20; and Sean Naylor, *Not a Good Day to Die: The Untold Story of Operation Anaconda* (New York: Berkley Books, 2005).

22 International Crisis Group, *Pakistan's Tribal Areas: Appeasing the Militants* (Brussels: ICG, December 2006), p. 14.

23 Zaffar Abbas, 'Operation Eyewash', *Herald*, August 2005, p. 64.

24 Author interview with Robert Grenier, CIA station chief in Islamabad, Washington DC, 6 November 2007.

25 Ashley J. Tellis, *Pakistan and the War on Terror: Conflicted Goals, Compromised Performance* (Washington DC: Carnegie Endowment for International Peace, 2008), p. 7.

26 In June 2002, for example, al-Qaeda militants attacked the Pakistani army in Azam Warsak, near Wana in South Waziristan, killing nearly a dozen soldiers. 'Descent Into Anarchy', *Herald*, March 2004, p. 62.

27 *Ibid.*

28 ICG, *Pakistan's Tribal Areas*, p. 14.

29 Amir Mohammad Khan, 'Spiralling into Chaos', *Newsline* (Pakistan), March 2004, p. 34–6.

30 M. Ilyas Khan, 'Who Are These People?', *Herald*, April 2004, pp. 60–68.

31 Khan, 'Spiralling Into Chaos'.

32 Khan, 'Who are these People?'; Sailab Mahsud, 'Caught in the Crossfire', *Herald*, April 2004, p. 66–7.

33 Mahsud, 'Caught in the Crossfire'.

34 Musharraf, *In the Line of Fire*, pp. 269–70.

35 Rahimullah Yusufzai, 'Whose Country is it Anyway?', *Herald*, February 2006, pp. 27–32; 'Hit and Run', *Herald*, February 2006, p. 58; Intikhab Amir, 'Waziristan: No Man's Land?', *Herald*, April 2006, p. 78.

36 The Pakistani army tried to depict these deals as part of long-standing precedent in the region, noting that the British negotiated with local Pashtun tribes in the North-West Frontier Province during their rule (see, for example, Christian Tripodi, 'Peacemaking through Bribes or Cultural Empathy? The Political Officer and Britain's Strategy towards the North-West Frontier, 1901–1945', *Journal of Strategic Studies*, vol. 31, no. 1, March–April 2008, pp. 123–51). However, the Pakistani deals differ in many serious ways from those of the British.

37 Author discussions in Pakistan.

38 Locals denied the existence of the last clause, and argued that they did not agree to register all foreigners with the government.

39 Mariam Abou Zahab, 'Changing Patterns of Social and Political Life Among the Tribal Pashtuns in Pakistan', unpublished paper, 2007. As Zahab notes, weapons were not surrendered but rather 'offered', and after the recent deal 'exchanged'.

40 Khan, 'Who are these People?'; Owais Tohid, 'The New Frontier', *Newsline* (Pakistan), April 2004; Ismail Khan, 'Five Militants Pardoned for Peaceful Life: Aliens Asked to Surrender by 30th', *Dawn*, 25 April 2004, http://

www.dawn.com/2004/04/25/top1.htm.

41 For a discussion of traditional *jirga* practices see Zahab, 'Changing Patterns'.

42 Iqbal Khattak, 'I Did Not Surrender to the Military, Sayd Nek Mohammad', *Friday Times*, 30 April–6 May 2004.

43 Ismail Khan and Dilawar Khan Wazir, 'Night Raid Kills Nek, Four other Militants', *Dawn*, 19 June 2004; Khattak, 'I Did Not Surrender'.

44 Pakistan Army, General Headquarters, Military Operations Directorate, *Record on Pakistan's War on Terror as of 28 December 2006*.

45 Ahmed Rashid, *Descent into Chaos: The United States and the Failure of Nation Building in Pakistan, Afghanistan, and Central Asia* (New York: Viking, 2008), p. 270.

46 Intikhab Amir, 'Whose Writ is it Anyway', *Herald*, April 2006, pp. 80–82.

47 'Accord in Bajaur to Curb Terrorists', *Dawn*, 31 May 2005; 'The Bajaur Massacre', *Dawn*, 1 November 2006; Mohammad Ali, 'Peace Deal in Bajaur Soon, Says Aurakzai', *Dawn*, 24 February 2007.

48 Joby Warrick, 'CIA Places Blame for Bhutto Assassination', *Washington Post*, 18 January 2008, p. A01.

49 According to a Pakistan army account, 'about 200 militants charged the fort from four sides … they broke through the fort's wall with rockets'. 'Militants Overrun Pakistan Fort', BBC News, 17 January 2008. See also 'Pakistani Troops "Flee Border Post"', al-Jazeera, 17 January 2008.

50 'Al-Jazeera TV Interviews Pakistan Taleban Chief', BBC, 29 May 2008.

51 'Taliban Chief Ideologist Survives "Zalzala"', *Daily Times*, 26 May 2008.

52 *Ibid.*; Iqbal Khattak, 'Army in Waziristan Better Equipped, More Relaxed', *Daily Times*, 21 May 2008.

53 Iqbal Khattak, 'Pakistan: Mehsud says Local Taliban to begin Media War; Slams Reporter's Murder', *Daily Times*, 27 May 2008.

54 Khattak, 'Army in Waziristan Better Equipped'.

55 Zaffar Abbas, 'Taliban Ousted, but Spinkai is now a Ghost Town', *Dawn*, 19 May 2008.

56 Author interviews with Pakistani and British government officials, Islamabad, April 2009.

57 Abbas, 'Taliban Ousted'.

58 *Ibid.*

59 Zulfiqar Ali, 'Over 4,000 Houses Destroyed in Waziristan Operation: Report', *Dawn*, 8 November 2008; Iqbal Khattak, 'Deserted Town shows Human Cost of Operation Zalzala', *Daily Times*, 20 May 2008.

60 Abbas, 'Taliban Ousted'; see also Declan Walsh, 'Demolished by the Pakistan Army: The Frontier Village Punished for Harboring the Taliban', *Guardian*, 20 May 2008.

61 Author interviews with Pakistani and British government officials, Pakistan, April 2009.

62 Amir Mir, 'Story Behind Manawan Fidayee Attack', *News*, 1 April 2009.

63 Author interviews with Pakistan and British government officials, Pakistan, May 2009.

64 Pakistan Institute for Peace Studies, *Pakistan Security Report 2008* (Islamabad: Pakistan Institute for Peace Studies, 2009), p. 3.

65 Stephen Graham, 'Ghost Village Haunts Pakistani Plans to Make Peace with Tribal Militants', Associated Press, 19 May 2008.

66 Anwarullah Khan, 'ISI Official, Three Others Killed in Bajaur Ambush', *Dawn*, 28 March 2007.

67 Mukhtar A. Khan, 'A Profile of Militant Groups in Bajaur Tribal Agency', *Terrorism Monitor*, vol. 7, no. 6, 19 March 2009, p. 1.

68 Anthony Lloyd, 'Captured Battle Plan Shows Strength and Training of Taleban Forces', *Times*, 11 November 2008.

69 Ismail Khan, 'Battle to be Won or Lost in Bajaur', *Dawn*, 21 September 2008.

70 The NWFP government and the TNSM had signed an agreement in May 2007 permitting a TNSM leader, Mauluna Fazlullah ('Mullah Radio'), to continue FM broadcasts, while Fazlullah agreed to support government efforts to maintain law and order, education for girls and polio vaccination. Akhtar Amin, 'Government Moves Additional Army Contingents to Swat', *Daily Times*, 19 October 2007.

71 Khashnud Ali Khan, 'Why and How did the Operation Commence in Mohmand Agency and Bajaur Agency?', *Jinnah*, 30 September 2008.

72 Nizam e Adl Regulation 2009. A copy of the text can be found at 'Text of Pakistan's Shari'ah law 2009', BBC Monitoring South Asia, 14 April 2009.

73 Abdur Rehman Abid, 'Taliban Ambush FC Convoy, Foil Buner Deployment', *Dawn*, 24 April 2009; Daud Khattak and Delawar Jan, 'Operation against Taliban on Government Mind', *News*, 24 April 2009; 'Taliban turn Troops back from Mingora', *News*, 26 April 2009; Abdur Rehman Abid, 'Buner Falls to Swat Taliban', *Dawn*, 22 April 2009; Ghulam Farooq, 'Taliban Step into Shangla as Buner Showdown Looms', *Daily Times*, 24 April 2009.

74 Zahid Hussain, 'From Much Sought After to "Most Wanted"', *Dawn*, 31 May 2009.

75 Iftikhar A. Khan, 'Security Forces Advance on Strategic Kamber Bridge', *Dawn*, 21 May 2009; Iftikhar A. Khan, 'Army Takes "Complete Control" over Mingora', *Dawn*, 30 May 2009.

76 Author interviews with non-governmental organisation personnel in Pakistan, May 2009; International Committee of the Red Cross, *Pakistan: ICRC and Pakistan Red Crescent Substantially Expanding Operations*, News Release 09/116 (Islamabad: International Committee of the Red Cross, June 2009); Office of the United Nations High Commissioner for Refugees, *Newly Displaced Pakistani Civilians Report Grim Conditions in Swat Valley* (Islamabad: Office of the United Nations High Commissioner for Refugees, June 2009).

77 Interview with Maulana Abdul Khaliq Haqqani in the *Herald*, July 2007, pp. 66–7.

78 This discussion draws from C. Christine Fair, 'Pakistan's Own War on Terror: What the Pakistani Public Thinks', *Journal of International Affairs*, vol. 63, no. 1, Autumn–Winter 2009 (forthcoming).

79 Author interviews in Pakistan in July 2007, February 2008, April 2008, February 2009 and April 2009. See also various polls on the army's popularity

and that of Musharraf conducted by the International Republic Institute at http://www.iri.org/mena/pakistan.asp.

80 See C. Christine Fair, Clay Ramsay and Steve Kull, *Pakistani Public Opinion on Democracy, Islamist Militancy, and Relations with the U.S.* (Washington DC: USIP/PIPA, 7 January 2008).

81 *Ibid.*

82 International Republican Institute (IRI), 'IRI Index: Pakistan Public Opinion Survey', 15–30 October 2008, http://www.iri.org/mena/Pakistan.asp.

83 IRI, 'IRI Releases Survey of Pakistan Public Opinion, March 7–30, 2009', 11 May 2009, http://www.iri.org/newsreleases/2009-05-11-Pakistan.asp. Notably, more recent polling data from June 2009 suggest significant public shifts in opinion with respect to military operations and peace deals. However, the period of coverage of that poll exceeds the timeline of this study. See Fair et al., *Pakistani Public Opinion.*

84 Fair et al., *Pakistani Public Opinion.*

85 C. Christine Fair, 'From Strategy to Implementation: The Future of the U.S.–Pakistan Relationship', testimony presented before the House Foreign Affairs Committee on 5 May 2009; Hassan Abbas, 'Police & Law Enforcement Reform in Pakistan Crucial for Counterinsurgency and Counterterrorism Success', Institute for Social Policy and Understanding, 2009, http://www.ispu.org/files/PDFs/ISPU - Police Reforms in Pakistan Report.pdf; C. Christine Fair and Peter Chalk, *Fortifying Pakistan: The Role of US Security Assistance to Pakistan* (Washington DC: USIP, 2006).

86 Seth G. Jones and Martin C. Libicki, *How Terrorist Groups End: Lessons for Countering al-Qa'ida* (Santa Monica, CA: RAND, 2008); C. Christine Fair and Sumit Ganguly, *Treading on Hallowed Ground: Counterinsurgency Operations in Sacred Spaces* (New York: Oxford University Press, 2008).

Forum

Progress, Dissent and Counter-Insurgency: An Exchange

Editor's note

In the August–September 2009 issue of *Survival* (vol. 51, no. 4, pp. 31–48), Philipp Rotmann, David Tohn and Jaron Wharton argued that the US military's change to a counter-insurgency posture in the on-going conflicts in Afghanistan and Iraq was catalysed by two products of an institutional culture that strove to be self-learning: the response of junior leadership to tactical problems and senior institutional dissidents driving deep, controversial changes in doctrine and culture. In this *Survival* Exchange two experts offer US and European perspectives on the authors' argument and recommendations to preserve and advance this dynamic in anticipation of future requirements for rapid change. A response from Rotmann, Tohn and Wharton concludes the debate.

Learning, Adapting and the Perils of the New Counter-insurgency

Gian P. Gentile

The essay 'Learning Under Fire: Progress and Dissent in the US Military' by Philipp Rotmann, David Tohn and Jaron Wharton is a perfect exposition of the current paradigm of war that the US Army has, over the last three years, come to embrace. For those who want to understand how the American army thinks about itself and about war and conflict in general, this essay is the place to start.

The authors set out all the stock explanations for the US Army's failings at counter-insurgency over the last 40 years and its recent triumphal suc-

Gian P. Gentile is a serving US Army Colonel and currently runs the Military History Program at West Point. He commanded a combat battalion in Baghdad in 2006.

 DOI 10.1080/00396330903461724

cesses in Iraq following the 'surge' of troops that started in February 2007, and the promise of carrying that triumph through to Afghanistan. Their essential argument is that efforts to bring about change within a hidebound, conventionally minded army by a band of hard-charging, Young Turk army officers currently fighting in Iraq and Afghanistan combined with a move from the top by certain inspired senior officers who also wanted to change the recalcitrant army. The combination of these groups enveloped, from top to bottom, an American army that, the authors suggest, only wanted to fight 'big-battle' conflicts such as the Second World War and *Operation Desert Storm* (1991). These two groups, however, shocked the big-battle army into a phase of deep learning so that the US Army, along with other parts of the US military, is now on the right track. In short, the essay is a tale of an army that figured out how to learn, adapt and win at counter-insurgency.

The thrust of the authors' argument is the necessity for an army, as an organisation, to 'learn and adapt' at the tactical, operational and strategic levels while engaged in conflict. And with the introduction of the US Army's new counter-insurgency doctrine, Field Manual (FM) 3-24, put into practice by the inspired senior leadership of General David Petraeus, the US Army turned on a dime, and as a result succeeded in Iraq. The authors trot out, as exceptional cases of the counter-insurgency 'gets it' club, H.R. McMaster's 3rd Armored Cavalry Regiment in Tal Afar in 2005 and Sean McFarland's 1st Brigade, 1st Armored Division in Ramadi in 2006, which adopted better counter-insurgency practices prior to Petraeus and the surge. In contrast, in the authors' view (shared by counter-insurgency expert Thomas Ricks), the majority of other army units prior to February 2007 dreamt rather of fighting a reincarnated Soviet army in the Sunni Triangle.[1] Officers such as Petraeus, McMaster and McFarland seem to personify the ability to 'learn and adapt'. In fact one can argue that this organisational mindset has taken over the US Army and other parts of the military. Yet there are deep, fundamental and potentially dangerous flaws with this paradigm that Rotmann, Tohn and Wharton overlook in their zeal to portray the positive.

Any military engaged in combat must, of course, learn and adapt; only a fool would argue otherwise. What great captains of past wars, both regular and irregular, failed to grasp that they had to adapt in the face of a hostile enemy force at all levels of war in order to succeed? King Frederick II of Prussia, known as 'Frederick the Great', made critical errors at the battle of Mollwitz in 1741 with the tactical disposition of his army, and learned from that battle and others the importance of terrain selection and an appreciation for tactical flexibility and combined arms in combat. American combat battalions facing staunch German infantry opposition in the hedgerows of Normandy in summer 1944 adapted through tactical innovation and under inspired leadership from generals such as Norm 'Dutch' Cota. The US Army in Iraq in spring and summer 2003 very quickly shifted from major combat operations against Saddam Hussein's army to full-spectrum operations, and by the end of 2003 were also employing best practices for counter-insurgency.[2] Armies that do not learn and adapt, however, can suffer catastrophic defeat, as the French Army did in June 1940 when it tried to halt the German onslaught with an army built on flawed lessons drawn from the First World War.

Armies learned because they knew how to fight

So what allows successful armies to learn and adapt quickly to the problems that confront them? History shows that this ability has not been driven by a paradigmatic mindset, but rather by grounding in the core competencies of combined-arms fighting at all organisational levels. Armies learned and adapted because they knew how to fight, because they knew how to combine arms in the face of hostile enemy foes. From the core competencies of combined-arms warfare comes the inherent ability to gain and maintain the initiative, and from the initiative – the ability to act first – comes the ability to adapt. The process does not work in reverse, yet Rotmann, Tohn and Wharton seem to think that accepting the paradigm, along with all its concomitant theories of organisational change, myths of past counter-insurgency campaigns and hagiographic generals, will be enough for success in future conflicts.

The idea of learning and adapting has placed the US Army in a conceptual straitjacket. While the driving theme of a previous US Army doctrinal manual from 1986 was how to gain the initiative, as Conrad Crane, one of the principle authors of FM 3-24, has stated, the driving theme throughout this vaunted doctrine is for the army to be able to 'learn and adapt'.[3]

But the problem is that this must perforce be in the direction of better population-centric counter-insurgency, which in practice is nation building at the barrel of American guns. The rules of the paradigm do not allow a reverse gear; a military organisation cannot learn and adapt its way out of doing population-centric counter-insurgency. Given the permeating effect of the paradigm as put forward by FM 3-24 on the rest of the US Army, this is worrisome indeed: it has dangerously eclipsed America's ability to develop strategy.

Petraeus recently noted the differences between Iraq and Afghanistan, but in the same breadth he said the principles of counter-insurgency 'learned' in Iraq (starting, naturally, after February 2007) are applicable to Afghanistan.[4] The United States has thus devolved to a strategy of tactics, allowing tactics and operations to eclipse strategy and the consideration of alternatives. As Chinese philosopher Sun Tzu put it, 'strategy without tactics is the slow road to victory', but 'tactics without strategy is the noise before defeat'.[5] Essays such as Rotmann, Tohn and Wharton's that present the idea of creativity, adaptability and initiative through the paradigm of an army that learns and adapts are, paradoxically, examples of how hidebound and straitjacketed the US Army has become toward its new way of counter-insurgency warfare.

The American army needs to get back to basics. Of course it needs to learn and adapt, but first and foremost it must be able to fight through combined-arms competencies. Rotmann, Tohn and Wharton, like so many others of the counter-insurgency persuasion, want to make the US Army feel guilty about its competencies to fight conventional wars, because they believe it was that very ability that made it difficult to conduct counter-insurgency and stability operations in Iraq and Afghanistan. But armies that are trained and proficient in combined-arms warfare are more able to adapt to counter-insurgency and other forms of irregular warfare than the other way around. Israel's experience in south Lebanon in summer 2006 shows what happens to an army when it focuses over-much on counter-insurgency warfare and loses the ability to combine arms. All the learning and adapting in the world could not get Israeli combat units up and moving once entangled with a Hizbullah enemy that stood and fought. If it is not careful, the US Army is heading down the same road with its fetishisation of learning and adapting.

Notes

1 See Thomas Ricks, *Fiasco: The American Military Adventure in Iraq* (New York: Penguin, 2006).

2 See Donald P. Wright and Timothy R. Reese, *On Point II: Transition to the New Campaign. The United States Army in Operation Iraqi Freedom, May 2003–January 2005* (Fort Leavenworth, KS: Combat Studies Institute Press, 2008).

3 For the 1986 manual, see Huba Wass de Czege and L.D. Holder, 'The New FM 100-5', *Military Review*, June 1982. For FM 3-24, see Department of the Army, *Field Manual 3-24, Counterinsurgency* (Washington DC, Headquarters Department of the Army, 2006); also Conrad Crane, personal communication. Holder and Crane were principal authors on the respective manuals.

4 From Fred W. Baker III, 'Petraeus Parallels Iraq, Afghanistan Strategies', American Forces Press Service, 28 April 2009.

5 Sun Tzu, *The Art of War*, trans. Samuel B. Griffith (London: Oxford University Press, 1963).

Counter-insurgency and the Allies

Thomas Rid

Philipp Rotmann, David Tohn and Jaron Wharton argue that two 'active ingredients' have critically contributed to the US military's successes in Iraq: the 'happy coincidence' of a 'proactive' and empowered junior cadre, and a senior cadre of 'institutional dissidents'. Together these groups helped turn the armed services into a 'self-learning organisation'. To bring about the necessary innovation in counter-insurgency doctrine and practice, 'it took activism from both ends of the leadership spectrum to force the middle to change'. The practical success of these organisational and doctrinal changes will be 'tested' in Afghanistan.

Thomas Rid is a Fritz Thyssen Fellow at the Shalem Center and at Hebrew University in Jerusalem.

Institutionally, the US Army and Marine Corps still seem to be less adapted to counter-insurgency than the authors imply. Discussions and doctrines on counter-insurgency are one thing, implementing these principles while being shot at is another. Yet their argument has a lot of merit. And it highlights a development with important consequences for America's European allies. Can the same happy coincidence be replicated in Britain's or Germany's armed forces? The answer has to grapple with an aspect of both wars neglected by the authors. Empowered and innovative commanders have made the US military more effective, but so did a laissez-faire approach by Washington's political elite at home and an inept enemy in the field in Iraq. The three combined reasons make it unlikely that America's allies can duplicate the counter-insurgency revolution in Afghanistan.

America's allies are unlikely to duplicate the counter-insurgency revolution

The security situation in Iraq deteriorated steeply in the three years following the invasion. Increasing numbers of casualties, both military and civilian and both American and Iraqi, increased the pressure to adapt and act. The 'surge', as Thomas Ricks and others have chronicled, happened perhaps not despite but because of a political leadership that seemed unsure what to do. Neither George W. Bush's White House nor the Pentagon under Donald Rumsfeld seem to have been where a new strategy for Iraq, or rather a new operational approach to counter the insurgency, was hatched.[1] Instead, in the critical phases of the Iraq War, not only the execution of strategy but also a great deal of the critical decision-making and the overall design of national security policy increasingly devolved to military commanders. The surge could be seen, to put it more provocatively, as the outcome of a beneficial crisis in civil–military relations.

When the administration of President Barack Obama took office, it fulfilled one of the new president's campaign promises and shifted attention from the seemingly successful 'bad' war in Iraq to the deteriorating but 'good' war in Afghanistan. But while Obama's civilian national-security team was new to the job and relatively unfamiliar with the on-going operations, the opposite was true for the military establishment.[2] Its most prominent generals, David Petraeus and Stanley McChrystal, exuded a near-heroic authority in national-security affairs that the White House had difficulty countering. When some senior military officials took the discussion about the best strategy for Afghanistan public, both anonymously and with attribution, they put the nation's civilian decision-makers under notable political pressure to follow their advice, perhaps even to the point of raising serious questions of civil–military oversight in a twenty-first-century counter-insurgency environment.[3]

This situation contrasts sharply with the non-American part of the International Security Assistance Force (ISAF). Europe's armies cannot match America's resources in men, materiel and money, and most NATO armies are already at the limit of what they can contribute in Afghanistan. But logistical limitations are only one side of the coin. In no other country of the Atlantic Alliance do generals and admirals and their current and former staffs have comparable influence on national policymaking and the surrounding debates. Military establishments in Europe tend to be much weaker politically, while the public tends to be more sceptical of counter-insurgency and the opposition parties in national parliaments less supportive. This could spell trouble for NATO. The more the operation in Afghanistan is Americanised, the more likely the Atlantic Alliance will find itself headed towards a wicked dilemma: in the case of failure, Americans will find it hard to not to blame allies; in the case of success, many US officers might conclude that they succeeded not because of allied help, but in spite of it.[4]

Perhaps even more importantly, the enemy in Iraq unwittingly played into the hands of the coalition. The success of the surge was, to some extent, the outcome of a development that started even before the strategic and doctrinal reorientation of US land operations. The 'Awakening' movement that spread across Baghdad and Iraq started in Anbar Province, where the attitudes of the local tribes had already begun to shift in early 2005. 'This shift in the strategic calculus of the tribes made a successful US–Iraqi tribal strategy possible', Austin Long wrote in *Survival* in 2008.[5]

Scholars and analysts have singled out a number of triggers for the Awakening: al-Qaeda's excessive use of brutality and violence, such as the killing of Sheikh Sattar Abdul Abu Risha's family; tribal loyalties and al-Qaeda's marriage policies;[6] the battle of Falluja in November 2004;[7] the Iraqi elections in January 2005; Sunni sheikhs' concerns about loss of power and sources of revenue to the foreign intruders; or a combination of these.[8] What is not controversial, however, is that the Anbar Awakening started before the surge and was caused to a significant extent by the tactical blunders of al-Qaeda in Mesopotamia. The conditions for one of the most important operational developments of the Iraq War were rooted in complex tribal relations and local history, not principally in general counter-insurgency doctrine and practice, although US forces did subsequently facilitate the spread of the movement.

The situation Rotmann, Tohn and Wharton describe might be an historical exception rather than the rule. In war, both politics and the enemy have a vote, and both might limit the military's room for manoeuvre in a way that makes it much more difficult to implement boilerplate counter-insurgency lessons.

Although the US military is now widely considered well prepared for counter-insurgency operations, Rotmann, Tohn and Wharton write, 'whether or not it can succeed in practice will be seen in Afghanistan'. But applying Iraqi lessons to Afghanistan is a fraught approach for at least three reasons.

Firstly, the mission is fundamentally different. The objective in Iraq always has been more limited than the goal in Afghanistan. When Iraq was at the brink of civil war in 2006, the goal was to pull the country back from the abyss and to restore the status quo ante — stability and security — albeit with a new and preferably democratic government. In Afghanistan, the goal has always been more ambitious: 'to defeat, disrupt, and destroy' al-Qaeda, in Obama's words, and to prevent Afghanistan from again becoming a 'safe-haven' for terrorists. The goal, in other words, is to overcome the status quo ante, not to restore it.

Secondly, the adversary is different. The main enemy, al-Qaeda, has morphed from a hierarchical organisation into a vague entity that is more difficult to describe. Experts vehemently disagree on whether jihad in the twenty-first century is still managed by a central cadre of leaders.[9] It is highly questionable that Salafism can be 'defeated' or 'destroyed' in Afghanistan and Pakistan. In Iraq, the relationship between counter-terrorism and counter-insurgency was less jumbled and twisted than it is in Afghanistan, both tactically and strategically. How, precisely, countering the Afghan insurgency, even if successful, will counter and disrupt global terrorism remains an open question.

Finally, conditions for success are difficult to replicate across ISAF. A remarkable coincidence brought about the rise of counter-insurgency in the US military at a moment of immense stress and strain. It is highly unlikely that history will repeat itself for America's allies in Afghanistan and beyond. NATO's European land forces and their operations in Afghanistan lack a number of essential ingredients: most European armies do not have the same cadre of strong-willed and Iraq-tested junior officers in combination with senior dissidents, but they also lack two further elements: the political clout in domestic capitals and the same degree of doctrinal and operational freedom. And in Afghanistan NATO does not benefit from an equally inept enemy; the various Taliban sub-groups (increasingly in coalition with hardened mujahadeen fighters, their former enemies[10]) seem more capable than al-Qaeda in Mesopotamia and certainly much older and better established in the complex patchwork of Afghanistan's local cultures.

The US land forces might be 'knowledge-based' organisations that 'learn under fire', albeit within limits. But organisational self-examination has limited utility in grappling with multinational counter-insurgency in Afghanistan and global counter-terrorism beyond.

Notes

1 Thomas Ricks, *The Gamble: General David Petraeus and the American Military Adventure in Iraq, 2006–2008* (London: Penguin, 2009).

2 See George Packer, 'The Last Mission,' *The New Yorker*, 26 September 2009, pp. 38–55.

3 Bruce Ackerman, 'A General's Public Pressure', *Washington Post*, 3 October 2009.

4 Various discussions on background with US participants at a major counter-insurgency conference, 'Irregular War', US Naval War College, Newport, Rhode Island, 15–16 September 2009.

5 Austin Long, 'The Anbar Awakening', *Survival: Global Politics and Strategy*, vol. 50, no. 2, April–May 2008, p. 78.

6 See David Kilcullen's description at http://smallwarsjournal.com/blog/2007/08/anatomy-of-a-tribal-revolt/.

7 Long, 'The Anbar Awakening', p. 77.

8 John A. McCary, 'The Anbar Awakening: An Alliane of Incentives', *Washington Quarterly*, vol. 32, no. 1, January 2009, p. 44.

9 Bruce Hoffman, 'The Myth of Grass-Roots Terrorism: Why Osama bin Laden Still Matters', *Foreign Affairs*, vol. 87, no. 3, May–June 2008, pp. 133–8; Marc Sageman, *Leaderless Jihad* (Philadelphia, PA: University of Pennsylvania Press, 2008); Marc Sageman and Bruce Hoffman, 'Does Osama Still Call the Shots? Debating the Containment of al-Qaeda's Leadership', *Foreign Affairs*, vol. 87, no. 4, July–August, 2008, pp. 163–7.

10 Thomas Ruttig, 'The Other Side', Afghanistan Analysts Network Thematic Report no. 1, July 2009, http://www.aan-afghanistan.org/uploads/200907 AAN Report Ruttig – The Other Side.pdf.

Response

Philipp Rotmann, David Tohn and Jaron Wharton

Gian Gentile and Thomas Rid address a number of salient issues. Gentile's warning is well taken: nothing is won if the military ends up replacing the combined-arms hammer, to which every problem looks like a nail, with a counter-insurgency screwdriver to which every problem looks like the right kind of screw. The adoption of population-centric counter-insurgency in Iraq did, as Rid points out, allow the US military to exploit the opportunity provided by the Anbar Awakening, which should make it a welcome addition to the doctrinal toolkit, and one that was notably absent before. Whether

Philipp Rotmann is a McCloy Scholar at the John F. Kennedy School of Government, Harvard University, and a fellow at the Global Public Policy Institute in Berlin and Geneva. He is a co-author of the forthcoming *Learning to Build Peace? UN Peace Operations and Organizational Learning*. **Colonel David Tohn**, a veteran of operations in Iraq, Haiti and Somalia, is an active-duty Military Intelligence Officer in the United States Army and a National Security Fellow at the John F. Kennedy School of Government, Harvard University. He is a co-author of *On Point: The United States Army in Operation Iraqi Freedom*. **Captain Jaron Wharton** currently serves as a Public Service Fellow at the John F. Kennedy School of Government. He is an active-duty infantry officer in the US Army and served in Afghanistan (2002) and Iraq (2003–06). The views expressed in this article are those of the authors and do not reflect the official policy or positions of Harvard University, the US Government, the Department of Defense or the United States Army.

that tool is appropriate for the situation in Afghanistan today, the major policy question lurking behind several of the points raised by Gentile and Rid, is a different question. At the same time, Gentile's question as to how a military develops and maintains the ability to do operational-level planning is valid. We know what the operational level looks like in a conventional war; do we know what it looks like in a counter-insurgency environment? This a legitimate question that the military intelligentsia ought to explore.

Since a counter-insurgency strategy has been adopted in Afghanistan, Rid raises another important strategic issue: will our allies be able to similarly adapt while in contact with a resourceful and persistent enemy, especially given their respective political and social constraints? This is a crucial question, since the coalition in Afghanistan must sustain a level of operational homogeneity for the current strategy to have a chance of success. It is necessary to understand that nations will likely come to the fight with caveats, to welcome their contributions and to move on. Barring a fundamental retooling, coalition partners need to tackle missions closely suited to their current strengths for them to be operationally relevant and effective. But, as Winston Churchill put it, 'there is at least one thing worse than fighting with allies – and that is to fight without them'.[1]

Training equally along the full spectrum of warfare is difficult

Gentile's concerns about the inherent risks to core warfighting competencies at the expense of the strategic theory *du jour* are certainly warranted, especially in a resource-constrained environment. These comments reflect the healthy scepticism within professional military thinking about sacrificing core conventional warfighting skills for a 'boutique' capability and represent real concerns about what the next war will look like and how long it would take to rebuild those skills. The military does need to maintain its core competencies, but training equally along the full spectrum of warfare is difficult given the strain of current operations. However, as long as the US military remains engaged in a counter-insurgency war, such training will remain necessary, along with creative ways of limiting the trade-offs as much as possible.

The argument that mastering conventional combined arms is all that is necessary for success echoes the flawed arguments of the 1990s that counter-insurgency (like nation building, peacekeeping or stability operations) is a secondary skill set automatically covered by an army that mastered the core, 'hard' things. The persistence of this argument is interesting, given that nearly every US military operation since *Desert Storm* in 1991 has marked a move away from pure combined-arms operations to something else, and that the rise of the insurgency in Iraq owes at least partly to the inadequacy of the US-led coalition's military occupation. Of course, the discipline, leadership and enabling equipment and organisation developed and honed in preparing for combined-arms operations are the same core characteristics and abilities that enabled successes later, but these are part of the army's core institutional culture that enables change.

Many of Gentile's and Rid's comments focus on the relevancy and effectiveness of the specific counter-insurgency strategy rather than the main thesis about learning and dissent. Most troubling is Gentile's assertion that learning and adaptive leadership are inextricably linked to the specific strategy of counter-insurgency, with all the associated risks, real and imagined. By extension, one could conclude that a learning and adaptive leadership cadre is contrary to good old-fashioned combined-arms fighting – 'nation building at the barrel of American guns'.

Military leaders such as David Petraeus, Stanley McChrystal and Raymond Odierno have emerged as a cadre of adaptive leaders who acknowledge that all things good do not happen solely through the application of combined-arms warfare. For example, McChrystal's July 2009 tactical directive limits the application of combined-arms warfare in order to fundamentally change the operational culture in which the military has operated in Afghanistan. This has led to a marked decrease in civilian casualties, recognising the Afghan people as the centre of gravity. The adaptive junior cadre, many of them veterans of the Iraq conflict, understand this and are responding accordingly. We heartily agree with Gentile that 'any military engaged in combat must, of course, learn and adapt; only a fool would argue otherwise'.

Our essay in *Survival* was a critical view on *how* the military changed since 11 September 2001, not an assessment of the ultimate efficacy of the chosen strategic solution, population-centric counter-insurgency, operationally and tactically implemented following Army and Marine Corps Field Manual 3-24. Whether that solution was the best or only option available in Iraq, or in Afghanistan today, is an open question. Rather, we detailed what we believe was a success story of innovation, mainly on the tactical and operational levels, by a historically rigid institution – but an institution that already had some established mechanisms to embrace internal criticism. The catalysts for change were both bottom-up (necessary but insufficient) and top-down (sufficient but ultimately driven by necessity). The bottom-up component provided an indispensable source of ideas, experimental innovation and pressure for change, a body of experience that informed senior leaders to make fundamental changes in how the army trains, equips and fights. But it was the top down that locked this change in.

This was not the case just a generation ago. Then Andrew Krepinevich was scorned for his assertion that 'the Army (after Vietnam) ended up trying to fight the kind of conventional war that it was trained, organized, and prepared for (and that it wanted to fight) instead of the [counter-insurgency] war that it was sent to fight'.[3] He was actually banned by the superintendant of West Point from speaking at the academy.[1] In contrast, today you can (as the army's Training and Doctrine Command recently announced) edit selected manuals 'wiki-style' or collaboratively. The Supreme Allied Commander Europe, Admiral James Stavridis, welcomes Facebook friends, and the chairman of the Joint Chiefs of Staff, Admiral Michael Mullen, recently announced a YouTube channel. This, of course, raises the question of how much 'free speech' is too much, but it also engages *all* of the military's intellectual capital to seriously address fundamental challenges. And, for the long term, it reinforces the cultural imperative that change will always be necessary and that every leader has a stake and a role in achieving it. The United States military, as an institution, may not be afforded the luxury of several years under fire to enact change in the future.

Notes

1 P.G. Tsouras, *The Dictionary of Military Quotations* (London: Greenhill Books, 2005), p. 30.

2 David Cloud and Greg Jaffe, *The Fourth Star* (New York: Crown Publishing Group, 2009), pp. 62–4.

3 Andrew F. Krepinevich, *The Army and Vietnam* (Baltimore, MD: Johns Hopkins University Press, 1986), p. 271.

Review Essay

Secrets of a Chinese Patriot

Dennis C. Wilder

Prisoner of the State: The Secret Journal of Premier Zhao Ziyang
Bao Pu, Renne Chiang and Adi Ignatius, trans. and eds. New York: Simon & Schuster, 2009. £20.00/$26.00. 306 pp.

When Zhao Ziyang, former general secretary of the Communist Party of China, died on 17 January 2005, China's state media was ordered to publish only a terse announcement, about 50 characters in length, on the inner pages of the major Chinese newspapers. After all, even though Zhao was still a member of the party, 16 years earlier it had found him guilty of 'supporting turmoil' and 'splitting the party' for his attempts to avert the bloodshed of the 4 June 1989 Tiananmen Square crackdown. During his years of house arrest, he had appealed on several occasions for a reversal of the Tiananmen Square verdict, which laid the blame for the Tiananmen protests and their violent outcome on a small group of 'counterrevolutionaries', while at the same time staunchly refusing to admit any wrongdoing. With the publication of *Prisoner of the State*, however, Zhao posthumously has found a way to get a hearing, this time in the court of international opinion.

Zhao's memoir, transcribed from recordings secretly made by Zhao while under house arrest and subsequently smuggled out of China by supporters, is a riveting read for those of us who have spent most of our professional lives trying to discern from afar the opaque inner workings of

Dennis C. Wilder authored this essay while a visiting fellow in the John L. Thornton China Center at the Brookings Institution. He served as China director and then senior director for East Asian affairs at the National Security Council from August 2004 to January 2009.

Survival | vol. 51 no. 6 | December 2009–January 2010 | pp. 203–210 DOI 10.1080/00396330903461732

the Chinese leadership cloistered in the Zhongnanhai complex, and who watched the events of June 1989 unfold with anguish and dismay. Western Sinologists have gleaned what we can from China's news media, but the personal dimensions of Chinese leadership politics have come to us only in rare and fleeting glimpses. To have a first-person account of the internal tensions and struggles of the Chinese Communist Party from the time Zhao became an alternate member of the Politburo in 1977 until his abrupt ouster from power in May 1989 is an unprecedented opportunity for scholars of Chinese politics and history. To be sure, there are glaring omissions in Zhao's memoirs, and those seeking an account of his personal feelings about the events and his interpersonal relationships with the rest of China's top leaders will be disappointed. Zhao is protective of his emotional life and much more comfortable providing a straightforward historical account and reflecting on political theory. Nonetheless, this memoir could well be the inspiration for a new generation of Chinese to fundamentally alter China's political landscape, much as Zhao was a major player in transforming China's economic system.

A government apart

One of the most striking aspects of the book is the way it confirms the profound emotional distance that exists between the Chinese leaders living and working in the Zhongnanhai compound and the population they govern. In my travels to Beijing as part of President George W. Bush's staff, I was fortunate to get a chance to attend meetings at Zhongnanhai. I could only imagine the intrigues and political machinations of the place. The compound's lakeside pavilions, marvels of architectural serenity and tranquillity, belie Zhongnanhai's status as the epicentre of Chinese political power in a teeming metropolis of over 17 million people.

In detailing the political deliberations in the run-up to the Tiananmen atrocity, Zhao never once mentions speaking to any ordinary Chinese about the evolving situation. While his empathy for the student demonstrators is obvious, he only refers to discussions with his family and other members of the party elite. For example, Zhao notes that he got his information on the students' views by requesting and watching visual recordings of their activities and by interviewing the president and vice-president of two of Beijing's most prominent universities. The 'Zhongnanhai bubble' around the senior Chinese leadership exists just as much today as it did in 1989. Many observers criticise the bubble in which US presidents must regrettably live for their personal safety, but the Chinese version is far more restrictive and deleterious to leaders' personal understanding of events in China and to China's image in the world.

Prominently featured in the book is the famous image of Zhao tearfully addressing the pro-democracy hunger strikers through a megaphone in the early-morning hours of 19 May 1989. But Zhao does not make even passing reference in his account of the Tiananmen tragedy to that one, deeply personal interaction he had with the student demonstrators, during which he told them that he regretted having come too late to talk with them. Yet, to most outsiders, this demonstration that at least one Chinese leader was trying desperately to avert the pending disaster was one of the most profoundly human moments of the entire crisis. Unfortunately, because of his lack of commentary, we may never know whether Zhao went to address the demonstrators because he thought he could convince them to leave Tiananmen Square before disaster struck or because he thought that somehow his presence might soften the hearts of the hardliners on the Politburo whom he knew – just a few hours after his impassioned remarks – would declare martial law and send in the military. The one man, still alive, who may have unique insight into Zhao's motives is current Chinese Premier Wen Jiabao, who is seen in the famous photograph standing stone-faced at Zhao's shoulder while Zhao speaks.

When, as a White House official, I worked with Chinese diplomats to arrange visits to Washington by senior Chinese leaders, they insisted that the mere sighting by a Chinese leader of an anti-China demonstrator was unacceptable. In April 2006, a Falun Gong demonstrator managed to gain access, using her journalist's credentials, to the press section on the White House lawn and create a well-publicised scene during the welcoming ceremony for Chinese President Hu Jintao. This, of course, was not something President Bush had wanted to happen, and he apologised to Hu for the incident. But the Chinese reaction, which included pressing for prosecution and a severe sentence for the demonstrator, led me to understand that Hu, in his entire career, had never been subjected to such a hostile verbal demonstration, even though it lasted for less than three minutes. One wonders if China's leaders would be more sympathetic to the grievances of China's minority groups and others who feel disenfranchised if they had greater personal exposure to them.

Reforming the PLA

Another element of Zhao's account that is notable by its absence is how little he says about the decision-making and dynamics within the People's Liberation Army (PLA) and its leadership during the 4 June debacle. This omission is deeply disappointing to China specialists who have speculated for years about how Deng Xiaoping, who had worked so hard after the Cultural Revolution to divorce the military from politics, could have convinced the generals to use force against the students. We know, for example, that Deng deliberately drew troops from all over China to carry out the final assault on the night of 4 June so that no military or regional leader could claim that his region was above reproach if events went against the Communist Party. And we are also fairly certain that Deng had to work to convince the military leaders that it was their duty to intervene even though it was clear that there were divisions within the Politburo on whether to declare martial law.[1] But what we do not know, and what Zhao does not explain, is whether Zhao participated in any meetings or conversations with PLA commanders or whether he ever tried to reach out to the military to urge restraint in his capacity as deputy chairman of the powerful Central Military Commission. In fact, Zhao's secret journal contains only brief references to the PLA.

We can only speculate that these issues were far too sensitive for Zhao to comment upon even in his secret journal. Perhaps he worried that, if he even alluded to any discussions with PLA officers in his tapes, there would be a manhunt and purge in the military ranks if the tapes were ever discovered by the Chinese government. This reminds us that Zhao was not entirely free of the influence of Chinese censors even while taping his thoughts in secret after his political career had ended.

Despite his reticence on these sensitive matters, Zhao clearly believed that a key element of political reform in China should be a dramatic change in the command and control structure of the military. One of the conclusions Zhao tells us he drew from his life in politics was that China needed to become a parliamentary democracy in which not just a few people were in charge but in which all Chinese were empowered to choose their leaders. In this regard, he alludes to the need for 'nationalisation' of the military. While he does not elaborate in his journal, Zhao almost certainly was referring to the fact that the PLA, harking back to its civil-war days as a revolutionary force, remains even now under the direct authority of the chairman of the Communist Party's Central Military Commission and not of the Chinese president, the executive branch (the State Council) or the legislative branch (the National People's Congress).

In 1989, as a way of possibly stopping the military crackdown on the students, Zhao tried unsuccessfully to engineer the early return from the United States of fellow political reformer National People's Congress Chairman Wan Li. Zhao clearly understood that, with Deng Xiaoping as the Central Military Commission chairman, the cards were stacked against him in the Military Commission, so he hoped that a special session of the Standing Committee of the National People's Congress might be called to, as he describes it in his secret journal, 'use the means of democracy and law to turn the situation around'. But even if Zhao had succeeded in convening an ad hoc session of the Standing Committee, this was a very thin reed, because its constitutional authority over the PLA was doubtful at best.

For many years, questions surrounding the PLA's status have been among the most sensitive in Chinese politics.[2] The issues of the appropriate constitutional command authority over the PLA and the force's proper command structure are inextricably linked and go to the core of the political problem which Zhao Ziyang confronted. By remaining an internally focused entity under the direct authority of the Communist Party, the PLA is a readily available instrument for settling domestic political disputes and carrying out internal suppression. As in 1989, today in China the only authority that needs to, and indeed can, authorise a military mobilisation is the chairman of the party's Central Military Commission.[3]

While many aspects of Chinese economic and political life are far more open and transparent today, deliberations over the deployment and uses of the PLA are not. This helps to explain why it is so difficult for outsiders to get clear answers from Chinese diplomats about such actions as the anti-satellite test on 11 January 2007, during which China surprised the world by successfully testing a direct-ascent hit-to-kill interceptor against one of its old weather satellites. As military decision-making is controlled by the party, such government entities as the Ministry of Foreign Affairs are not necessarily participants in the deliberations. Yet the foreign ministry may be the only segment of the Chinese government that has considered or even understands the international ramifications of heating up the arms race in space. Thus, on occasions like this, the senior political leadership of China may be genuinely surprised and confused by strong international backlash against actions authorised by the Central Military Commission and taken by the PLA, because the pre-briefings received from Chinese military authorities do not adequately explain the full extent of potential adverse reactions.

Zhao's call for moving control of the PLA from the party to the state was recently resurrected in an anonymous article that circulated for a short time on the Internet within China, until it was permanently deleted by official censors. According to reporter S.L. Shen, the author called for a multiparty system with real elections and described China under the current system as the party's state.[4] Many observers have speculated that this article was the work of Wan Li, chairman of the National People's Congress in 1988–93, the man whose intervention Zhao sought to stop the military crackdown. Whether the publication of Zhao's secret journal spurred one of his old colleagues to speak out is unclear, but what is certain is that the debate over the appropriate role and command structure for the PLA has not faded away and likely will be reinvigorated by Zhao's memoirs.

Pragmatic idealism

The ultimate impact of *Prisoner of the State* on Chinese politics is impossible to gauge. There is little doubt that China's leaders worry that such authoritative accounts from within the Communist Party ranks will erode domestic confidence in the wisdom of China's past and current leaders, and tarnish the party's reputation. Since it was released in May 2009, China's state-run news media has ignored the book, though many Chinese know of its publication and have gained access to its content from the Internet.

This memoir may well have a large impact on the thinking of the Chinese people about the direction of political reform. Zhao establishes himself as a pragmatic and dedicated Chinese patriot and a starry-eyed idealist. He goes into great detail on his role in China's economic reforms and opening to the outside world and argues convincingly that he was the true implementer of many of the most successful reform initiatives that have been credited to Deng Xiaoping. Furthermore, he persuasively argues that a modern China will need not only the kind of market economy that he helped build but ultimately also a parliamentary democracy in order to avoid 'the commercialization of power, rampant corruption, and a society polarized between rich and poor'. As befits his reputation as a pragmatist, he embraces the notion that the Communist Party may well be the ruling party of China for a considerable period. He warns, however, that the party must no longer use the constitution to monopolise power and argues that the first steps to a parliamentary democracy should be for the party to allow other political parties and a free press to exist.

I am convinced that many within and outside the Chinese Communist Party are still searching for the right model for reforming the political system and that – now that China's celebration of its 60th anniversary is over – there may be greater political space for this kind of debate in the run-up to the 18th Party Congress in 2012. With the political struggle of the Tiananmen era now safely 20 years in the past and most of the key protagonists no longer in power, Zhao's wisdom can be studied and absorbed with greater dispassion. As another reviewer, Richard Rigby of the Australian National University, has noted, Zhao has ensured that his name will be added to the list of upright Chinese officials who throughout history did the right thing at great personal cost, but also to their own, and to their nation's, ultimate credit.[5] Many of us who hope for a bright future for the Chinese people would like to believe that the legacy of Zhao Ziyang and his memoir may be even greater. Let us hope that it ultimately leads to a serious reappraisal of the Tiananmen Square crackdown and consideration in China of the kinds of political reforms that Zhao so clearly understood were necessary to transform China into a truly stable and prosperous nation in the modern era.

Notes

1 The US government has declassified a unique CIA research paper detailing Deng's manoeuvring with the Chinese military in the run-up to 4 June 1989 titled 'The Road to the Tiananmen Crackdown: An Analytic Chronology of Chinese Leadership Decision Making', dated September 1989. A copy can be found at http://www.gwu.edu/~nsarchiv/NSAEBB/NSAEBB47/doc13.pdf.

2 Some in China have argued that the PLA should be reorganised from its long-standing structure of seven internally focused military regions (Shenyang, Beijing, Lanzhou, Jinan, Nanjing, Guangzhou and Chengdu) into an organisation with perhaps five strategic zones (northern, eastern, western, southern and central reserve) more appropriate to defending against external threats. For more on this issue, see L.C. Russell Hsiao, 'Major Restructuring of the PLA Military Regions?', The Jamestown Foundation, China Brief, vol. 9, no. 16, 5 August 2009, available at http://www.jamestown.org/programs/chinabrief.

3 Given his position as Central Military Commission chairman, it was not surprising to see Chinese President Hu Jintao abruptly cut short his trip to Italy for the G8 summit in July 2009 so that he could take personal command of the mobilisation of forces to curb the unrest in Xinjiang among the Uighur minority community.

4 S.L. Shen, 'Former Cadre Critiques China's CCP Rule', UPI Asia Online, 12 August 2009, http://www.upiasia.com/politics/2009/08/12/former_cadre_critiques_chinas_ccp_rule/1090.

5 Richard Rigby, 'Can China Embrace its History and Zhao Ziyang's Memoir?', 24 May 2009, http://www.eastasiaforum.org/2009/05/24/.

Review Essay

Learning from Europe on Climate Change

Andrew Holland

Energy and Climate Change: Europe at the Crossroads
David Buchan. Oxford: Oxford University Press, 2009. £25.00/ $55.00. 218 pp.

As Paula J. Dobriansky and Vaughan C. Turekian point out in their commentary elsewhere in this issue, with the world gathering in Copenhagen this December to replace the Kyoto Protocol, the relative successes of existing regional and national approaches are of great interest. It is particularly useful to look for lessons from the only region of the globe that has moved in a coordinated and effective way to limit its greenhouse-gas emissions: Europe. David Buchan's *Energy and Climate Change: Europe at the Crossroads* gives a comprehensive overview of the European Union's energy policy, and how the shared threat of climate change encouraged collective action, in effect creating a common energy policy within the EU. This book should be a guide for international and national policymakers for how to create a climate-friendly energy policy.

Scientists say that the levels of carbon in the atmosphere have not been this high for 15 million years, and the last time they were, global temperatures were 3–5°C warmer and sea levels approximately 23–37 metres higher than today.[1] The unambiguous scientific consensus, as stated in the Intergovernmental Panel on Climate Change's most recent assessment, is 'warming of the climate system is unequivocal' and there is 'very high con-

Andrew Holland is Programme Manager and Research Associate for the Transatlantic Dialogue on Climate Change and Security at the IISS.

Survival | vol. 51 no. 6 | December 2009–January 2010 | pp. 211–220 DOI 10.1080/00396330903461740

fidence' that this warming is probably caused by man-made emissions of carbon dioxide and other greenhouse gases.[2] An international agreement in Copenhagen would ask the countries of the world to come together to bring emissions below dangerous levels by 2050.

An agreement to stabilise and reduce emissions must overcome the differing priorities of each nation. The least-developed countries call for funding for direct adaptation, so that they are not overwhelmed by the effects of climate change. Tropical nations seek a reliable way to finance the protection of their forests from the pressures of deforestation, the source of 20% of greenhouse-gas emissions. Small island nations want assurances that they will retain some form of sovereignty should they slip beneath the waves. Large growing nations, particularly China and India, say that they cannot agree to a cap on their emissions, as that will only prevent them from enjoying the economic growth that the West has already achieved. Meanwhile, developed countries, particularly the United States, maintain they cannot abide a reprise of Kyoto, with mandatory caps on the developed world and no commitments from the developing world. Oil-producing nations like Saudi Arabia have asked for financial reimbursement to replace revenues lost because of limitations on oil sales. Bridging these divides will be a substantial challenge.

How can such a diverse set of agendas be brought into agreement? For a possible answer we may look to Europe. The 27 states of the EU exhibit significant diversity: some are large, rich or growing fast, while others are small, poor or economically stagnant. Europe has crafted a common climate policy that includes the coal miners of Silesia, the bankers and traders of London, the auto manufacturers of Germany, impoverished rural farmers in the Carpathians, and environmentalists throughout. As Buchan reveals, action on climate change has come to define the EU's common energy policy both domestically and internationally.

Why the EU leads on climate change

The European Union perceived the threat of climate change far earlier than the rest of the world. Buchan notes that even before the United Nations' 1992 Earth Summit in Rio de Janeiro, Brazil, which produced the first major international agreement recognising the threat of climate change, the ministers of the EU were beginning to talk about stabilising emissions 'in the Community as a whole' (p. 1). One of the reasons for this early and enduring embrace of collective action was the EU's emphasis on the 'precautionary principle'. This states that the lack of scientific certainty about serious or irreversible damage should not be used as an excuse to prevent harm. It was enshrined as part of EU law in the 1992 Maastricht Treaty and guides EU consumer and environmental law.[3]

Europe's embrace of the precautionary principle has been vindicated as scientists have exposed the potentially catastrophic risks of unmitigated climate change. As economists have begun to tackle this issue, it has also become clear that the costs of action need not be crippling. The Stern Report of 2006, for example, argued that 'the benefits of strong and early action far outweigh the economic costs of not acting'. The report noted that an investment of approximately 1% of global GDP per year could prevent future annual losses of at least 5%, and possibly over 20%, in the future.[4]

Energy and
Climate Change:
Europe at the Crossroads
David Buchan

The other source of EU leadership on climate change is the wide support that action receives. In an early 2009 poll, conducted as the global recession was reaching its height, 50% of Europeans identified climate change as one of the greatest threats facing the world, behind only 'poverty, lack of food and drinking water' and 'a major global economic downturn'.[5] This support can be contrasted with the United States, where a recent poll indicated that only 37% of Americans believe that there is solid evidence that the earth is warming because of human activity.[6]

The European Union has been able to use popular support and its legal traditions to put together a comprehensive energy plan to address climate change. Only a decade ago, there was little that was 'European' about the continent's energy policy. Each country had set its own policies for decades. But as Buchan makes clear, attempts to address the problem of climate change effectively created EU energy policy. The newly ratified Lisbon Treaty offers a crucial caveat to the EU's energy policy, saying that the

EU 'shall not affect a member state's right to determine the conditions for exploiting its energy resources, its choice between different energy sources and the general structure of its energy supply'.[7] However, decisions made over the last decade indicate that national governments prefer to address climate change through international collective action at the EU level.

The European model

Europe's early embrace of action on climate change has resulted in considerable successes. Although some countries are likely to overshoot their Kyoto targets, as a whole, Europe will meet its Kyoto-agreed targets for emissions reductions. The European Environment Agency has reported that the overall domestic emissions of the 27 EU nations were 9.3% below 1990 levels in 2007, and the 15 western EU nations will meet the 2012 target of reducing emissions by 8% below 1990 levels.[8] This success is in contrast to some other Kyoto signatories, such as Canada, which will overshoot its target by over 30%.[9] The key to the EU's effectiveness in reducing emissions lies in a regulatory environment characterised by a balance of power between the EU in Brussels and national capitals across Europe.

The most visible representation of the EU's action on climate change is the Emissions Trading Scheme (ETS). Within the European Union, there is a price for emitting carbon. This price is set by daily trading of permits to emit greenhouse gases. The EU has set a national cap on emissions for each of the 27 member countries that applies to large emitters, including utilities, refineries and major manufacturers. This cap covers approximately 40% of total emissions. Emitters are allocated a specific number of permits over a commitment period, which they can then trade among themselves. This cap-and-trade mechanism allows a free market to determine the price of carbon, while the EU determines the total emissions allowed. As of early November 2009, the spot price for a tonne of carbon was approximately €14. Trading takes place every day across Europe, and industry and utilities must factor the price of carbon into every business decision they make.

Buchan is clear that implementing the ETS took a great deal of trial and error over the last four years in order to reach the relatively stable and predictable level the world sees now. The first phase of the ETS, which began in January 2005, was a failure. Prices jumped in the first six months from approximately €7 to over €25 per tonne and peaked at over €30 in April 2006, before collapsing to near zero by September 2007. As this experience showed, any market depends on scarcity to provide demand. As businesses began to turn in their permits for emissions, most began to realise that they had more than enough to continue to emit at current levels, and had no need for extra permits.

The problem was that the EU had delegated the right to determine the number of emission permits that were allocated to national governments. The predictable result was that, in the absence of quality information about recent emissions, each government listened to its industrial lobbies and claimed a high level of permits in order to give its home industries an advantage. When it became clear that there was a surplus of permits being traded on the market, prices collapsed. By the end of the first phase in 2007, permits were effectively worthless.

For the second commitment period (2008–12), the EU revised its permit-allocation policies to address its earlier failures. While the first phase did not succeed in reducing emissions below its baseline level, it did provide the European Commission with better information about the actual levels of emissions that were driving the use and trading of permits. With this firm information, the Commission was better able to allocate permits based on real, not claimed, emissions. So far, this has resulted in a second commitment period that is more stable, even though prices have fallen in response to the economic slowdown, much as one would expect. The ETS is still not perfect, it but it has shown to the world that such a system can work on a large scale.

More important than the specific policies established by the EU are the supranational negotiations that determine them. The unique nature of policymaking within the EU provides an important model for international institutions seeking to address climate change. Though anyone who has worked with the EU can attest to the maddening bureaucracy of Brussels, the institutional balance between the European Commission, the European Parliament and national capitals has proved to be a workable and coherent way to craft EU climate policy. Buchan's analysis of how the European

Commission acts to balance power between large and small, rich and poor states is excellent. His discussion of the process leading to the EU's 20/20/20 pledge in December 2008 is particularly valuable, and should be required reading for climate negotiators in the UN process. This plan would reduce European emissions by 20%, increase energy efficiency by 20%, and make renewable power 20% of the energy supply by 2020. The story of how this complex and detailed plan came about shows how negotiations among parties acting in their own interests can still produce progress towards an ambitious goal. In particular, Buchan credits French President Nicolas Sarkozy's 'demonic style of chairing the EU' (p. 118) in the second half of 2008 for pushing through such an ambitious plan. Sarkozy made use of the powers of the EU presidency, placed relentless pressure on national capitals, and engineered rigorous coordination in the European Parliament to push through the plan. He balanced the economic and security needs of Eastern European states, especially coal-dependent Poland, with the more environmentally oriented desires of richer states. And he accomplished all this in the middle of an economic calamity.

That the EU could agree to such an ambitious plan despite the significant economic divisions among its members shows the unity of Europe in addressing the challenge of climate change, and the efficacy of the EU's power structures in setting up an international agreement. The key is that each state accepted the authority of the EU to make these decisions, felt that its concerns were addressed and, most importantly, understood the urgency of reducing carbon emissions. For the EU process to become a model for the UN process at Copenhagen, these three factors will have to come together among the top emitters.

Failures of the model

Though the EU approach to climate change provides a model for the world, there are some areas where its efforts to assert leadership have not been successful. Firstly, a general lack of budget authority has undercut the EU's ability to fund the research, development and deployment of environmental technologies. Secondly, its approach to nuclear power shows how divisive issues can sometimes create muddled and self-defeating policies.

Most experts agree that new technologies, including wind, solar, carbon-capture and sequestration, will be vital in mitigating climate change. Government-sponsored research will be particularly important in making the basic advances that can then be developed and deployed by private firms. Currently the EU is spending about €3 billion a year on research and development in clean energy, and the European Commission has proposed to increase this to €8bn per year. While this may sound like a large amount, it falls well behind American plans to spend $112bn over the coming two fiscal years on 'green' funding and Chinese plans to spend approximately $221bn over the next two years.[10]

The EU is a supranational body that has been given a great deal of regulatory authority, but its budgetary authority is still small relative to that of national governments. As a result, clean-technology policy is driven by subsidies from individual states. Buchan cites the example of Germany, where the government guarantees a long-term, above-market price to renewable electricity producers. The German government's decision to offer a 'feed-in tariff' on solar power has guaranteed a market for this form of energy. However, Germany has successfully prevented that subsidy from applying to solar projects built in other countries. Clearly, an EU-wide policy allowing Germans to invest their solar-technology funding in much sunnier Spain in exchange for some sort of clean-energy credit would have been a more economically efficient model. But this would not have provided jobs and prestige to German industry. Moreover, national governments have successfully undermined any attempts by the European Commission to open trade in clean energy across borders, and the Lisbon Treaty provides for national control over energy policy. Under this policy, and without additional budget authority, the EU as a whole will never become a leader in renewable-energy research, development or deployment to the extent that the United States or China seem poised to do.

Buchan makes clear his view that deploying nuclear power on a large scale will be essential for any move to a low-carbon economy. Indeed, there seems to be little chance of providing large-scale baseload, zero-emissions electricity without atomic power, despite the cost of building nuclear plants. But EU nuclear policy, in another instance of individual states undermining collective action, has been undercut by competing views within Europe on the utility, cost, safety and future of atomic power. Calling nuclear power 'the impossible consensus', Buchan gives the EU's nuclear-power policy an 'A–' for potential, but only a 'D' for performance. Although the European Atomic Energy Community (Euratom) was created in 1957 to ensure stable and predictable access to nuclear power, efforts by the European Commission to increase the EU's nuclear-regulatory authority, including a 2003 draft directive to this effect, have been resisted by national governments. Euratom could have set standards for safety, waste disposal and reactor design. The fact that it has not been allowed to live up to its potential is a testament to the enduring power of the Chernobyl accident to evoke fear among Europeans. Atomic power is a highly politicised issue, perhaps more than any other energy issue. Therefore, it might be logical to leave nuclear decision-making to local governments. If, however, the promotion of efficient, safe and productive atomic power is a genuine goal, and not just a political smokescreen, a Europe-wide regulator could ensure a better nuclear future.

* * *

The EU's precautionary principle acts to prevent damage to the environment by pre-empting harmful action. This philosophy has led to a policy that effectively limits current emissions and promotes efficiency through a price mechanism. While far from perfect, European energy policy presents us with a road map for how the world can begin to address climate change. Individuals and nations will have to learn to use our existing energy supply more efficiently and cost effectively, and we will have to deploy existing renewable technologies on a larger scale.

Europe came to a consensus about the dangers of climate change prior to the rest of the world, and has a head start in crafting the policies to mitigate its worst effects. Europe's common foreign policy prioritises taking action on climate change. It was only through European action that the Kyoto Protocol was finally brought into effect, and European leadership over the last decade has ensured that climate change has risen to the top of the international agenda. Buchan's book, by detailing the successes and failures of Europe's trailblazing efforts, can act as a guide for how other nations can achieve a climate-friendly energy policy before it is too late.

Notes

1 Stuart Wolpert, 'Last Time Carbon Dioxide Levels Were This High: 15 Million Years Ago, Scientists Report', ScienceDaily.com, 9 October 2009, http://www.sciencedaily.com/releases/2009/10/091008152242.htm.

2 Intergovernmental Panel on Climate Change, *Climate Change 2007: The Physical Science Basis*, Working Group I Contribution to the Fourth Assessment Report (Cambridge: Cambridge University Press, 2007), Summary for Policymakers, pp. 2–3.

3 For more on the precautionary principle and EU climate policy, see John R. Schmidt, 'Why Europe Leads on Climate Change', *Survival: Global Politics and Strategy*, vol. 50, no. 4, August–September 2008, pp. 83–96.

4 Nicholas Stern, *The Economics of Climate Change: The Stern Review* (Cambridge: Cambridge University Press, 2006).

5 'Europeans Attitudes Towards Climate Change', Special Eurobarometer 313, July 2009, http://ec.europa.eu/public_opinion/archives/ebs/ebs_313_en.pdf.

6 Pew Research Center for People and the Press, 'Modest Support for "Cap and Trade" Policy: Fewer Americans See Solid Evidence of Global Warming', 22 October 2009, http://people-press.org/reports/pdf/556.pdf.

7 Treaty of Lisbon, Title XX: Energy, Article 176A (2), 2007/C 306/01, available at http://europa.eu/lisbon_treaty/full_text/index_en.htm.

8 European Environment Agency, 'EU Greenhouse Gas Emissions Fall for Third Consecutive Year', Press release, 29 May 2009, http://www.eea.europa.eu/pressroom/newsreleases/2009-greenhouse-inventory-report.

9 'National Inventory Report: Greenhouse Gases Sources and Sinks 1990–2007', Submission by Greenhouse Gas Division, Environment Canada, to the United Nations Framework Convention on Climate Change, April 2009.

10 Ben Furnas, 'We Must Seize the Energy Opportunity or Slip Further Behind: A Primer on Global Competition in Green Technology Investments', Center for American Progress, 20 April 2009.

Book Reviews

United States

John L. Harper

War of Necessity, War of Choice: A Memoir of Two Iraq Wars
Richard N. Haass. New York: Simon & Schuster, 2009. $27.00. 336 pp.

Part personal memoir, part historical analysis, this book is above all a clear exposition of the George H.W. Bush–Brent Scowcroft 'realist' view of the world. Richard Haass introduced a simple but compelling distinction between necessary wars (waged in self-defence and to secure vital interests) and wars of choice (embarked on despite alternatives to force, and to carry out a political design) into the current debate in a November 2003 *Washington Post* article called 'Wars of Choice'. The book makes about as good a case as can be made that, although the United States could have done more to deter Saddam Hussein, once he had occupied Kuwait war was unavoidable and produced tangible benefits. The second Iraq War, a preventive–demonstrative war hyped as pre-emption, was an act of hubris for which the United States and Iraq have paid a frightful price.

Haass adds nothing startlingly new to what we know from an already vast literature, but he was in a good position to derive insights and lessons from the wars. As an assistant to National Security Adviser Scowcroft, he was involved in day-to-day policymaking in 1990–91. In 2002–03, he was in a rather more detached role as a roving ambassador and head of the State Department's Policy Planning Staff. He is particularly interesting on the first Bush's handling of the Saudi Arabians, who were reluctant to be protected even with the Iraqis on their doorstep. Oddly, Haass glosses over the significance of the late October 1990 decision to double US troop strength, for all practical purposes a decision for war and one which probably made Saddam less likely to back down or compromise

 DOI 10.1080/00396330903461757

in ways that would have complicated life for Washington. (Unintended effects are not always negative.) Haass speculates on Saddam's motives for not trying to avoid war in 2003 by 'coming clean' on his (lack of) nuclear, biological and chemical weapons. One he doesn't mention (remarkably, it occurred to almost no one in a position of power) was Saddam's well-founded assumption that the Americans would invade in any case.

Haass's boss Colin Powell emerges as someone distrusted by the White House but himself overly trustful of his colleagues' common sense. The thumbnail portraits of Powell's rivals are unflattering but apt. Paul Wolfowitz was 'something of an intellectual romantic' (and, one could add, a historical determinist). Haass suggests that Condoleezza Rice's role as courtier led her to discard her realist views. Bush himself was a 'retail politician' nonpareil who unfortunately convinced himself he could change the course of history. Haass admits that his opposition to the second conflict was 'not fundamental' (60–40 rather than 90–10) since he believed Iraq had weapons of mass destruction. This is one reason why he didn't push back harder when Rice famously told him to 'save his breath' rather than try to stop the war, and why he decided to stay with the Bush administration until mid 2003. Haass makes a thoughtful, if debatable, case for the decision not to quit despite significant disagreements over Afghanistan and the Israel–Palestine peace process (or lack thereof) as well as Iraq.

The Rebellion of Ronald Reagan: A History of the End of the Cold War
James Mann. New York: Viking, 2009. £25.00/$27.95. 396 pp.

This engaging study looks at a set of relatively neglected aspects of Ronald Reagan's second term (the 40th president's relationship with Richard Nixon and moderate conservatives; his ties to Suzanne Massie, an author of popular books on Russia; the story behind his 'Mr Gorbachev, tear down this wall!' speech in Berlin; his 1987–88 summitry) and uses them to sharpen our understanding of why the Cold War ended as it did.

A central theme of the book is that in betting on Mikhail Gorbachev Reagan 'rebelled' not only against the Republican right but the still-influential centrists who had earlier pursued détente. Nixon and Henry Kissinger viewed the Cold War as a long-term geopolitical struggle and dismissed the possibility that Gorbachev aimed at anything but strengthening the Soviet system. This is an important and oft-forgotten point. Still, it seems a little misleading to say that opposition in Washington to an Intermediate Nuclear Forces (INF) bargain was led by Nixon, Kissinger and Brent Scowcroft. As Mann himself shows, the former president had privately encouraged Gorbachev to deal with Reagan and did not oppose an INF treaty in principle. It is hard to imagine that if fate had matched Nixon and Kissinger with Gorbachev they would not have reached agreements with him (though they might not have tried to convince him of the existence of God, as Reagan did during the 1988 Moscow summit).Their basic problem with Reagan was that they suffered from an 'own indispensability' complex and thought he and Secretary of State George Shultz were inexperienced and naive.

Mann shows that it was precisely Reagan's superficial knowledge, and view of the Cold War as an ideological more than a geopolitical contest, that provided an opening for Massie, someone to whom Nixon would not have given the time of day. Massie whetted Reagan's curiosity about Russian life and encouraged him to think something fundamental was afoot, including a spiritual reawakening. The Kremlin used her to send messages to Reagan, including a February 1987 appeal. The recent Reykjavik meeting had failed to produce an arms agreement. Gorbachev was under pressure and in dire need of 'something to show'. Prompted by Massie (as well as Shultz and Nancy Reagan), Reagan responded positively rather than trying to exploit the Soviet Union's troubles. In so doing he bolstered Gorbachev, buying him time and allowing Moscow to consider unilateral arms reductions and the end of Soviet hegemony over Eastern Europe, as well as democratisation at home. In the meantime, while committed to relaxing tensions, Reagan used the 1987 Berlin speech to try to cover his right flank.

What emerges from Mann's revealing account is that the East–West confrontation wound down at the time and in the way it did because Gorbachev's need for 'something to show' in 1987–88 happened to coincide exactly with Reagan's own. For this one can blame – or thank – Oliver North, John Poindexter and Reagan himself, for the Iran–Contra affair. The scandal left him floundering and even more eager than Gorbachev for high-visibility summits and agreements that would allow him to salvage his presidency and recover his coveted popularity. Along with his flexibility and pluck, Reagan's vanity, too, helped to bring the Cold War to an end.

Great Powers: America and the World after Bush
Thomas P.M. Barnett. New York: G.P. Putnam's Sons, 2009.
$29.95. 488 pp.

Pentagon consultant Thomas P.M. Barnett believes the key to the world's future lies in the example of America's nineteenth-century conquest of its hinterland and creation of a single, continental market. The New World's destiny is, or should be, the 'source code for freedom's viral advance around the planet'. His recommended grand strategy (it 'resides in America's DNA') is to press on with a project already well advanced despite recent setbacks: the integration of recalcitrant 'Gap' areas (Africa, the Middle East, Central Asia) into the growing 'Core' (the United States and Europe, plus newcomers China, India and Russia) of interconnected economies, giving rise to a 'super-empowered' global middle class.

A self-declared economic determinist, Barnett argues that Washington has focused excessively on terrorism, democratisation and nuclear proliferation instead of the quasi-cure-all of globalisation. Al-Qaeda's plans for 'civilizational apartheid' are headed for history's dustbin. Democracy will come on its own, demanded by (Barnett sometimes sounds like a Marxist) the rising bourgeoisie. Nuclear weapons are a good thing because they have practically ruled out great-power conflict. Rather than a league of democracies, he favours a league of capitalist powers, including Russia and China, combining to develop backward areas. Rather than the current 'Leviathan' useful mainly for fighting an unnecessary war with China and enriching defence contractors, he calls for a US military whose forte is counter-insurgency and post-conflict stabilisation. And instead of an 'off-shore balancing' and energy-conservation strategy, he supports America's head-long plunge into the Middle East. But on Iraq he is schizophrenic. Bush and Cheney, he says, should be forgiven for connecting Saddam to the 11 September attacks because 'democracies such as our own always have to make it personal before we can launch a war of choice'. Yet he also warns against demonising adversaries. The war, he writes, has had the positive effect of 'locking America into real, long-term ownership of strategic security in the Gulf'. But its 'main beneficiary' has been Iran.

In the end, Barnett raises more questions than he answers. Why and how would China and Russia help the United States in Afghanistan, and can subduing the Taliban really be usefully compared to pacifying the Lakota Sioux? Would the middle-class capitalist powers (the United States, Europe, China, Russia, India and so on) making up the world he imagines live in peace and harmony or might they find reasons to fight in spite of economic interdependence? What kind of international political infrastructure would such a world call for? Will liberal democracy automatically arrive after a certain level of per-capita income is attained? Does it really matter? Will important parts of the West decide to shield themselves from the negative consequences of economic and financial openness? The author himself seems to harbour doubts about his messianic, homogenising vision. 'Humanity's paths to happiness', he concludes, 'are as varied as the human condition'. If so, predictions of the triumph of Americanisation-cum-globalisation would be premature.

After America: Narratives for the Next Global Age
Paul Starobin. New York: Viking, 2009. $26.95. 352 pp.

Paul Kennedy and the late 1980s 'declinists' saw the United States as the latest big power to fall afoul of 'imperial over-stretch', the gap between domestic resources and foreign commitments. Both conservatives and liberals pooh-poohed the argument, but it served as a kind of self-denying prophecy. By calling attention to the problem, 'declinism' helped galvanise the political class to bring enormous federal budget deficits under control. Twenty years on, journalist Paul Starobin's arguments will be harder to dismiss.

Strarobin sees America not simply as a great power beset by serious economic problems and unwinnable wars on the periphery (although that is an essential part of the story), but a broader, Braudelian 'civilisation' approaching 'the end of its long ascendancy in the world'. The revival of Russian nationalism and the genuine popularity of the Putin model, alone, give the lie to 'the end of history'. Across a spectrum of activities – architecture, robotics, health-care delivery, Internet services, green technology, business practices – America has ceased to be the 'preeminent benchmarks producer' and is heading toward 'middling' status. What will the post-American world look like? Starobin's travels and interviews with an astonishing variety of people (Cossack students, Turkish Muslim teachers, Chile-based Chinese diplomats, Indian admirals, Hollywood executives and a US Supreme Court justice, to name a few) suggest a range of possibilities: chaos across an 'arc of crisis' stretching from the Middle East to Western China, a multipolar world of great powers, an age of city-states presiding over mega-regions, a Chinese Century, and global governance. And what's in store for America 'after America'? For Starobin, the future as usual arrives first in California, a multicultural society whose economy no longer relies on the Pentagon, and where both Silicon Valley and Hollywood do more and more business outside the United States.

Starobin's book is more a collage of arresting vignettes and vivid snapshots than a rigorously argued thesis à la Kennedy. But the overall picture is plausible and it is only prudent to allow for a variety of 'after America' scenarios. Could this and similar books serve as another self-denying prophecy for those hoping to prolong US pre-eminence? Maybe, but the rich variety of evidence marshalled here suggests there would be little point. There is no turning back the clock and, as Britain's post-1945 experience suggests, America is not fated to be miserable in a post-American world.

Parallel Empires: The Vatican and the United States – Two Centuries of Alliance and Conflict
Massimo Franco. Roland Flamini, trans. New York: Doubleday, 2009. $26.00. 223 pp.

Scholars have oddly ignored the subject of US–Vatican relations. This book (updated since the 2005 Italian edition) by a *Corriere della Sera* columnist tries to fill the gap. Massimo Franco gives a useful survey of the century and a half before 1939, but his treatment of the war years is cursory. The reader would like to know more, for example, about Washington's relations with Pope Pius XII, and the controversy surrounding his role during the German round-up of Rome's Jews in October 1943. The book errs in portraying a 1944 *Life* magazine article (reporting the Vatican's fears of approaching Communist hordes) as 'the message that the United States wanted to convey'. William Bullitt, the article's author, had broken with the Roosevelt administration and its policy of post-war collaboration with the USSR. Franco offers little evidence for saying that the Americans initially trusted Christian Democratic leader Alcide De Gasperi because the Vatican did, and that Cardinal Francis Spellman of New York played a key role in shaping US strategy toward Italy in the early post-war years.

The book's title is misleading. Its real focus and merit lie in its account of the complex relations between the George W. Bush administration and the Vatican under Pope John Paul II and Benedict XVI. There are fascinating accounts of the meetings between four American cardinals and National Security Adviser Condoleezza Rice, and between Papal Nuncio Pio Laghi and Bush, on the eve of the Iraq War. The book says that the pope 'did not support the anti-war positions of France and Germany'. But the Holy See's position was, if anything, more radical than that of Jacques Chirac and Gerhard Schröder. Franco quotes the Vatican foreign minister's statement that unilateral US action would amount to 'a war of aggression and therefore a crime against humanity'.

Equally striking, as Franco shows, is how quickly the Vatican and the White House settled their quarrel in 2004. Even as conditions in Iraq were going from bad to worse (much as church officials had predicted), the Vatican (and by and large American Catholics) preferred the born-again Methodist Bush to the anti-war but lukewarm-Catholic John Kerry. Bush's opposition to abortion and same-sex marriage readily trumped a foreign policy that (in the church's view) risked triggering a Christian–Muslim clash of civilisations. The episode casts an interesting light on the Vatican's attitude toward the current Italian government. Prime Minister Silvio Berlusconi is no model of Catholic family values and his television networks are known for their vapid game shows and scantily clad dancing girls. But when a Berlusconi-owned newspaper brutally slapped down the editor of a Catholic paper who had dared to question the premier's personal morality, the Vatican was eager to calm the waters. One reason is that Berlusconi's government has promised to deliver a law on living wills that will satisfy restrictive Catholic standards. For the Vatican, reason of state, or rather reason of souls, prevailed again.

Europe

Hanns W. Maull

European Union Security Dynamics: In the New National Interest
Janne Haaland Matlary. Basingstoke: Palgrave Macmillan, 2009. $50.00/$74.95. 234 pp.

In Search of Structural Power: EU Aid Policy as a Global Political Instrument
Patrick Holden. Farnham: Ashgate, 2009. £55.00/$99.95. 222 pp.

Energy Security: Europe's New Foreign Policy Challenge
Richard Youngs. Abingdon: Routledge, 2009. £70.00/$140.00. 230 pp.

These three books each tackle an important segment of European external relations. Janne Haaland Matlary deals with European security policies in the traditional, military sense, asking what has driven the rapid development of the European Security and Defence Policy (ESDP). Patrick Holden discusses European development aid and thus much of Europe's relations with the South and the East, probing the ability of the EU to use its 'structural power' vis-à-vis developing and Eastern European countries to achieve their economic ('development') and political ('good governance') transformation. Richard Youngs dissects the external dimensions of European energy security, asking how – and how well – the EU has integrated its new concern with energy security into its overall external relations. Together, the authors provide a fairly comprehensive picture of Europe's position in the international system.

Certainly, Europe does not occupy the position of a traditional great power, nor is it much like an empire, despite Jan Zielonka's claims to the contrary in his book, *Europe as Empire* (Oxford University Press, 2006), though the EU does have a pervasive global presence and significant influence in certain spheres. That influence, however, rests more on what the EU *is* than on what it *does*. It is a community of peaceful, (mostly) rich and (largely) democratic states, and as such is an attractive club to belong to. This has produced a series of enlargements, in which the EU has been able to integrate the newcomers into its own principles, rules, practices and institutions. (This influence has not been a one-way street, however: enlargement has profoundly affected the European Union's collective identity.) Some of its neighbours still want to join, which gives the EU leverage, and the Union can also exercise influence beyond its own sphere of influence through the weight of its practices, norms and standards in international economic relations. But, as Holden points out (p. 184), much of the EU's influence would dissipate if it behaved like, say, the United States, China or India, as a traditional great power; Europe enjoys influence precisely because it does *not* try to project power, and therefore is not feared.

The focus of these authors, however, is on what the EU *does*, and all three make it clear that the EU's active influence in international relations is quite limited. Patrick Holden's careful analysis of the EU's aid policy shows that while the EU has tried to develop its own structural power over countries to its south and east, its influence there is still shallow. EU efforts have been sufficient to bring some of the societies targeted by EU aid policies into its orbit and to make them dependent on Europe, but they have failed to achieve the kind of structural social, economic and political transformation seen in countries that have actually joined the EU. As Holden's in-depth case studies of Morocco, Ghana and Ukraine reveal, the EU's economic and political presence in those countries has grown, and their formal institutions have adapted to European expectations. Below the surface, however, entrenched informal power structures have largely resisted the EU's efforts to achieve 'good governance'.

The EU has also, as Richard Youngs shows, been rather less than successful in its efforts to enhance European energy security through its external policies. In essence, the EU has tried to do so with a markets- and institutions-based approach, ostensibly eschewing geopolitics. To that end, it has arranged bilateral and regional energy dialogues, hoping to export intra-European energy-market principles, rules and norms to its energy suppliers. To evaluate how well this has worked, Youngs looks at the energy dimension of EU foreign policies towards the Middle East, Russia, the Caucasus and Central Asia, and sub-Saharan Africa, and finds that the realities of EU policies have lagged far behind the rhetoric. In practice, energy-security concerns in EU external relations have often been crowded out by other issues, and where they have loomed large in a bilateral relationship, such as with Russia, the EU has seemed unable to do much about allaying those concerns.

Similarly, while Matlary does identify real and important advances in the ESDP, she also argues cogently that a lack of political integration represents a fundamental deficiency in European security policy. As a result, the EU has largely avoided robust military power projection or coercive diplomacy, focusing instead on humanitarian interventions, crisis management and state-building. While most ESDP missions have been quite successful in a technical sense, they have lacked ambition and strategic vision. Matlary sums up her argument with a paradox: the EU may be able 'to deploy force with increasing capability and legitimacy; but it cannot be expected to threaten the use of force effectively' (p. 204).

The limitations of Europe's power and influence in international relations lie, as all three books show, in the very nature of the European Union as a global player. On the one hand, its external relations and the drive for a Common Foreign and Security Policy reflect the inescapable logic of mutual dependence. In this age of globalisation and global power shifts, even the large member states, such as Germany and erstwhile great powers Britain and France, must, in Benjamin Franklin's famous phrase, hang together or, most assuredly, they will hang separately. Their governments recognise this, more or less reluctantly. (Most small and medium-sized EU member states know they need the European Union as a 'force multiplier', and Germany, for historical reasons, has also long followed this logic.) On the other hand, member governments have generally been anxious to retain as much of their national sovereignty and freedom of action as possible. Their responses to this dilemma have usually involved the construction of essentially technocratic, politically deficient European policies and institutions. This holds true for the arrangements and mechanisms through which the European Union dispenses aid, such as the Lomé and Cotonou conventions, the European Development Fund, or TACIS; for ESDP institutions and capabilities within the framework of the Common Foreign and Security Policy (CFSP), particularly in the realm of military security; and for the toolbox of 'energy dialogues' and 'strategic partnerships' meant to enhance European energy security, again within the framework of the CFSP. These arrangements are all inherently flawed in important ways, reflecting the contradictory impulses behind their creation and subsequent evolution. As a result, political leaders can use European institutions not only to pursue their country's strategic objectives, but also to serve their own domestic concerns and priorities. Matlary aptly calls this the 'blame game': political leaders, she argues, use Europe to advance national interests, but also to score at home and shield themselves from domestic criticism if European action does not deliver expected results. Holden similarly concludes that the EU has so far developed only one effective strategy to achieve its objectives, that of offering membership. Beyond that – very expensive – policy, Europe has not been able to come up with a coherent and consistent development policy. The EU's energy-security strategy, too, is seriously flawed – 'a toolbox without tools', in the words of one senior EU diplomat quoted by Youngs.

Thus, in all three policy areas we find institutional arrangements that make it virtually impossible to develop consistent political strategies, and external policies that are inherently weak and inconsistent. All three studies point to a significant qualitative gap between the EU's ambitions and its institutional and material capabilities – a gap, in other words, that could not be narrowed by simply providing more money and people, but which also calls for strong political leadership and, most likely, new institutional designs. It is not just that EU policy is conceived as a supplement to national policies, the supplements are also systematically constructed in ways that cannot but limit their effectiveness. Thus, the 'European Security Strategy', as Matlary points out, is a fine document spelling out risks and threats which the EU will face, and providing a vision for addressing these challenges, but is ultimately not a strategy. Similarly, the EU does not have a strategy to redress its energy insecurity through its foreign policy, nor to promote 'good governance' in Africa and Eastern Europe.

The second, and more familiar, problem with EU policies in all three areas is that the Union is seriously divided in its allegedly 'common' foreign- and security-policy efforts. This is true not just of the various players in Brussels, such as the EU Commission and EU Council, with regard to aid and energy security, but above all of member states, who often pursue their own, independent national agendas in parallel to – and not infrequently at cross-purposes with – the common policy line. Holden contents himself (somewhat disappointingly) with stating the problem: his figures show that total EU-level official development assistance (ODA) in 2007 was about twice that of the combined national ODA budgets of two medium-sized European donors, Spain and the Netherlands. In his conclusions, he observes, with some understatement, that member-state aid policies have been 'imperfectly aligned with the collective EU programme' (p. 184). For Matlary, the ESDP suffers not only from the tensions between the different (though, as she sees it, increasingly convergent) strategic visions of its principals, France and the United Kingdom, but also – and perhaps even more so – from the tendency of national leaders to instrumentalise the ESDP to offset domestic constraints or score points with national audiences. And Youngs shows how the pursuit of energy security is still widely held to be a national rather than a European task by governments, which frequently undercut the EU's emphasis on markets- and institutions-based approaches. France, Germany and Italy, in particular, have been much keener on their own, bilateral arrangements with suppliers than on common approaches, and frequently have refused to share information and establish transparency about those deals with Brussels.

National approaches, but also the positions taken by governments in Brussels, above all reflect the intricate interaction of domestic and European politics which today characterises even military security policies. To describe and analyse that interplay, Robert Putnam coined the felicitous metaphor of 'two-level games', in which political leaders are constantly trying to win at two tables simultaneously. One game is played domestically, with the stakes usually consisting in re-election; the other at a European (or international) level, with peers from other governments. Matlary explicitly uses this metaphor in her analysis, and the fact that in Europe, security policy now is (almost?) as enmeshed in domestic politics as any other policy is, in her view, one key element in what she calls 'the new European security dynamics'. (The other is that within Europe, there are few, if any, purely national security interests any more, pushing governments into pursuing 'common interests' through common efforts.) But the metaphor is also well illustrated by Young's account of energy security in EU external relations, in which some of the big European utilities and energy corporations loom large as sources of policy influence, and it occasionally also surfaces in Holden's analysis of EU aid policies. What gets lost in the maze of these multi-level games played within and about European external relations is, as all three accounts show, the coherence, consistency and effectiveness of European foreign and security policies. As a consequence, Europe still punches much below its weight in world politics.

The Euro: The Politics of the New Global Currency
David Marsh. New Haven, CT, and London: Yale University Press, 2009. £25.00/$35.00. 340 pp.

This is a gripping account of how the euro came about, taking a long historical view but concentrating, in considerable detail drawn from an impressive array of documents and interviews, on the critical years from 1988 to 1995. The book is particularly good on the crises in the European Exchange Rate Mechanism (ERM) in 1992–93, which first forced Britain and Italy to leave the ERM and then almost exploded the core of the system, the Franco-German exchange-rate parity. The 'battle of the Franc' was, as Marsh shows, won on the strength of the political cooperation and leadership of François Mitterrand and Helmut Kohl, who were both determined to defend their pro-European visions. This paved the way to European Monetary Union and the successful introduction of the euro, a currency which by 2008 had achieved a worldwide circulation, in cash terms, some 15–20% above that of the US dollar.

Yet Marsh is profoundly ambivalent about the future of this new global currency. He recognises the benefits of greater economic security and the absence of exchange-rate pressures, but also points to a slackening of economic reforms in the Southern European economies once they joined the common currency, and notes that overall there has been no discernible difference in economic performance between European countries within the Eurozone and those without. In fact, Marsh argues, the jury is still out on the success or failure of European Monetary Union. For the euro presents its member governments (and the European Union as a whole) with a challenge: to overcome the fundamental tensions inherent in the project, between a dominant German economy geared towards perennial export surpluses and the structural deficits of France, in particular; between hugely divergent economic circumstances and performances within the Eurozone and the one-size-fits-all interest-rate policies of the European Central Bank; and, above all, between the essentially technocratic arrangements of the bank, which governs the euro, and its vast political significance. Tellingly, Marsh's account of the euro barely mentions one important dimension of the 'politics of the new global currency' – the role of the Eurozone in contributing to a viable international monetary and financial order. But who would represent the euro in negotiations with the United States, Japan and China on those crucial issues?

Counter-terrorism

Jonathan Stevenson

The Search for Al Qaeda: Its Leadership, Ideology and Future
Bruce Riedel. Washington DC: Brookings Institution Press, 2008. £15.99/$26.95. 190 pp.

This straightforward, concise and sensibly organised book sets forth a balanced assessment of al-Qaeda and its capabilities and prospects. Given that Riedel was a long-serving CIA officer and a senior Pentagon official and National Security Council staffer, and led the Obama administration's policy review on Afghanistan and Pakistan, it also offers a good approximation of the United States government's operative view of al-Qaeda. Laying blame for public ignorance about al-Qaeda squarely at the Bush administration's doorstep, Riedel recounts the genesis of the 11 September 2001 attacks and then casts light on al-Qaeda through the prisms of four of the global jihad's key players: Ayman al-Zawahiri ('the thinker'); Osama bin Laden ('the knight'); Mullah Omar ('the host'); and the late Abu Musab al-Zarqawi ('the stranger'). Others, notably Daniel Benjamin, Steven Simon and Lawrence Wright, have ably explained the significance of these men, and Riedel's topical mini-biographies, though lucid, have little new to offer. But they lay the foundation for the most enterprising chapters of the book, on al-Qaeda's plans and a US-led counter-terrorism strategy.

In Riedel's view, al-Qaeda's leaders intend to engineer the collapse of the United States and its allies in the manner that the West brought about the demise of world communism: through 'bleeding wars' (p. 122), particularly in Afghanistan. Subsidiary to this strategic objective are the goals of acquiring nuclear, biological and chemical weapons, maintaining safe havens, and nurturing regional and local franchises to keep up the pressure. Among these, the grand prize would be a dominant jihadist group in Palestine, preferably via the penetration and transformation of Hamas.

The obituary for al-Qaeda that some analysts, such as John Mueller, have begun drafting, says Riedel, amounts to 'wishful thinking' (p. 135). At the same time, he concludes that the group's demise 'should not take decades to achieve' (p. 154). Indeed, he believes Washington has squandered opportunities to hasten its decline by abandoning conflict resolution in the Middle East and diverting military resources from Afghanistan to Iraq. Ameliorating these mistakes is key, but he pins a successful US-led counter-terrorism campaign on a favourable 'outcome of the battle for the soul of Pakistan' (p. 140), whose tribal areas now host al-Qaeda's core leadership. The most novel element of this approach would be more aggressive American diplomacy on the Kashmir problem, which has been perennially dismissed in light of India's customary rejection of outside involvement. More predictably, Riedel prescribes an enhanced US military, political and economic commitment to Afghanistan, a policy adopted by the Obama administration but currently facing heavy criticism and scrutiny as it comes under review.

Awkwardly inserted, and sometimes rather precious, insider scene-setting anecdotes and self-consciously dropped names slightly compromise the narrative's otherwise detached, authoritative tone, but are mercifully kept to a minimum. In essence, Riedel presents a clear and useful précis of the United States' current understanding of al-Qaeda and its approach to countering transnational jihadist terrorism.

Al'Qa-ida's Doctrine for Insurgency: 'Abd Al-'Aziz Al-Muqrin's *A Practical Course for Guerrilla War*
Norman Cigar. Dulles, VA: Potomac Books, 2009.
£16.00/$26.95. 224 pp.

The New Counterinsurgency Era: Transforming the U.S. Military for Modern Wars
David H. Ucko. Washington DC: Georgetown University Press, 2009. £20.75/$26.95. 268 pp.

Abdul Aziz al-Muqrin, who was killed by Saudi security forces in 2004, is transnational jihad's answer to Carl von Clausewitz, and in translating and explaining his doctrine and guidance Norman Cigar has provided estimable assistance to analysts, officials and scholars. There are no major surprises in al-Muqrin's ideas. They incorporate in detail familiar approaches to unconventional and asymmetric conflict, such as 'bleeding wars', for which he uses equally evocative metaphors such as 'the war of the flea and the dog' (p. 92) and 'the strategy of a thousand cuts' (p. 97). While such tactics are usually presented in broad terms as elements of al-Qaeda's strategy, details matter, and Cigar plumbs them. The overarching point of his analysis is that while al-Muqrin's doctrine does advocate terrorist tactics, it also dictates genuine insurgency – that is, the constructive if violent upheaval of existing political arrangements and their replacement with new ones, which not all terrorist movements contemplate.

In Cigar's view, on al-Muqrin's evidence the al-Qaeda insurgency, while global in strategic scope, remains essentially regional and local in operational practice. This suggests that spectacular attacks like those of 11 September may be less central to the jihadist strategy than Western governments have often viewed them, and may help explain why a comparable operation has not materialised so far. Beyond that, jihadist terrorism, unlike 'simple' terrorism, calls for a 'more comprehensive approach' to counter-terrorism, in which the military plays only a supporting role, winning the war of ideas is central, and local governments take the initiative (p. 55). Cigar acknowledges the hurdles that politically retrograde and often brutal regimes face in making the 'systemic reforms' (p. 56) needed to win hearts and minds and defeat insurgencies, and implicitly leaves room in counter-insurgency for discreet political suasion and limited military action on the part of external actors. But his reading of al-Muqrin, alongside the large body of recent work criticising the United States' treatment of the global counter-terrorism effort as a 'war', clearly counsels a less militarised and more finely calibrated political response to transnational jihadist terrorism on the part of the major powers than the approach that has thus far held sway.

David Ucko's *The New Counterinsurgency Era*, while embodying remarkably assiduous research and analysis, cuts in a very different direction. The author beholds a string of historical American small wars, from Vietnam to Afghanistan, and concludes that there is no 'real evidence to suggest that this effort will end with the current campaigns' (p. 13). He takes it as given that US-waged counter-insurgency and stability operations are 'a growth business' (p. 12) and that they are desirable, or at least inevitable, in engaging jihadists and other adversaries. In light of the consensus that Iraq has imposed heavy strategic costs on the United States, increasing doubts about muscular counter-insurgency in Afghanistan and the rising salience of realist constraints on US policy, these appear to be questionable assumptions.

For better or worse, however, provisional institutional change in the general direction of counter-insurgency is indeed under way in the US military. Ucko seeks mainly to dissect the cultural, bureaucratic, technical, budgetary and operational challenges the American military faces in remaking itself from an exclusively major-war force, unduly focused on direct action, into a more flexible one, also capable of tackling the subtler tasks that proper counter-insurgency requires. Within those self-imposed boundaries, he succeeds admirably. Ucko's book is an impressive effort, and an invaluable resource for anyone who wants to understand the halting, ambivalent and, as Ucko wisely notes, quite reversible evolution of the US military.

The Globalization of Martyrdom: Al Qaeda, Salafi Jihad, and the Diffusion of Suicide Attacks
Assaf Moghadam. Baltimore, MD: The Johns Hopkins University Press, 2008. £24.00/$45.00. 357 pp.

The Terrorist in Search of Humanity: Militant Islam and Global Politics
Faisal Devji. London: Hurst and Company, 2009. £45.00/$24.95. 239 pp.

Diverging from Cigar's and Ucko's concerns, which involve mainly geographically concentrated terrorist efforts, Assaf Moghadam of West Point's exceptional Combating Terrorism Center explores the global spread of jihadist terrorism. Acknowledging the spate of recent books on jihadist suicide terrorism, he cites as his primary reason for adding another one the fact that previous explanations for the phenomenon 'have all but ignored the importance of ideology' (p. 3). This is particularly true of Robert Pape's *Dying to Win* (2005), the most prominent of the earlier books, which holds foreign occupation to be the prime culprit. Moghadam argues convincingly that Pape 'overstates the importance of occupation, while understating the role that religion and ideology – however distorted they may be from true Islam – play in the eyes of the group' (p. 34).

Pape has deservedly drawn many critics, but Moghadam mounts an especially cogent repudiation of his and kindred arguments. Noting first that al-Qaeda places a premium on suicide attacks because they emphatically signal tenacity and fearsomeness, Moghadam identifies three main factors in the globalisation of this tactic: al-Qaeda's dedication to the *umma*, the notional worldwide community of Muslims; the dispersal of Afghan Arabs following the Soviet Union's withdrawal from Afghanistan; and al-Qaeda's decision to outflank its 'near enemies' (apostate Arab regimes) by first attacking its 'far enemies' (their Western supporters, principally the United States) (pp. 43–4).

To be sure, much of the author's historical analysis reprises previous efforts, but *The Globalization of Martyrdom* remains welcome for its case studies and a cohesive marshalling of disparate facts. Particularly incisive is the account of al-Qaeda's adaptive strategy. Against improved US homeland security, al-Qaeda has focused pragmatically on soft targets elsewhere so as to erode support for the United States; tried to expand its own base of support beyond Sunni Muslims by appealing to 'all oppressed and wronged people in the world' (p. 142, quoting al-Zawahiri); and increasingly exploited the Internet to facilitate planning, training, recruitment and fundraising. This tack has served to bolster a Salafi-jihadist ideology geared to aggressively spreading Islamism on a transnational basis.

Faisal Devji complements Moghadam's essentially ideological approach to the globalisation of Islamist terrorism with a psychological and philosophical argument that brazenly seeks to transcend conventional analysis. His thesis is that jihadist terrorists, while ostensibly brutal and nihilistic, have acquired such broad geographical appeal not on account of 'some impossibly political identification with the suffering of unknown Muslims in unknown lands' – an argument which demotes the Israeli–Palestinian conflict as a source of jihadist ire – but by addressing themselves to the more universal problem of 'calling humanity into being through sacrifice' (p. 22). He suggests that 'it might well be that this intimacy between the terrorist and the humanitarian is what lends militant Islam its popularity, and poses therefore its greatest threat as well' (p. 23).

Devji's long essay is eclectic, inventively drawing on Gandhi's principles, existentialism and Hannah Arendt's 'terror of the idea of humanity' among many other twentieth-century ideas, as well as religious texts, historical analysis, current events and statements of al-Qaeda leaders. Some will no doubt find his argument hopelessly idiosyncratic and unbounded, and simply too cheeky. But it is also, in places, brilliantly provocative. 'Though separated from Osama bin Laden by a vast gulf', writes Devji, 'Mohandas Karamchand Gandhi does join him in the rejection of a humanity that is defined by life alone, thus breaking with the politics of states and NGOs alike, which take life as their object by invoking security as an ideal' (p. 219). One subtext of such thinking is that the study of terrorism has in relatively short order become narrowly gauged and hidebound, and Devji's argument is sufficiently passionate and coherent to potentially inject new energy and adventurism into the field and inspire more searching analyses.

How Terrorist Groups End: Lessons for Countering al Qa'ida
Seth G. Jones and Martin C. Libicki. Santa Monica, CA: RAND Corporation, 2008. £18.55/$33.00. 252 pp.

Walking Away from Terrorism: Accounts of Disengagement from Radical and Extremist Movements
John Horgan. Abingdon: Routledge, 2009. £20.99/$36.95. 214 pp.

Seth Jones and Martin Libicki of the RAND Corporation provide several typically thorough and workmanlike case studies on the decline and fall of terrorist groups, including Japan's Aum Shinrikyo, the Frente Farabundo Martí para la Liberación Nacional (FMLN) in El Salvador, and al-Qaeda in Iraq, along with a comprehensive 'End-of-Terror Data Set' and more focused and prescriptive analyses of the weaknesses of the United States' counter-terrorism strategy and the ending of the 'war' on terrorism. Supporting what is by now the consensus that 'U.S. efforts have relied too much on military force' (p. 105), the authors advocate a more varied set of responses, including sanctions against state sponsors, law enforcement, efforts to resolve critical conflicts such as those in the Middle East and Kashmir, redressing Muslims' political grievances and debunking al-Qaeda's ideological positions, as well as selective military action. Programmatically, there is nothing terribly novel in these recommendations. But the authors apply a critical eye to their implementation, noting that 'a "kitchen sink" approach does not prioritize a finite amount of resources and attention' or 'provide an assessment of what is most likely to be effective' (p. 121).

That, indeed, is the rub. Al-Qaeda's maximalist agenda makes any strictly political accommodation unlikely. Thus, Jones and Libicki propose a two-front strategy of which law enforcement and intelligence cooperation are the core components, with the US military avoiding politically incendiary presences in Muslim countries and instead working to build indigenous military capabilities for countering jihadist insurgencies. Ironically, a fair number of analysts put forward essentially the same proposal shortly after the 11 September attacks, before the Bush administration undertook the invasion of Iraq and adopted the unfortunate 'war on terror' terminology. That two respected RAND analysts now see fit to circle back and reiterate the recommendation, though remedially salutary, also seems to reflect how little progress has been made and how much time wasted.

John Horgan, a leader in the study of terrorist psychology and counter-radicalisation, focuses on the individual in exploring the question of how terrorism ends. Academically cautious, his book comprises a serviceable survey of the literature on how and why terrorist movements decline; six case studies of persons with varying extremist backgrounds (two loyalists and one republican from Northern Ireland, two former jihadists and one right-winger from Norway) who quit terrorist groups; and final thoughts on how to facilitate individual disengagement.

Like a number of analysts from Ireland and the United Kingdom, Horgan, who is Irish, believes that the ethno-nationalist Northern Irish conflict, despite admittedly stark disparities, is highly relevant to the current jihadist challenge posed by al-Qaeda. That the research community seems to have ignored social and psychological indoctrination and disengagement processes, especially with respect to Provisional Irish Republican Army volunteers, he says, 'reflects a lack of imagination … as well as an overly narrow view of how a counter-radicalisation initiative might develop' (p. 77). While he does not follow up this assertion with a tight argument about the claimed parallels, he does distil several interesting guidelines from his case studies. One is that while public policy cannot appreciably influence the personal factors in terrorist motivation, effecting 'change at the level of the *social, organisational and political context*' (p. 160; emphasis in original) is an important strategy. The book ends rather dispiritedly with a mere exhortation to think more about how to do so, but it is better to be honestly tentative than disingenuously conclusive.

Law, Ethics, and the War on Terror
Matthew Evangelista. Cambridge: Polity Press, 2008.
£12.99/$49.95. 202 pp.

The Cost of Counterterrorism: Power, Politics, and Liberty
Laura K. Donohue. Cambridge and New York: Cambridge
University Press, 2008. £18.99/$28.99. 500 pp.

These two volumes move past the justifiable consternation over post-11 September counter-terrorism measures in the area of law enforcement – prompted mainly by American practices such as indefinite detention, extraordinary rendition, domestic eavesdropping and 'enhanced interrogation' (the Bush administration's euphemism for torture) – to a calmer deliberation about how to balance security and individual rights in a time of crisis. Cornell professor Matthew Evangelista's treatment is elegant and broadly thematic, dealing with foundational issues: the definition of terrorism; the applicability of the Geneva Conventions; whether there is an emerging international consensus behind preventive war; and the challenge to humanitarian actors, especially non-governmental organisations (NGOs), to remain neutral in interventions undertaken for humanitarian purposes or to effect regime change.

His principal contention is that the 11 September attacks have effectively ended the brief post-Cold War period during which civil-society groups and NGOs largely determined the norms governing international behaviour, thus re-establishing the primacy of states in that enterprise. Concentrating on the United States' leading role in the counter-terrorism effort, Evangelista judges that 'things got pretty bad' (p. 156) when the Bush administration decided it was above the law, militarised counter-terrorism, and authorised extreme extra-legal measures. But perhaps surprisingly, he finds hope in the consciences of disillusioned military, intelligence and law-enforcement professionals who 'expressed their opposition to the Bush administration's lawlessness' (p. 163) by leaking information to journalists and working within bureaucratic channels, often against the scornful resistance of other officials, to reform reprehensible practices.

Hope, of course, is not enough, and Laura Donahue, a fellow at both Stanford Law School and Cambridge University, puts forward a more systemic solution. To get there she undertakes a learned comparative analysis, as exhaustive as it is exacting, of the United Kingdom's handling of Northern Irish terrorism and the United States' response to 11 September. In both contexts, 'the reductive "security or freedom" framework' (p. 111) was used to justify practices such as indefinite detention, domestic surveillance and curbs on free speech, which undermined liberal norms by sidelining the legislative and judicial branches of government in favour of the executive branch. This, Donahue says, has resulted in an array of serious operational and political costs, including the further alienation of those who sympathise with terrorists, a loss of international credibility, and the consequent difficulty in attaining foreign-policy goals. While this general formulation is well known, Donahue links the causes and consequences of actual cases to legal and political theory with singular specificity and judiciousness.

Donahue agrees with Evangelista that the 'accretion of dangerous executive power is indeed the hallmark of counterterrorist law' (p. 359). She argues that the institutional remedy for counter-terrorist excess is legislation, and that the legislature 'can mediate between representative democracy and the pressures of terrorism by emphasizing a culture of restraint that resists extraordinary procedures and encourages the immediate institution of an inquiry after a terrorist attack' (p. 336). Her view, while tinged with a lawyer's disdain for governmental abuses, is not a broad-gauged polemic but a finely calibrated appeal. She recognises that the structure of the state may have to change to meet terrorist threats. Her sensible plea is that any such possibility be confronted directly, explicitly and honestly through democratic channels, and not cynically 'backed into' (p. 360) on the pretext of providing security against emergent threats.

Brief Notices

United States

America's Grand Strategy and World Politics
Robert J. Art. Abingdon: Routledge, 2009. £85.00/$135.00. 400 pp.

Eleven essays explore how the United States employs its military power to support its foreign policies and national interests. Art argues that politics nearly always drives strategy, and that military power is central to the successful conduct of a great power's foreign policy.

Balance Sheet: The Iraq War and U.S. National Security
John S. Duffield and Peter J. Dombrowski. Stanford, CA: Stanford University Press, 2009. £25.50/$29.95. 243 pp.

The authors explore the effects of the Iraq War on the 'war on terror', nuclear non-proliferation, Middle East stability, the US military, America's global standing, and the ability of the United States to pursue its security interests now and in the future.

FDR's World: War, Peace, and Legacies
David B. Woolner et al., eds. New York and Basingstoke: Palgrave Macmillan, 2008. £45.00/$79.95. 254 pp.

Ten essays assess Franklin Roosevelt's presidency, examining his foreign policies, his role as a war leader, his contribution to the creation of the national security establishment, and the 'China Question'.

Foreign Policy, Inc.: Privatizing America's National Interest
Lawrence Davidson. Lexington, KY: University Press of Kentucky, 2009. £25.95/$27.50. 188 pp.

Davidson argues that well-funded and well-organised private-interest groups are capitalising on Americans' ignorance of world politics to shape US foreign policy to serve their own ends rather than the national interest.

From Colony to Superpower: U.S. Foreign Relations Since 1776
George C. Herring. Oxford: Oxford University Press, 2009. £18.99/$35.00. 1035 pp.

The only thematic title in Oxford's *History of the United States* series, this volume tells the story of America's foreign relations from the country's earliest days to its decades-long struggle against Soviet communism and on-going conflicts in Afghanistan and Iraq.

Imbalance of Power: US Hegemony and International Order
I. William Zartman, ed. Boulder, CO: Lynne Rienner Publishers. $25.00/£23.50. 288 pp.

Kenneth Waltz, Francis Fukuyama, Seyom Brown and others explore the shifting world order and the place of the United

 DOI 10.1080/00396330903461765

States within it. Topics include empire and hegemony, international justice and energy security.

In the Shadow of the Oval Office: Profiles of the National Security Advisers and the President they Served – From JFK to George W. Bush
Ivo H. Daalder and I.M. Destler. New York: Simon & Schuster, 2009. $27.00. 386 pp.

The authors profile the 15 national security advisers who have held office since McGeorge Bundy served under President Kennedy, discussing their personalities, relationships with their presidents, and successes and failures.

The Legacy of George W. Bush's Foreign Policy: Moving Beyond Neoconservatism
Ilan Peleg. Boulder, CO: Westview Press, 2009. £13.99/$24.00. 202 pp.

Peleg looks at the factors that shaped the 'Bush Doctrine', claiming that the Bush administration has revolutionised both the ends and means of US foreign policy. He makes suggestions for overcoming what he sees as past failings.

The Origins of Canadian and American Political Differences
Jason Kaufman. Cambridge, MA: Harvard University Press, 2009. £49.95/$55.95. 368 pp.

Kaufman looks at the development of Canada and the United States since colonial times in an attempt to account for persistent differences in the countries' political cultures, including division over such issues as gun ownership and same-sex marriage.

Out of the Shadow: George H.W. Bush and the End of the Cold War
Christopher Maynard. College Station, TX: Texas A&M University Press, 2009. $34.95. 192 pp.

In this study of President George H.W. Bush's role in bringing about the end of the Cold War, Maynard argues that historians have downplayed Bush's contribution, focusing instead on the 'strong ideological rhetoric' of Ronald Reagan and Mikhail Gorbachev.

America and the World: Conversations on the Future of American Foreign Policy
Zbigniew Brzezinski and Brent Scowcroft. David Ignatius, moderator. London and New York: Basic Books, 2008. £15.99/$27.50. 304 pp.

Two former US national-security advisers reflect on the challenges presented to American foreign policy by the Middle East, Russia, China, Europe, globalisation and what Brzezinski terms 'the global political awakening' in unscripted conversations moderated by David Ignatius of the *Washington Post*.

Presidential Decisions for War: Korea, Vietnam, the Persian Gulf, and Iraq (2nd ed.)
Gary R. Hess. Baltimore, MD: The Johns Hopkins University Press, 2009. $21.95/£11.50. 328 pp.

Hess analyses the reasoning behind four presidential decisions to go to war, compares the leadership and performance of each commander-in-chief, and evaluates how effectively each understood US interests, explored alternatives to war, adhered to constitutional processes, and built congressional, popular and international support.

War and Decision: Inside the Pentagon at the Dawn of the War on Terrorism
Douglas J. Feith. New York: HarperCollins, 2008. $27.95. 656 pp.

Former US Under Secretary of Defense Douglas Feith provides his insider account of the first five years of the Bush administration, describing a White House that was intent on avoiding another terrorist attack but which was hindered by failures of intelligence, inter-agency friction and personal mistrust among officials.

What Happened: Inside the Bush White House and Washington's Culture of Deception
Scott McClellan. New York: PublicAffairs, 2008. £16.99/$27.95. 368 pp.

Former White House press secretary Scott McClellan offers his account of some of the defining moments of the Bush administration, including 11 September 2001, the Iraq War and Hurricane Katrina, and provides an assessment of the president and his top aides.

Europe

Conflict, Negotiation and European Union Enlargement
Christina J. Schneider. Cambridge: Cambridge University Press, 2008. £50.00/$99.00. 211 pp.

Noting that each wave of EU enlargement has been accompanied by political tensions and conflict, Schneider argues that enlargement is usually successful provided the overall gains of enlargement are sufficiently great and distributed so to as to compensate any relative losers among existing members.

European Identity
Jeffrey T. Checkel and Peter J. Katzenstein, eds. Cambridge: Cambridge University Press, 2009. £15.99/$29.99. 265 pp.

While European economic integration has made great strides, the contributors argue, Europe's sense of identity is fragmenting as transnational European policies create a political backlash.

European Perceptions of Islam and America from Saladin to George W. Bush: Europe's Fragile Ego Uncovered
Peter O'Brien. Basingstoke: Palgrave Macmillan, 2009. £42.50/$74.95. 230 pp.

In this study of Europe's self-perception vis-à-vis its chief historical rivals – first Islamic civilisation and then the United States – O'Brien argues that low self-esteem has played a significant role in the formation of a European identity.

European Security Culture: Language, Theory, Policy
Monica Gariup. Farnham: Ashgate, 2009. £60.00/$114.95. 334 pp.

Drawing on a variety of analytical tools, including linguistic analysis and international-relations theory, Gariup analyses the implications of the discourse and practice of the EU's European Security and Defence Policy.

European Security Governance: The European Union in a Westphalian World
Charlotte Wagnsson et al., eds. Abingdon: Routledge, 2009. $70.00/$115.00. 168 pp.

Asserting that the EU approach to security governance has been largely successful within its own boundaries, rendering armed conflict within the union 'inconceivable', the contributors ask whether the EU model could be applied further afield.

European Security in a Global Context: Internal and External Dynamics
Thierry Tardy, ed. Abingdon: Routledge, 2009. £70.00/$140.00. 236 pp.

A variety of issues surrounding Europe's security posture are explored in this volume, including the roles of the EU, NATO and the OSCE, patterns of interaction between Europe and other parts of the world, and external perceptions of European security.

The Europeanization of National Foreign Policy: Continuity and Change in European Crisis Management
Eva Gross. Basingstoke: Palgrave Macmillan, 2009. £50.00/$74.95. 194 pp.

Noting that member states of the European Security and Defence Policy have more than one international-security institution on which they can rely, the authors explore how policymakers in Britain, France and

Germany are influenced by and respond to European and transatlantic bodies during times of crisis.

Euroscepticism: Images of Europe Among Mass Publics and Political Elites
Dieter Fuchs, Raul Magni-Berton and Antoine Roger, eds. Opladen: Barbara Budrich, 2009. £19.95/€29.90. 296 pp.

This volume discusses European identity and its relationship with national identities; Euroscepticism among European citizens and its construction in the mass media; and the connection between Euroscepticism and the party systems of European countries.

Going to War: British Debates from Wilberforce to Blair
Philip Towle. Basingstoke: Palgrave Macmillan, 2009. £45.00/$74.95. 227 pp.

In this study of how pressure groups, religious bodies, military officers, commentators and journalists have tried to influence British public opinion about intervention in overseas conflicts through the years, Towle challenges the notion that Britons are enthusiastic about foreign interventions.

The Meaning of Sarkozy
Alain Badiou. David Fernbach trans. London: Verso, 2008. £12.99/$24.95. 117 pp.

In Badiou's view, French President Nicolas Sarkozy is part of a 'reactionary tradition', based on fear, that goes back to the early nineteenth century. He proposes a 'communist hypothesis' to correct the failings of modern electoral democracy.

The New Eastern Europe: Ukraine, Belarus and Moldova
Daniel Hamilton and Gerhard Mangott, eds. Washington DC: Center for Transatlantic Relations, 2007. £13.99/$22.95. 292 pp.

The authors argue that the location of Ukraine, Belarus and Moldova between the EU and Russia and astride key military, transportation and energy routes means that the challenges they face – infectious diseases, organised crime, drug and human trafficking, pollution and illegal migration – have implications beyond their borders.

The Rise of Political Islam in Turkey
Angel Rabasa and F. Stephen Larrabee. Santa Monica, CA: RAND Corporation, 2009. £17.99/$24.50. 113 pp.

This study evaluates how the secular Turkish political system has been affected by the ascent to power of the Islamic Justice and Development Party. It suggests actions the United States could take to nurture its relationship with Turkey and to promote liberal interpretations of Islam worldwide.

The Search for a European Identity: Values, Policies and Legitimacy of the European Union
Furio Cerutti and Sonia Lucarelli, eds. Abingdon: Routledge, 2008. £70.00/$140.00. 232 pp.

The contributors consider problems of political identity and legitimacy in the European Union following the referendums on the Constitutional Treaty. Topics examined include foreign policy, human-rights promotion and external views of European identity-building.

Serbia in the Shadow of Milošević: The Legacy of Conflict in the Balkans
Janine N. Clark. London: Tauris Academic Studies, 2008. £53.50/$85.00. 236 pp.

Based on interviews with Serbians from all walks of life, Clark presents an analysis of the way former Serbian leader Slobodan Milošević is perceived by those he governed.

Shaping German Foreign Policy: History, Memory, and National Interest
Anika Leithner. Boulder, CO: FirstForum Press, 2008. £48.50/$55.00. 178 pp.

Leithner argues that a reinterpretation of the Second World War and new memories of interventions in the Balkans and the Middle East are contributing to Germany's pursuit of an assertive foreign policy.

The Search for a Common European Foreign and Security Policy: Leaders, Cognitions, and Questions of Institutional Viability
Akan Malici. Basingstoke: Palgrave Macmillan, 2008. £42.50/$79.95. 219 pp.

While the European Union has made efforts to develop a common foreign and security policy, Malici asserts that the policy's viability is questionable. He argues that the key to understanding why an institution succeeds or fails lies in studying the changing thinking of the national leaders seeking to build it.

A Stranger in Europe: Britain and the EU from Thatcher to Blair
Stephen Wall. Oxford: Oxford University Press, 2008. £20.00/$39.95. 230 pp.

Drawing on his personal experience as a British diplomat, Wall recounts how successive UK governments have sought to reconcile Britain's national and European interests.

The Struggle for the European Constitution: A Past and Future History
Michael O'Neill. Abingon: Routledge, 2008. £85.00. 564 pp.

O'Neill looks at the development of the European Constitution against the background of the current 'crisis of confidence' between the EU and its citizens. Topics addressed include how power politics shaped the constitutional negotiations and how the constitution affects EU policymaking.

West European Politics in the Age of Globalization
Hanspeter Kriesi et al. Cambridge: Cambridge University Press, 2008. £9.99/$39.99. 428 pp.

Contending that new political cleavages have emerged in Western Europe as a result of globalisation and denationalisation, the authors describe a new 'tripolar configuration of political power' pitting the left against the moderate and populist right in six European countries. Cultural issues, they say, have supplanted economic issues as the focus of debate.

Counter-terrorism

Analyzing Intelligence: Origins, Obstacles, and Innovations
Roger Z. George and James B. Bruce, eds. Washington DC: Georgetown University Press, 2008. £17.75/$29.95. 340 pp.

Intelligence experts provide an assessment of the state of intelligence analysis in the United States, looking at the ways the field has evolved over time, how analysts work with policymakers and strategists, and how they guard against pitfalls such as analytical bias. New challenges since the 11 September attacks are discussed.

Beyond the Law: The Bush Administration's Unlawful Responses in the 'War' on Terror
Jordan J. Paust. Cambridge: Cambridge University Press, 2007. £17.99/$29.99. 311 pp.

This volume documents the actions and decisions of the Bush administration which the author believes violated international law, including interrogation tactics, prisoner transfers and secret detentions. Paust provides details of cases which he says establish that all US presidents are bound by the laws of war and that the commander-in-chief is subject to restraints by Congress.

From Bullets to Ballots: Violent Muslim Movements in Transition
David L. Phillips. New Brunswick, NJ: Transaction Publishers, 2008. $49.95. 238 pp.

Phillips looks at several non-state Muslim organisations, including the Muslim Brotherhood, Hizbullah and the Kurdistan

Workers Party, as examples of movements that have attempted, with varying degrees of success, to abandon violence and pursue their goals through a political process.

The CIA and the Culture of Failure: U.S. Intelligence from the End of the Cold War to the Invasion of Iraq
John Diamond. Stanford, CA: Stanford University Press, 2008. $29.95. 536 pp.

Diamond places the intelligence failures that contributed to the attacks of 11 September 2001 in historical perspective, looking at the CIA's role in such key events as the end of the Soviet Union, the Gulf War, and early al-Qaeda attacks.

Counterterrorism
Ronald Crelinsten. Cambridge: Polity, 2009. £14.99/$22.95. 328 pp.

This primer on the problems of fighting terrorism in democratic societies includes chapters on coercive, proactive, persuasive, defensive and long-term counter-terrorism.

Crush the Cell: How to Defeat Terrorism Without Terrorizing Ourselves
Michael A. Sheehan. New York: Crown Publishers, 2008. $24.95. 309 pp.

Aiming to discredit the 'experts' and pundits he believes are misleading America, Sheehan argues that billions of taxpayers' dollars are being wasted on defensive counter-terrorist strategies when offensive operational intelligence is needed. Would-be terrorists, he says, are often much weaker than they are made out to be.

Enemy Combatants, Terrorism, and Armed Conflict Law: A Guide to the Issues
David K. Linnan, ed. Westport, CT: Praeger Security International, 2008. $85.00. 400 pp.

The contributors explore the legal dilemmas raised by the wars in Afghanistan and Iraq, arguing that the 'war on terror' has challenged even long-standing legal principles. They look at current debates surrounding intelligence-gathering, civil liberties, responses to terrorist threats, limits on interrogation, treatment of prisoners and preventive conflicts.

Global Jihadism: Theory and Practice
Jarret M. Brachman. Abingdon: Routledge, 2008. £20.99. 212 pp.

Brachman delves into jihadist strategic scholarship, exploring the thinking that underpins the activities of al-Qaeda and similar groups, and situating it within the broader Salafist religious movement. This leads to a discussion of the evolution of jihadism in Saudi Arabia and the United Kingdom, and how jihadist ideology might be countered.

In Their Own Words: Voices of Jihad
David Aaron, ed. Santa Monica, CA: RAND Corporation, 2008. £15.99/$35.00. 333 pp.

The statements and writings of jihadis are grouped by theme under such headings as 'Islam Under Threat', 'Tactics' and 'Recruitment', and supplemented by an original introduction and commentary.

Invitation to Terror: The Expanding Empire of the Unknown
Frank Furedi. London: Continuum, 2008. £17.99/$26.95. 204 pp.

Furedi discusses what he perceives as widespread confusion about the nature of the 'war on terror', noting that there is doubt about who the key belligerents are and even what terms should be used to describe the conflict.

Islamic Radicalism and Global Jihad
Devin R. Springer, James L. Regens and David N. Edger. Washington DC: Georgetown University Press, 2009. £15.95/$26.95. 320 pp.

Drawing on Arabic-language sources, the authors explore the philosophical foundations, strategic vision, organisational dynamics and tactics of the modern jihadist movement, with a special emphasis on al-Qaeda.

The Mind of Jihad
Laurent Murawiec. Cambridge: Cambridge University Press, 2008. £14.99/$24.99. 342 pp.

Drawing on history, anthropology and theology, Murawiec analyses the origins and belief structures of modern jihadist movements. Among his conclusions is that the 'political technologies' employed by jihadists can be traced to the Bolsheviks, whose doctrines of terror as a system of rule were appropriated by radical Islam.

The New Age of Terrorism and the International Political System
Adrian Guelke. London: I.B. Tauris, 2008. £14.99/$27.50. 238 pp.

This inquiry into the nature of terrorism looks at the varying perceptions of, and reactions to, violent acts, both domestic and international, around the world. Guelke argues that the fundamentals of terrorism have changed very little since 11 September 2001.

The New Protective State: Government, Intelligence and Terrorism
Peter Hennessy, ed. London: Continuum, 2007. £10.99/$19.95. 184 pp.

This volume focuses on debates surrounding the gathering of intelligence by the British government. Expert contributors explore how intelligence is collected, assessed and used; how new threats and a changing legal environment have shaped the intelligence-gathering process; and what the ethical responsibilities of the Intelligence Services are.

Old and New Terrorism: Late Modernity, Globalization and the Transformation of Political Violence
Peter R. Neumann. Cambridge: Polity, 2009. £14.99/$22.95. 218 pp.

Drawing on case studies ranging from the IRA to al-Qaeda, Neumann identifies what he sees as shifts in the practice and reception of terrorism over the years, and argues that many of these changes have been facilitated by globalisation.

The Shadow Factory: The Ultra-Secret NSA from 9/11 to the Eavesdropping on America
James Bamford. New York: Doubleday, 2008. $27.95. 395 pp.

An expert on the US National Security Agency tracks its evolution from the days before the 11 September attacks to the present.

Small Boats, Weak States, Dirty Money: Piracy and Maritime Terrorism in the Modern World
Martin N. Murphy. London: C. Hurst & Co., 2009. £35.00/$60.00. 539 pp.

Murphy explores the connection between piracy and terrorism, noting that while piracy may be a marginal problem in itself, linkages between pirates, criminal networks and corrupt governments could undermine states, destabilise regions and disguise insurgent and terrorist activity.

Talking to Terrorists: Making Peace in Northern Ireland and the Basque Country
John Bew, Martyn Frampton and Inigo Gurruchaga. London: C. Hurst & Co., 2009. £15.99. 327 pp.

While some believe the Northern Ireland peace process demonstrates the necessity of engaging in dialogue with terrorists in order to end violent conflicts, the authors contend that the act of talking to terrorists is less important than a range of other variables.

Terrorism: How to Respond
Richard English. Oxford: Oxford University Press, 2009. £12.99/$24.95. 208 pp.

English looks at historical instances of terrorist violence to determine why such violence occurs, why it continues, and how and why it ends. He argues that the problem of terrorism cannot be effectively addressed without first being honest about the complexity of its causes.

Treading on Hallowed Ground: Counterinsurgency Operations in Sacred Spaces
C. Christine Fair and Sumit Ganguly, eds. New York: Oxford University Press, 2009. $24.95. 227 pp.

This study looks at how insurgents around the world have adopted the strategy of positioning themselves on the 'hallowed ground' that surrounds place of religious worship, and analyses efforts to counter this strategy in Israel, Iraq, India, Kashmir, Pakistan, Thailand and Saudi Arabia.

Ungoverned Territories: Understanding and Reducing Terrorism Risks
Angel Rabasa, et al. Santa Monica, CA: Rand Corporation, 2007. £26.99/$44.00. 364 pp.

Noting that ungoverned territories can become sanctuaries for terrorist organisations, the authors suggest strategies to discourage terrorist infiltration of such areas. Their analysis includes discussion of the conditions that give rise to ungoverned territories, and examines case studies including the Pakistani–Afghan border region and the East Africa Corridor.

Closing Argument

Beijing Calling

Adam Ward

The following is the partial transcript of an imaginary phone conversation between Chinese President Hu Jintao and Iranian Supreme Leader Ayatollah Sayyid Ali Khamenei, which has come into the hands of Adam Ward.

Hu: I hope that the weeks since the incidents of June have not placed too heavy a strain on you. My colleagues on the Politburo and I know from our own not-too-distant history that June can be a trying and dangerous month. We place importance on the Islamic Republic's well-being, and are glad that a semblance of order has been restored to your country. We congratulate you on having achieved this without quite the level of coercive exertion that, alas, proved all too necessary in our own case in 1989. Surveying the scene after that challenge to Communist Party rule – a crisis that revealed alarming fissures and diffusion in our power structures, and what we call 'contradictions' in our wider society – the Politburo under our Paramount Leader, Deng Xiaoping, took stock. We asked ourselves this question: how is a political survival strategy for the Party to be amalgamated with a new, more expansive set of mutually reinforcing geopolitical and economic objectives for our country? I wonder, Mr Supreme Leader, if, in all the tumult of recent months, you have had the opportunity to ask yourself a similar question? My colleagues and I see some parallels with your predicaments and those we have laboured under. May I point them out?

Adam Ward is Director of Studies at the IISS.

Survival | vol. 51 no. 6 | December 2009–January 2010 | pp. 249–252 DOI 10.1080/00396330903461773

Khamenei: Do go on.

Hu: You have a long and continuous civilisation. So do we. Your people are ethnically distinct from those of your immediate neighbours. So are ours. You derive some internal coherence and cohesion from this, but it makes your neighbours suspicious; and you certainly have no love for them. We feel the same way. Your modern state was forged in the bright fires of revolution. Ours was too. Armed with a powerful and compelling ideology, you cast off foreign oppressors and their local puppets. Favouring for our own reasons Marx and Mao over the Prophet Muhammed, we fought the same fight. For years you bristled in defiance, and repelled threats from near and afar. We did not shrink from such a task ourselves. But your ideological fervour, if you will permit me, shines a little less brightly than before; and so, to be perfectly honest, does ours. The imperatives of governing and of feeding your often fretful and restive population have long since intruded, as they did in our case.

You do not recede from your ideological attachments, and neither, publicly, do we. How could we? But your central purpose now, like ours, is to find solace and legitimacy in the status of a rising great power. You feel your smaller neighbours owe you deference; some in China are nostalgic for the Asian tributary systems of former centuries. You feel cramped and fettered by the overweening presence in your vicinity of the United States; we dislike the East Asian alliances it has ranged against us.

Khamenei: Indeed: all this we have in common.

Hu: And yet, Mr Supreme Leader, this is where the parallels end. Consider the strategy we have unfolded to carry us to our destination and that which you have – forgive me – improvised. For years we have engaged our tiresome neighbours and shown our softer side. We have flattered and we have fawned. We have resolved border disputes. Trade and investment has flourished. Our neighbours do not trust us, and many still cling to the United States. But we take a long view. We have vast reserves of strategic patience and perseverance. Under the magnetic force of our economy a

Sino-centric region is coming into being and the marginalisation of the Americans is assured. We glimpse epochal change. To soothe our neighbours and the US itself, we have joined with the Americans in a long, tight handshake. But it is a farewell and not a welcome.

Let us now consider your case. You have few friends and no reliable allies. In Palestine you meddle in emotional historical disputes that your Arab neighbours see as their own special preserve and which are intimately bound up with such legitimacy as Arab elites can claim at home. Your nuclear programme is incinerating any bridges you had to the West. It has bought you no deference, only hostility and sanctions. Rather than occupying more strategic space, your condition has become claustrophobic. Israel may strike at any moment. The Arabs are turning to the Americans for arms. Quietly they are being choreographed into a posture of containment against you. Soon, some may follow you down the nuclear road. What then?

Khamenei: Our cause is legitimate. Our enemies are divided.

Hu: But so are your friends. I ask you to be mindful of this. Of course we in China rely on your gas and oil. We have no immediate interest in hampering your exports through sanctions. Still less do we wish to see military action to cripple your nuclear programme, when the consequences would carry far and wide, perhaps inflaming the whole Middle East for an interval. And, like our Russian friends, we have no inherent reason to do the Americans' bidding in the Security Council.

But lately we have in our reflections begun to see – reluctantly, perhaps, but unmistakably – that the dimensions of China's interests must be broader. If I may dispense with the strict formalities of Iran's diplomatic position, Sir, we consider that these interests cannot be served by your possession of a nuclear weapon or several of them. We worry this outcome would permanently unsettle the regional equilibrium in a most destructive way. We are unsure whether – pardon me – your fragmented polity could enter into reliable deterrence relationships with other nuclear powers. We fret about nuclear accidents. The Arabs, who have their own oil to offer us, are asking persistent and unwelcome questions about our allegiances. The Americans and Europeans are in respect of our policy towards your government setting benchmarks for 'responsible' behaviour in a way that is cramping our style around the world. As your scientists and engineers race towards the nuclear finish, our discomfort is growing. In our diplomacy we deprecate the forcing of issues; 'time the great healer' as they say in the West. But your nuclear haste is boxing us in. It would be irresponsible not to review our policies. The Geneva agreement of October on sending low-enriched uranium to Russia and receiving medical isotopes in return raised our hopes of a respite; but now we are not so sure.

Might you not take a leaf from our diplomatic textbook? It is not enough that the region knows you have the means to become weapons-capable for them to show you grudging respect? Forgo the temptation to cross the line, and call this restraint magnanimity. Speak to the Americans about a new regional dispensation. Let them confer prestige upon you. Have the Gulf states hedge their bets in your direction. Tap the trade, technology and investment of the West. Entrench your power and standing at home. And relieve me of my dilemma...

Supreme Leader, are you still there...?

Printed and bound by CPI Group (UK) Ltd, Croydon, CR0 4YY
01/11/2024
01782609-0003